ALTERNATIVE PARADIGMS IN ENVIRONMENTAL EDUCATION RESEARCH

Edited by

Rick Mrazek
Faculty of Education
The University of Lethbridge

**MONOGRAPHS IN
ENVIRONMENTAL
EDUCATION
AND ENVIRONMENTAL
STUDIES
VOLUME VIII**

**The North American
Association for Environmental
Education
P. O. Box 400
Troy, Ohio 45373 U.S.A.
1993**

NORTH AMERICAN
ASSOCIATION FOR
ENVIRONMENTAL
EDUCATION

ISBN 1-884008-04-6

THE NORTH AMERICAN ASSOCIATION FOR ENVIRONMENTAL EDUCATION

Since its beginning in 1971, the North American Association for Environmental Education has been dedicated to promoting environmental education and supporting the work of environmental educators around the world. NAAEE is an integrated network of professionals in the field of environmental education with membership throughout North America and in 25 additional countries.

There are many environmental interest groups and many organizations dedicated to the improvement of education. NAAEE uniquely combines and integrates both of these perspectives. NAAEE is deeply committed to environmental education, but it is not a partisan advocacy organization. Its approach to promoting environmental education is neither confrontational nor adversarial.

The Association is made up of people who have thought seriously -- over lifetimes -- about how people become literate concerning environmental issues. NAAEE members believe education must go beyond consciousness-raising about these issues. It must prepare people to think together about the difficult decisions they have to make concerning environmental stewardship, and to work together towards the resolution of environmental problems.

NAAEE recognizes the need for a coherent body of information about environmental issues, but its members also recognize that information and analysis are only part of an effective education program. To be truly effective, this body of knowledge must be integrated into all aspects of the curriculum and into all types of educational institutions for the widest array of audiences.

In order to translate theory into reality, and provide tangible support for environmental education and environmental educators, NAAEE engages in a variety of programs and activities. Perhaps the single most important activity of the Association is the annual conference. Each year educators from around the world gather at a site in North America to share knowledge and experiences with fellow experts in the field. The conference features a diverse mixture of concurrent sessions on topics of interest. In addition, the conference features a browsing library where participants can inspect new environmental education materials, and a film and video festival where conference goers can view the best in audio-visual productions. Additional conference activities include field trips, symposia to provide an in-depth look at a particular topic, global briefings on environmental issues, exhibits and noted speakers.

The conference is only one aspect of the Association's activities. A highly professional publication program is another key feature of NAAEE. The Association produces a bi-monthly newsletter with timely articles, resource listings and announcements. In addition, NAAEE maintains a series of professional publications of interest to environmental educators, and adds to this series of scholarly monographs and practical manuals on a yearly basis. Various catalogues and the conference proceedings round out the publication program.

While the conference and publications form the core of NAAEE's member-directed programs, other important activities include testifying in support of environmental education legislation and innovative programs, maintaining a consultant and volunteer data base, providing information on environmental education techniques and programs in response to inquiries, and working cooperatively with other organizations in North America and throughout the world.

In addition to ongoing activities, on a regular basis, the Association undertakes the development of model programs and other selectively targeted initiatives. Recent initiatives include creation of environmental materials for use in NAAEE's Environmental Issues Forums, development of an agenda identifying environmental education priorities for the 1990's, implementation of training courses in international environmental education, organization of career development internships for minority students, and development of a Resource Bureau to provide support for provincial and state environmental education organizations.

For more information contact:

NAAEE
P. O. BOX 400
TROY, OHIO 45373
U.S.A.

(513) 676-2514 (Telephone and Fax)

TABLE OF CONTENTS

TABLE OF CONTENTS (cont'd)

TABLE OF CONTENTS: (cont'd)

THE HOLY GRAIL AND OTHER QUESTS

Rick Mrazek

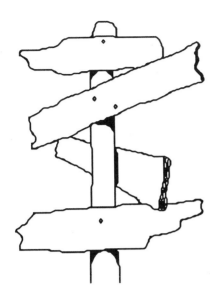

Abstract

Alternative Paradigms in Environmental Education Research represents to many much more than a contribution to a body of knowledge being catalogued in a series of monographs by the North American Association for Environmental Education. It represents a quest not unlike the journey undertaken by knights in search of the Holy Grail in medieval times.

In the Beginning

This monograph began with questions raised in 1989 at the North American Association for Environmental Education conference held in Estes Park where discussions at the North American Commission for Environmental Education Research meeting focused on the types of research being made available and promoted by various journals and publications. There was considerable doubt expressed concerning the match between the areas of research that are timely now and those which were being promoted. As a result of this, Ian Robottom, Paul Hart, and I put forward a proposal for a symposium to be held at the 1990 NAAEE conference to be held in San Antonio, Texas called Contesting Paradigms in Environmental Education Research. John Disinger and a number of other individuals involved in environmental education research helped identify individuals who may be willing to take part in the symposium, others involved in environmental education research that would be interested in knowing more about these efforts, and those who may be able to provide some insights as to the types of questions that should be raised in such a symposium. Using the North American Commission for Environmental Education Research membership as a starting point and adding those identified through the process just mentioned, a brief survey was circulated. Its purpose was to gather general and demographic information regarding those involved in environmental education research, identify in what capacity they were involved in environmental education research, and determine what role they might be willing to take regarding participation in the symposium and potentially a subsequent monograph. The symposium was to provide a forum for considering and appraising alternative approaches in environmental education research. Some of the topics to be addressed were

1. What is the nature of alternative paradigms in environmental education research?
2. What is the history of these traditions?
3. What are some of the assumptions these differing paradigms make about the relationship between theory and practice?
4. What assumptions are made about the four common places of education -- teachers, learners, subject matter, and milieu?
5. What differing methodologies are favored by these approaches?
6. What is or should be recognized as the professional status of practitioners in environmental education research?
7. What differing interpretations of such notions as rigor, validity, and generalizability are made by these alternative paradigms of educational research?
8. What should be the role of a professional education journal in providing a forum for discussing questions similar to those listed above?

At the time a concern was raised that the term "contesting" represented conflict and therefore the title of the symposium should be "Alternative Paradigms" rather than "Contesting Paradigms". In an attempt to communicate that the symposium was meant to be as inclusive as possible without intimidating anyone that might be interested, the change was made. However, as Ian Robottom suggests in his contribution in this monograph there are some educational concepts, and this may be one, which are necessarily contested and should be the subject of continuing critical discourse and debate. The reader will be left to make that decision. Based on the survey mentioned earlier, initial presenters and reactors were identified for the symposium. The symposium was structured in such a way that initial overview presentations were made by Paul Hart, Diane Cantrell, and Tom Marcinkowski reflecting different ways of viewing and approaching research in environmental education. This morning session used one-half hour presentations to focus on empirical studies, interpretive studies, and a critical approach to research. Following this, three reactors, Ian Robottom, John Disinger, and Esther Railton Rice responded to these initial presentations. Their job was to react to the three main papers and set the stage for small group discussions in the afternoon. These small group discussions were then followed by a plenary session which attempted to provide a summation and future directions regarding environmental education research. It was hoped that from this plenary session suggestions would come forward for potential research networks, collaborative efforts and/or proposals which may involve a greater number of NAAEE members. Some of the themes which came out of this section included a need for continuing our quest to look at the consequences of research as well as the different interpretations of terms being used such as "rigor". It was quite obvious that language became problematic. There was confusion between philosophical derivations of paradigms and the need for more emphasis of the specific questions being asked.

One of the major points upon which all those present agreed was that there was a need to involve more people in this discussion. This seemed to lead directly to the 1991 monograph proposal dealing with paradigms in environmental education research which had been proposed by Paul Hart and myself. Possible contributing authors were viewed initially as the participants from the 1990 symposium as well as interested members of the North American Commission on Environmental Education Research. In order to solicit a wide selection of opinion and array of issues associated with this topic, letters were sent out to individuals identified with a potential interest in contributing to the monograph, as well as soliciting contributions through the Environmental Communicator. This became an ongoing process as the monograph took shape. A serious attempt was made to take into consideration cultural differences in ways of viewing environmental education research by soliciting papers from as many countries as possible.

From this point the structure of the Monograph evolved from an attempt to share the presentations and ideas resulting from the symposium into a contribution which would grapple with the complexity of defining environmental education research in such a way that it would **invite participation** in the discussion and carry forward the quest to address the initial questions raised in the symposium to more members of the NAAEE. As in any quest we are seeking a path which ultimately has signposts which help provide direction. If one considers the contributions within this monograph as providing possible signposts, the challenge to the readers is to consider each of the contributions but **not** focus on the signs so intently that they lose sight of the path and subsequently become lost.

Icons have been used throughout the publication for a quick reference to specific articles or grouping of articles. These groupings reflect in part the evolution of the monograph. **Setting the Stage** presents articles which challenge the reader to define what we mean by terms such as environmental education, paradigms, and research. **Confronting the Issues** includes those articles which served as original platform presentations made at the 1990 symposium. **Raising Questions: Reactions to and Building on the Symposium** include articles which do exactly that. Ian Robottom's contribution as a reactor to the initial presentations at the symposium raised issues which are spoken to in the other four contributions in this section. These might also be considered as position papers on paradigms in environmental education research. **Shedding Some Light: Examples of Environmental Education Research** includes contributions resulting from a follow-up symposium at the 1991 NAAEE conference in St. Paul where a need for sharing more examples of different types of environmental education research which is being done was made. **Responding to Influences** provides some challenges to the reader regarding future directions for environmental education research.

There has been no attempt to priorize articles in terms of their importance of contribution. There is also a great variation in the length of articles which is due more to the intent of their initial use, for example, as a starting point in a symposium to that of a specific example of research being conducted. Submission guidelines for the monograph had indicated a length of 5-20 pages, however there were no clear guidelines on length for the written documentation of presentations in the symposium.

Through the monograph's long journey into print, a number of suggestions have been made by the publications committee, members of the research commission, and interested individuals. One included providing the reader with some semblance of context for the symposium and subsequent monograph by including research articles from the Environmental Communicator. These are included in **Appendix I: Pre-Symposium Research Articles from Environmental Communicator** and **Appendix II: Post-Symposium Articles from Environmental Communicator. Appendix III: Responses to Symposium Reactors** is provided as an example of what is more often found in portions of journals of research and that is the ongoing dynamic dialogue that exists in an attempt to make sense of differing views of potentially the same phenomena.

To encourage more NAAEE members to contribute to research publications, an example is provided in **Appendix IV: Research Publication Guidelines** of the types of manuscripts that are solicited and published in a journal. **Appendix V: Contact Information for Contributing Authors** invites the reader to not stop with what is contained in the monograph. Each of the contributions included in this monograph represent a small fraction of what these authors have to share. The reader is encouraged to take advantage of this information and to continue a dialogue with authors personally. Where possible, information about the author has also been provided with their contribution. However, once again, remember that this is a small snapshot that is part of a larger picture. **Appendix VI: Monographs and Publications of the North American Association for Environmental Education** directs the reader to other publications available through the NAAEE in which they may find other contributions by the same authors.

A sincere debt of gratitude is extended to all authors who have contributed to this monograph for your patience in seeing this work through to its completion. A very special thank you is extended to Judy Braus, the Publications Committee, Randy Champeau and Diane Cantrell for their review of the finished Monograph. A heartfelt thanks is extended to Barb Krushel for her dedication over the last two years and countless revisions to this publication.

As a final note to the reader, please remember that this monograph is not necessarily attempting to provide all the answers but rather initiate the beginning of a healthy dialogue of what is possible in environmental education research. Hopefully you will view this as your quest and establish your own path which sees you through **Setting the Stage** into **Appendix I** onto **Confronting the Issues** and partway through **Raising the Questions** then into **Appendix II** and who knows where from there. Pleasant journey.

SETTING THE STAGE

THROUGH WHICH LOOKING GLASS? DEFINING ENVIRONMENTAL EDUCATION RESEARCH

Rick Mrazek

Abstract

In recent years there has been a growing dialogue on the role played by language in the discussion of gender, race and culture. Similarly, as there are needs to identify and understand the differences in ways of communicating within each of these areas, there is also such a need in the area of environmental education research. Hopefully, if we can recognize the differences between different ways of viewing this research process, we might learn from each others' styles and subsequently be in a better position to confront real problems in environmental education using a shared language.

This monograph raises questions about how we view and use language in defining paradigms, environmental education, and research, as well as identify who the actual practitioners of environmental education research are.

Decoding and Demystifying

When those engaged in environmental education research, or research in any area of endeavour for that matter, are challenged to provide a method for involving a greater number of people in doing and using research, one of the common directions given is to demystify the language used and make the information more "user friendly". This article may not necessarily do that but hopefully it will at least make less problematic the use of language in interpreting and sharing environmental education research.

Quite often when one thinks of language, it is in terms of vocabulary and grammar. As a starting point let us say that language is a system of resources for making meanings and, in addition to a vocabulary and a grammar, our language gives us semantics. Consider then:

> The semantics of a language is a particular way of creating similarities and differences in meaning. We need semantics because any particular concept or idea makes sense only in terms of the relationship it has to other concepts and ideas. This web

9

of relationships of meaning is woven with the semantic resources of language. (Lemke, 1990:ix)

Here we encounter the first of our problems in defining terms used in environmental education. Language, through the use of symbols, makes things definite; it specifies and differentiates, thereby ruling out wholeness or an understanding of interconnectedness. If to dwell within the meaning of words is to loose the meaning of the whole, then the question becomes, how can we use language to give clarity to experience without sacrificing its experiential depth (Chappell, 1985)? If we accept that communication is a social process central to the reporting of research and that we communicate by creating and manipulating social situations and not by the transmission of signs or signals, can we also accept then that communication becomes the creation of community (Lemke, 1990)? Most will acknowledge that communication and teaching are social processes dependent upon attitudes, values, and social interests, not just our knowledge and skills. Perhaps it means then, when we speak of environmental education, that we also acknowledge:

> We are helping to create, or re-create a community of people who share certain beliefs and values. We communicate best with people who are already members of our own community; those who have learned to use language in the same ways that we do. When the people with whom we are trying to communicate use language differently, use it in ways that make sense of a subject differently than we do, communication becomes more difficult (Lemke, 1990:x).

Considering that environmental education and its associated research is not limited to one culture, one dialect of English, or one style of communication, we quickly see that language itself may be problematic in any discussion about environmental education research.

What of Paradigms?

Since paradigms are discussed further in the second part of this section by John Disinger as it relates to Kuhnian philosophy, let us focus here on some of the language used and its implications for making sense of environmental education research. Webster's Dictionary interpretation of paradigm is "a pattern or model which establishes boundaries or sets out rules and regulations, which may present a generalized, hypothetical description often based on an analogy, used in analyzing or explaining something" (Guralnik, 1980: 913). Is it then inherent in this definition that the strength of a model is in its grasp of the general or the common and that the weakness of that model is in its missing of the particular or the uncommon (Brickle, 1981). What then do paradigms have to do with environmental education research?

10

If we consider a simplified interpretation of paradigms as used by Joel Arthur Barker (1990) in <u>Discovering the Future: The Business of Paradigms,</u> there may be a few key points to consider. If we think of the models or paradigms in environmental education research as a lens or a way of using incoming experience, then they must also have some form of filtering which can possibly blind us to new ideas or changes in that field. In other words, we would still see what "we are supposed to see" and not accept or even be sensitive to data that doesn't meet our present paradigm. Any new rules, procedures, standards or routines must then be written at the edge and not at the core of the paradigm. The term Barker uses for this paradigm paralysis is where we are blinded by the success of our old paradigm and our investment in it to the point that we believe that there can only be one way to do things. Change occurs through what he calls a paradigm shift where there is a revolutionary new way of thinking about old problems. This dramatic, collective change in our perception usually occurs when the established "rules of the game" fail to provide effective solutions to our problems. When the old framework gives way to a new insight or alternative explanation, then the paradigm shift occurs.

The question the reader is left to ponder is whether or not we are dealing with replacement of paradigms in environmental education research or coexistence of multiple paradigms.

The EE in Environmental Education Research

Trying to define the term "environmental education" is a task which many publications have incorporated as a central purpose to which they filled hundreds of pages. It is also one that is evolutionary and becomes dated very quickly. For purposes of the discussion here I would like to draw upon the definition included in the preliminary review draft of the <u>National Report on Environmental Education</u> prepared by the North American Association for Environmental Education in June, 1992.

> Environmental education is widely understood to be an interdisciplinary process of developing a citizenry that is aware of and knowledgeable about the environment, in both its natural aspects, and in those which are built or altered by humans. This awareness and knowledge is understood by environmental educators to lay the groundwork for resolving environmental problems caused by human activity, and the value conflicts that often make these problems intractable, as well as for preventing new problems from arising. Further, environmental education aims to develop in the citizenry the capacity for, and the commitment to engage in inquiry, problem-solving, decision-making, and action that will achieve and maintain a high quality of life by assuring a high quality of environment.
>
> Based on the above understanding, environmental education can be defined as the interdisciplinary process of developing a

citizenry that is aware of and knowledgeable about the total environment, in its natural and built aspects, that has the capacity for, and the commitment to engage in inquiry, problem-solving, decision-making, and action that will assure environmental quality.

This definition is clearer and more precise when accompanied by the goals and principles that have guided the field for many years. Goals such as those put forward at Belgrade and Tbilisi have helped to clarify the focus of environmental education:

- To foster clear awareness of, and concern about, economic, social, political and ecological interdependence in urban and rural areas;

- To provide every person with opportunities to acquire the knowledge, values, attitudes, commitment and skills needed to protect and improve the environment; and
- To create new patterns of behavior of individuals, groups and society as a whole towards the environment.

The Tbilisi conference stated twelve guiding principles that are representative of those that guide the field. Under these principles, environmental education should:

- Consider the environment in its totality -- natural and built, technological and social (economic, political, technological, cultural-historical, moral, aesthetic);
- Be a continuous lifelong process, beginning at the preschool level and continuing through all formal and non-formal stages;
- Be interdisciplinary in its approach, drawing on the specific content of each discipline in making possible a holistic and balanced perspective;
- Examine major environmental issues from local, national, regional and international points of view so that students receive insights into environmental conditions in other geographical areas;
- Focus on current and potential environmental situations, while taking into account the historical perspective;
- Promote the value and necessity of local, national and international cooperation in the prevention and solution of environmental problems;
- Explicitly consider environmental aspects in plans for development and growth;

- Enable learners to have a role in planning their learning experiences and provide an opportunity for making decisions and accepting their consequences;
- Relate environmental sensitivity, knowledge, problem-solving skills and values clarification to every age, but with special emphasis on environmental sensitivity to the learner's own community in early years;
- Help learners discover the symptoms and real causes of environmental problems;
- Emphasize the complexity of environmental problems and thus the need to develop critical thinking and problem-solving skills;
- Utilize diverse learning environments and a broad array of educational approaches to teaching/learning about and from the environment with due stress on practical activities and first-hand experience. (NAAEE, 1992: 11-14)

The implications of inclusion of such a definition in environmental education research is that not only can such research focus on any one part or component within the interdisciplinary process of developing a citizenry that is aware of and knowledgeable about the environment, but can also focus on any one of the multitude of connectors (relationships) that make up such a field of endeavor. For example, if we focus on the term education, then it may conjure up visions of conceptualizations of schooling and cognitive processes where intellectual skills are secured as tools for adapting to and shaping future situations. Or, to others, it may mean curriculum which could be subsequently viewed through a curriculum technology approach as a consummatory experience of self-actualization or in terms of social reconstruction, academic rationalism and so on. For our purposes it may be fair to simply acknowledge the complexity of the area with which we are working and that we must be conscious of interpretations other than those which we ourselves hold.

Placing Environmental Education Research into Context

It is amazing how through repeated use of a term one often begins to simplify the meaning attached to that term. Many dictionaries give a definition for context as it applies to written work. Following from the definition which we had just given for environmental education, it may be more fitting to use a definition for contexture which is congruent with the meaning of context -- that is "the manner of interweaving several parts into one body; the disposition and union of the constituents parts of a thing with respect to each" (Guralnik, 1980). The purpose for applying such a definition is to acknowledge the process of definition within which we are engaged and to recognize the complexity of defining research in environmental education. Since this is a task to which each of the contributions in this monograph addresses itself at this point, it may suffice to raise some of the issues.

In an address delivered in celebration of Max Plank's 60th birthday (1918) before the Physical Society in Berlin, Albert Einstein presented his views on the principles of research which in his view demanded the highest possible standard of rigorous precision in the description of relations, such as only the use of mathematical language can give. In terms of physicists and their subject matter, they must limit themselves very severely and must content themselves with describing the most simple events which can be brought within the domain of our experience.

> All events of a more complex order are beyond the power of the human intellect to reconstruct with the subtle accuracy and logical perfection which the theoretical physicist demands. Supreme purity, clarity, and certainty at the cost of completeness. (Seelig, 1964: 226)

Hopefully our definition of research has evolved somewhat, like our knowledge of gender specific language, since 1918. At the same time since it may be argued that this view is still quite prominent within the scientific community, so what does this say about its influence on science related issue research in environmental education? If the language of environmental education is inclusive of three dimensions "about, in and for the environment" (Mrazek, 1990), then this also means that it demands a new dynamic of its research. As one moves from context of science to that of education, then the reader is challenged to consider what counts as good research and how one ensures that such research is practical, if that is indeed what the demand of this research should be. What of the challenge by Soltis (1984) that pedagogical and educational research needs to be empirical, interpretive, and normative, and both can be objective in the sense of being public and rational forms of inquiry? Does one truly need to view the tensions in contemporary educational research in the broader context of 20th century philosophical traditions concerned with the epistemology of human and social knowledge? Does this suggest that in this way the large variety of languages and logics of educational research must be viewed as a reflection of various reconstructive logics of traditions manifesting themselves in environmental education? Where do challenges by the likes of Barrow (1986), that empirical research does not make things right or wrong, or empirical findings are not a criterion of success and truth or that methodological questions are not philosophical, fit into our search for appropriate research in environmental education?

Which signs are we to use to find our path through this maze and which questions do we ask to provide the signposts in our quests? Beattie (1989) suggests academics who advocate the use of action research want respectability for their enterprise within the research community — meaning that a properly theoretical body of knowledge is required as a product. At the same time a respectable meta-theory is wanted to justify the methods in their results. Subsequent inclusions in this Monograph will speak to this issue, however, let me muddy the waters a bit more with this final inclusion regarding language and context;

> In a reflective conversation, the values of control, distance, and objectivity -- central to technical rationality -- take on new meanings. The practitioner tries, within the limits of his virtual world, to control variables for the sake of hypothesis-testing experiment. But his hypotheses are about the situation's potential for transformation, and as he tests them, he inevitably steps into the situation. He produces knowledge that is objective in the sense that he can discover error -- for example, that he has not produced the change he intended. But his knowledge is also personal; its validity is relative to his commitments to a particular appreciative system and overarching theory. His results will be compelling only for those who share his commitments (Schön, Donald, 1990:79).

Those that have spent time on a golf course have probably overheard a golfer describing their home course to another using the expression "you can't get there from here." What the person who knows the course is saying is that, depending on how you play your shot, it is still almost impossible to get to the green from where you are and at the same time avoid the many hazards that exist if you happen to fall a bit short or carry a bit too long (Mrazek, 1991). Could we be dealing with exactly the same situation here? Have we developed the necessary theoretical perspectives or conceptualizations which provide ways of viewing the complexity of environmental education phenomena in an orderly and meaningful pattern which take the important issues associated with everyday environmental education practice (i.e. authority, knowledge, teaching, theory, status of models) and use this philosophical treatment to get to an understanding of issues of environmental education (Mrazek, 1983). Do we have a theoretical perspective which can be translated into a clue structure or series of analytical questions which is broad enough to capture the important, generally accepted aspects of research in an environmental education context, which have meaning for many audiences, including those unsophisticated in research and in environmental education, and lend themselves to the operational definitions in terms of praxis in environmental education research? The question we are left to ponder is whether such a theoretical perspective and clue structure have already been developed or identified and can these serve as our signposts in our quest **or** is that in itself the pathway that we seek?

Identifying the Researcher

The final challenge in trying to form a picture of what alternative paradigms in environmental education research may look like, is to consider who is involved in this enterprise. Depending on which view or lens one uses, this community of researchers can be either inclusive or exclusive. Barth (1990) charges that there is useful and useless research and good and bad scholarship. Few would debate this point. Peshkin concludes that "no research paradigm has a monopoly on quality. None can deliver promising outcomes with certainty. None can have the grounds for saying 'this is it' about their designs, procedures, and anticipated outcomes" (1993:28). If this is true, what do our researchers in environmental education look like in terms of background and skills necessary to engage in "good quality" research? Barth presents that it is a mistake to take too seriously the capacity of educational research to directly improve schools and that academics have a far greater success reaching other academics then they will probably ever have directly touching school people. If this is so, how do researchers meet the many demands set out in our definition of environmental education? Where schools are concerned, Beattie (1990) claims that when action research is given the respectability within the research community that it requires, it means then that the aims of that research will be removed from the immediate concerns of teachers who wish to solve specific problems in their classrooms. Can these potentially different needs of the two groups be reconciled without destroying their common central aspirations -- improvements in classroom practice? At the other end of the continuum Wilson and Cowell (1989) push for inclusion of the philosopher as part of any research team particularly in the first stages of research. They argue that at the present philosophy is regarded as irrelevant to research; however, there is a great need for the conceptual consideration of the research topic and the philosophical monitoring of the research as it proceeds. They are concerned that without careful philosophical scrutiny and proper understanding on the part of the researchers, things will often go wrong at the start since it is very common for research to be set up and carried out by a vague mixture of political consensus and fashionable methodology. Who then do we call on as part of our research team when we are considering environmental policy or impact assessments? How does research in environmental education help us to understand what our choices are and what the consequences of making different choices will be in relation to our future and that of our planet? Which looking glass will give us the definition and clarity of understanding needed to fulfill our quest? It is this challenge I leave you with as you continue your journey through this Monograph.

References

Barker, Joel Arthur. (1990). Discovering the Future: The Business of Paradigms. Burnsville, Mn.: Charthouse International Learning Corporation.

Barrow, R. (1981). The Philosophy of Schooling. Brighton, Sussex: Wheatsheaf Books Ltd.

Barth, R. (1990). Improving Schools from Within. San Francisco: Jossey-Bass Publishers.

Beattie, C. (1989). Action Research: A Practice in Need of Theory? In Milburn, G., Goodson, I. and Clark, R. Re-Interpreting Curriculum Research: Images and Arguments. London, Ontario: The Althouse Press.

Brickell, H.M. (1981). Groping for the elephant. In Brandt, R.S. (Ed.). Applied strategies for curriculum evaluation. Alexandria, Va: Association for Supervision and Curriculum Development.

Chappell, E. (1985). The Azimuth of Language: Explorations into the Limits of Expression. Unpublished Doctor of Philosophy Thesis, University of Alberta, Edmonton.

Guralnik, D. (Ed.). (1980). Websters New World Dictionary. Second College Edition. New York: Simon and Schuster.

Lemke, J. (1990). Talking Science: Language, Learning, and Values. Norwood, New Jersey: Ablex Publishing Corporation.

Milburn, G., Goodson, I. and Clark, R. (Eds.). (1989). Re-Interpreting Curriculum Research: Images and Arguments. London, Ontario: The Althouse Press.

Mrazek, R. (1983). Defining Science Education in a Canadian Context. Elements. 14(5), 6-8.

Mrazek, R. (1990). Teaching Environmental Education in the 1990s. Faculty of Education. The University of Lethbridge. Lethbridge, Alberta.

Mrazek, R. (1991). You Can Get There From Here! Challenge. 28(1), 25-31.

North American Association for Environmental Education. (1992). Preliminary Review Draft for the Report to Congress on the Status of Environmental Education in the United States, Washington, D.C.

Peshkin, A. (1993). The Goodness of Qualitative Research. Educational Researcher. 22(2), 23-29.

Schön, Donald A. (1990). Educating the Reflective Practitioner. San Francisco: Jossey-Bass Inc. Publishers:

Seelig, C. (1954). Ideas and Opinions by Albert Einstein. New York: Wings Books.

Soltis, J. (1984). On the Nature of Educational Research. Educational Researcher. December. 5-10.

Wilson, J. and Cowell, B. (1989). Taking Education Seriously. London, Ontario: The Althouse Press.

About the Author

Rick Mrazek is an associate professor in the Faculty of Education at the University of Lethbridge, Canada. His present responsibilities include teaching methods in science and environmental education, as well as being responsible for professional development scholarship institutes for teachers which focus on agricultural education, water education, elementary science education, and implementing computer technology in the science classroom. Prior to joining the Faculty of Education at the University of Lethbridge eight years ago, Rick taught in the public school system in southern Alberta in classrooms ranging from Grade 3 to senior high school. His M.Ed. and Ph.D. from the University of Alberta were both in science education curriculum and instruction. He has served in a number of capacities in environmental education at the provincial and national level, as well as authoring curricula and supporting documents for junior and senior high school programs ranging from general science to a wildlife and natural resources curriculum. Rick is past president of the Environmental and Outdoor Education Council of The Alberta Teachers' Association and serves as an Alberta coordinator for Project WILD. He has been active as a western region representative to the UNESCO MAB/NET group of the Canadian Man and Biosphere Committee (Canada/MAB) and presently is involved with tri-lateral EE research and teaching initiatives between Canada, Mexico, and the United States.

Rick has been participating in the NAAEE since 1983 and has been a member of the North American Commission for Environmental Education Research since 1987. He has served as a member of the Board of Directors for the Association in 1990 and again from 1992 to the present as a Canadian representative. He served as publications editor for the Environmental Communicator 1991-92 and is presently serving as Proceedings Chair for the 1993 North American Association for Environmental Education conference to be held in Big Sky, Montana .

Due in part to Rick's involvement with a diverse array of groups working within environmental education, a major thrust of much of his work in the past few years has been oriented towards developing partnerships in education and research. When pressed to identify what paradigm his work is representative of, he would ask to be considered to be eclectic and where methodology is concerned "still searching" for the critical paradigm which will help provide a better global environment for Kristen, Evan and children throughout the world.

THE SEARCH FOR PARADIGMS FOR RESEARCH IN ENVIRONMENTAL EDUCATION

John F. Disinger

Abstract

The usefulness of paradigms as conceptual organizers of activities in scientific fields was demonstrated by Thomas Kuhn about 30 years ago. The idea of paradigms appeals to investigators in many areas of inquiry, including environmental education. This paper considers ramifications of the search for paradigms for research in environmental education, development of the field, present status, need, and future possibilities.

The Search for Paradigms for Research in Environmental Education

I am wary of the word "paradigm." My introduction to it came when I first read Thomas Kuhn's The Structure of Scientific Revolutions[1] shortly after its publication in 1962. I was, and remain fascinated by Kuhn's presentations of paradigms and paradigm shifts, and early on became engaged in a number of more or less scholarly discussions of both the book and the concepts. On several occasions I have revisited the book, mainly its 1970 revision[2], and have been exposed to many and diverse interpretations of it. Over time I have become more and more sensitive to uses of the word which to me are questionable, misled or misleading, either or both.

Many scholars imply that their use of the word "paradigm" is parallel to or derived from Kuhn's, though their purpose in doing so is not always clear, nor is the meaning they associate with it. Kuhn was not using a dictionary definition, which typically is limited to the synonyms "pattern, example, model." Those are simpler words, and do not convey the image most of us associate with Kuhn's presentation. To Kuhn, and to most of us, a paradigm is something different; at the very least it implies a more sophisticated construct than "pattern, example, model."

What Kuhn described was the difference between normal science, which leads to changes in conceptual understanding at a slow pace, and extraordinary science, which precipitates relatively rapid adjustments. Normal science is evolutionary, extraordinary science revolutionary. Normal science generally buttresses existing paradigms, whereas extraordinary

---

[1]Thomas S. Kuhn, The Structure of Scientific Revolutions (Chicago, IL: University of Chicago Press, 1962).

[2]Thomas S. Kuhn, The Structure of Scientific Revolutions, Second Edition, Enlarged (Chicago, IL: University of Chicago Press, 1970).

science expedites their reconsideration, and opens the way for new ones.

In Kuhn's view, a paradigm is an overarching conceptual construct, an understanding of how the world or some segment of it operates. Once established it becomes widely accepted, guiding the behavior of most people who have occasion to be concerned about it. A paradigm includes exemplars to which those in the field refer; these are qualitatively different from pre-paradigm, or previous paradigm, exemplars.

A paradigm shift is possible when discordant information forces re-evaluation of an existing paradigm. When new evidence is introduced into an accepted conceptual framework in such a manner that it must be accommodated or rejected, we are obligated to reconceptualize the framework to incorporate that information, or to reject it. The new framework and its exemplars form a new paradigm; the conceptual framework it replaced becomes a discarded or modified one. Because these frameworks or paradigms exist in the minds of those involved, adjustment to new ones is generally not instantaneous. Ways must be found to incorporate new evidence; consideration of possibilities first, then investigation, then development of responsive procedures and new exemplars, then creation of a new paradigm. Old paradigms die hard; they often are entrenched, and their adherents may not surrender them easily or quickly, even though the weight of evidence may call for it. There may be those who refuse to accept a new paradigm, preferring to cling to an old one. It is possible that others may develop yet other alternative paradigms capable of incorporating the new evidence[3].

At any rate, Kuhn's "paradigm" is not garden-variety "model." It means something significantly beyond ordinary "patterns" and examples; it focuses on major shifts in concepts and exemplars, it precipitates reconsideration of world views. Kuhn was not talking about evolutionary changes, nor was he addressing minor detail; his concern was "big pictures."

I do not believe that we currently have an initial paradigm, or a set of competing or alternative paradigms, for research in environmental education. We do have a number of research "patterns, examples, models" which come to us from the field of education, and from other fields of study; we use them for several reasons, one of which is that we do not have our own. Another is that most environmental educators have themselves come from other fields, and bring the research patterns and traditions of those fields with them. Yet a third is that, for most of us, our professional identities remain tied to those other fields, so we feel and perhaps are compelled to maintain identity with them. Thus, we may be practicing "environmental education," but we are professionally obligated to practice it in the context of "something else." For example, because a large number of environmental educators either once were or currently are science educators, there are obvious reasons to employ the research models of the

---

[3] I am grateful to Robert L. Vertrees, School of Natural Resources, The Ohio State University, for his input to, critical review of, and helpful comments on the discussion of Kuhn's work in this paper.

science education community. In turn, there is pressure in the science education community to use the research models of the natural sciences, as opposed to the behavioral sciences.

Whether or not environmental education should have its own paradigm, or set of alternative paradigms, for research is open to question. If it does not aspire to a unique paradigm, are existing paradigms from education, or other related fields, appropriate? Do such paradigms exist? What if no appropriate paradigm can be identified? These are the questions which this volume addresses.

We can describe current styles of, or approaches to, research in environmental education, and can initiate the process of seeking a paradigm of conceptualizing a workable "grand scheme" on which to base our common research thrusts. Whether or not a single paradigm can encompass all environmental education research interests is another open question. We will need to tread carefully, because we have so far been unable to reach consensus as to what the scope of environmental education is, what its purposes are, or which specific audiences we wish to educate. To elucidate:

With respect to scope. To various segments of the professional community, environmental education focuses in a content sense on one or more of: conservation, deep ecology, ecology, energy, environmental ethics, environmental science, global education, natural resource management, nature study, outdoor education, pollution, population, science/technology/society, sustainable development, urban environ-ments, and so on. Though these interface and overlap in various ways, they are not identical or even close[4].

With respect to purposes. Is the primary purpose of environmental education the communication of cognitive information? Are we really trying to change environmental behavior? Either? Both? What else? Other papers in this volume address these concerns carefully, thoughtfully, in a challenging manner. It is a basic question in environmental education, and must be addressed and resolved before any paradigm or set of paradigms for environmental education research can be specified.

With respect to audiences. According to cross-sections of environmental educators, targeted audiences apparently include the total human population, in formal and nonformal settings, cradle to grave. Will a single research paradigm suffice here? Probably not. It is difficult under these conditions to establish a finite set of models.

A specific note of caution is in order. Simply stated, many environmental educators, including those currently involved in the paradigm discussion, focus almost exclusively on formal (school-related) education. But others are concerned with nonformal (out-of-school) audiences. Generalizations

---

[4]An overview of definitions of environmental education was presented in John F. Disinger's, "Environmental Education's Definitional Problem," ERIC/SMEAC Information Bulletin 2 (1983). The selective list of environmental education's areas of concern in this paper has been informally updated, and appears here as illustrative rather than definitive.

dealing with research in environmental education must acknowledge differences in audiences, and recognize the necessity of different approaches; research procedures in school settings, or for school-age children in nonformal settings, may well be inappropriate in nonformal settings. This seems obvious, but is often implicitly ignored. For example, extensive media-related research dealing with the communication of environmental information to the general public has been and is being conducted, but this area has not been considered to date in the environmental education research paradigm discussion.

At the current point of development, it seems overly ambitious and potentially dangerous, to attempt to define a unique research paradigm for environmental education. If we characterize educational research in general as being of four types -- descriptive (preexperimental), survey (normative/status studies), correlational/ex post facto (relational studies), and experimental/quasi-experimental[5] -- we find that all have merits in terms of the present situation, in which we seek to achieve definition of scope, purposes, and audiences. A review of the environmental education research literature of the recent past indicates that all of the above are represented, as the field progresses from exploration, to description, to explanation/ prediction, to control. Papers dealing with exploration and description are far more frequently found in the literature of the field than are papers detailing studies involving explanation/prediction and control[6].

Controlled experimentation is difficult to achieve in environmental education, as it is in all areas of education; it may be more difficult for environmental educators than for educators in other areas because the field is so young, so ill-defined, so diverse, so dynamic, so interactive with so many areas of study. It is unfortunate that educators feel, and sometimes bow to, pressures to emulate the mathematically sophisticated physical sciences in their research efforts. Professional pressures for publication of research papers often force the researcher into highly academic modes which may not be appropriate to the situations under investigation.

Education is a behavioral science; as such, it is far behind the exact sciences in development of empirically demonstrable theories or in ability to exert control over observable events[7]. Kuhn's discussions of paradigms focus on the exact sciences, and understandably so. Are similar constructs appropriate to the behavioral sciences, including education? What will it take, to build a paradigm (or paradigms) for research in environmental education?

---

[5]This categorization of educational research is more or less standard; the immediate source is an unpublished, undated outline for a graduate-level course in educational research taught by Larry E. Miller, Department of Agricultural Education, The Ohio State University.

[6]John L. Hayman Jr., Research in Education (Columbus, OH: Charles E. Merrill, 1968).

[7]An informal review--i.e., categorizing and counting--of 275 papers published in The Journal of Environmental Education, as cited in ERIC's Current Index to Journals in Education between January 1980-December 1990 (eleven years), produced these tallies: descriptive (pre-experimental), 147 papers (53%); survey (normative/status studies), 57 papers (21%); correlational/ex post facto), 60 papers (22%); quasi experimental/experimental, 11 papers (4%).

A good deal of effort has gone into the development of prospective paradigms for research in environmental education. Stapp's seminal definition, still the most frequently quoted, though not always properly attributed and certainly not generally practiced, set a unique standard for all aspects of environmental education, and might serve as a precursor for a research paradigm:

> Environmental education is aimed at producing a citizenry that is knowledgeable concerning the biophysical environment and its associated problems, aware of how to help solve those problems, and motivated to work toward their solution[8].

Clearly, definitions are not paradigms, but they serve as the appropriate point of entry to any field. There must be a starting point, and a clearly stated, commonly accepted definition is an excellent one. But...

In addition to the intellectually intimidating breadth of necessary cognitive concern, the (total) biophysical environment and its associated problems, later identified as residing in both the biophysical and sociocultural environments[9], what makes the Stapp definition unique is the "motivation" aspect. Definitions of most areas of education are cognitive in nature. They verbalize goals dealing with awareness, knowledge, understanding, and sometimes values, but they do not specifically address motivation to work toward the solution of real-world problems.

For all our talk about behavioral objectives over the past 35 years[10], the behaviors typically described for education are cognitive in nature. Moreover, educational research has typically focused on cognition. Where affective behaviors are described and researched, they rarely go beyond paper-and-pencil identification of values. It may be argued that achievement of cognitive and affective objectives, even on paper, will logically lead to changes in real-world behavior, but evidence that this is the case is hard to come by[11].

The Stapp definition implies that the ultimate purpose of environmental education is education for environmental action at least to the point of working actively for environmental quality. Over two decades, Hungerford and his associates[12] have refined this concept by organizing and conducting

---

[8]William B. Stapp et al., "The Concept of Environmental Education," Environmental Education (1969):30-31.

[9] Robert E. Roth et al., Environmental Management Education Concepts-A List (Madison, WI: University of Wisconsin Center for Cognitive Learning, Technical Report No. 126, 1970). (ERIC ED 045376).

[10]Benjamin S. Bloom et al., Taxonomy of Educational Objectives, Handbook I: Cognitive Domain (New York: David McKay Company, 1956); David R. Krathwohl et al., Taxonomy of Educational Objectives, Handbook II: Affective Domain (New York: David McKay Company, 1964).

[11]Louis A. Iozzi, "What Research Says to the Educator: Part I, The Affective Domain," Journal of Environmental Education 20 (Spring 1989):3-9.

[12]Harold R. Hungerford and his colleagues (fellow faculty, students, and former students, including Gary D. Harvey, Gary Klingler, Thomas J. Marcinkowski, John M. Ramsey, Archibald P. Sia, Jody Hines Stone, Audrey N. Tomera, R. Ben Peyton, Trudi L. Volk, and Richard J. Wilke) at Southern Illinois University have published a number of papers reporting their research in the area of

a series of focused research studies dealing with education for the development of responsible environmental behavior. They have established a functional model with a viable research pattern and consistent examples. Another candidate for "potential paradigm for environmental education research" is action research[13]. It too has become established as a useful and productive model. A strong case has been made for the appropriateness of interpretive research in environmental education[14].

To this point, none of these has become pervasive in the field, nor has anything else. At this point, there is no established single paradigm, no initial paradigm, for environmental education research. Using the Kuhn description, none of the current candidates appear worthy of "paradigm status," though they clearly qualify as "alternative models." There is no apparent reason why they should instead be viewed as "contesting models;" as environmental education evolves, there is sufficient room and demand for a variety of research techniques, from descriptive to quasi-experimental[15]. It is understandable (and at this point still necessary) that most of the environmental education literature is descriptive; we are still learning the territory.

Whether or not research in environmental education eventually requires, or warrants, a true paradigm is problematic, and at this point not particularly important. However, the exercise of seeking one has remarkable merit as it encourages dialogue, focuses debate, promotes definition and re-definition, and places a premium on intellectual honesty and rigorously conceived and executed research of all kinds.

About the Author

John F. Disinger is a professor in the School of Natural Resources of The Ohio State University, Columbus, Ohio, and a courtesy professor in the Department of Educational Studies at Ohio State. Previously he was Associate Director of the ERIC Clearinghouse for Science, Mathematics, and Environmental Education, also at Ohio State. He has been associated with all of these since 1971, following receipt of a Ph.D. degree in Science Education at Ohio State. His earlier experience includes 15 years of public

---

responsible environmental behavior. An overview is presented in Hungerford's "Environmental Education and Student Behaviors," in Trends and Issues in Environmental Education: EE in School Curricula, ed. John F. Disinger (Columbus, OH: ERIC/SMEAC, 1987), 25-38 (ERIC ED 292608).

[13] Paul Hart, "Alternative Perspectives in Environmental Education Research: Paradigm of Critically Reflective Inquiry," a paper presented at the annual conference of the North American Association for Environmental Education (NAAEE), San Antonio, Texas, November 6, 1990.

[14] Diane C. Cantrell, "Alternative Paradigms in Environmental Education: The Interpretive Perspective", a paper presented at the annual conference of the North American Association for Environmental Education (NAAEE), San Antonio, Texas, November 6, 1990.

[15] The published title of the 1990 NAAEE conference symposium which served as precursor to this volume was "Contesting Paradigms in Environmental Education." The focus was described as research. The 1990 title has been replaced in this volume by a semantically softer, less contentious title, "Alternative Paradigms in Environmental Education." My personal preference would be for less pretentious terminology, on the order of "Alternative Models in Environmental Education Research."

middle school/junior high school science teaching in Upstate New York.

Dr. Disinger's vita lists, as author or editor, more than 100 publications--directories, case studies, survey reports, literature reviews, book reviews, "state of the art" papers, etc.--in environmental education over the past 20 years. He has been active in the North American Association for Environmental Education since 1975--as treasurer from 1979-1984, as conference and program chair in 1985, and as president during 1985-86. He received the Association's Walter Jeske Award in 1984.

CONFRONTING THE ISSUES

A CONTEXTUAL REVIEW OF THE "QUANTITATIVE PARADIGM" IN EE RESEARCH

Tom Marcinkowski

Abstract

This paper has been prepared as one of three initial papers to be presented at the Symposium "Alternative Paradigms in Environmental Education Research" to be held at the NAAEE Annual Conference in San Antonio. I was asked to present an overview of what is commonly referred to as the "Quantitative Paradigm" in educational research circles, and so, the central focus of this paper is just that. At the same time, I would feel remiss if I did not attempt to place the Symposium and attendant discussions of educational research in some broader context. Thus, I have preceded my presentation of this paradigm with some comments on how I have come to look at research, and on several apparent problems in the EE research arena which emerge from this view or are apparent in the literature. I have also preceded an overview of the quantitative paradigm with a broad comparative overview of the two paradigms of interest. Following a presentation of the quantitative paradigm, I wish to acknowledge up front that I hold some strong views on any possible and desirable relationships between these alternative paradigms (or methods). Specifically, I question whether there is any necessary incompatibility between the two paradigms. Thus, the fourth section of this paper contains a number of comments and questions along these lines. I have concluded the paper with several suggestions as to how we, as an educational field, might address some of the these apparent dilemmas and questions.

The paper which follows is an attempt to provide some philosophical, methodological and historical views on research in the field of environmental education. It has been organized as follows:

I. Foundations
    A. Some Basic Definitions
    B. A Model for Understanding and Interpreting Research
    C. Identifying Dilemmas and Problems in EE Research
    D. Closing Comments

II. An Overview of Quantitative and Qualitative Research
    A. Three Levels of Analysis in Understanding this Dilemma
    B. The Two as Research Paradigms

I. Foundations

A.   Some Basic Definitions

The apparent dilemma to be addressed herein pertains to qualitative and quantitative research. In order to discuss this dilemma with some degree of clarity, I would like to provide definitions for some of the key terms. These are not offered as "the" definitions for the respective terms. Rather, they are those definitions which have been used within this paper. Brief definitions, and sources consulted relative to each, are provided below.

<u>Research</u> is disciplined inquiry. "Disciplined inquiry, unlike opinion and belief, 'is conducted and reported in such a way that the argument can be examined painstakingly. The report does not depend for its appeal on the eloquence of the writer or any surface plausibility' " (Cronbach & Supples, 1969, p. 15, as quoted in McMillan & Schumacher, 1989, p. 9). The principles and methods of inquiry may vary from discipline to discipline.

<u>Inquiry</u> is the search for knowledge using recognized methods in the collection, analysis and interpretation of observations (adapted from McMillan & Schumacher, 1989, p. 8). As such, Kerlinger (1973) argues that inquiry is but one of a number of ways of "knowing." Other ways of knowing include revelation, tradition, authority, logic, intuition, and social compact/agreement.

<u>Scientific Inquiry/Research</u> "is systematic, controlled, empirical, and critical investigation of hypothetical propositions about the presumed relations among natural phenomena" (Kerlinger, 1973, p. 11). According to Borg and Gall (1983) the purposes of science and of scientific research are: "(1) to describe, (2) to predict (3) to control, and (4) to explain" the nature of and relationships among phenomena (p. 20). Scientific inquiry/research may be undertaken in an inductive or deductive fashion, and both are considered to be part of the 'positivistic' philosophic tradition (Borg & Gall, 1983, p.26).

<u>Social Inquiry/Research</u> is the systematic, empirical, and analytical investigation of social phenomena (i.e., including individuals and groups, events and processes). In educational settings, the phenomena of interest include "shared beliefs, practices, artifacts, folk knowledge, and behaviors" (Goetz & LeCompte, 1984, pp. 2-3, cited in McMillan & Schumacher, 1989, p. 386). An array of research methods have been used within the various social sciences. For example, social inquiry/research may be undertaken in an inductive or deductive fashion (e.g., ethnographies and single-subject case studies, respectively), and may involve the use of interactive and/or non-interactive strategies. As a result social inquiry/research may be undertaken in a positivistic fashion (i.e., as social science) or in another fashion which has been referred to under a number of associated labels including naturalistic, artistic, illuminative, and subjective (Eisner, 1981; Borg & Gall, 1983, p. 27; McMillan & Schumacher, 1989, p. 385).

<u>Educational Inquiry/Research</u> is the particular area of disciplined inquiry which focus upon the study of educational phenomena. "Education is a field of inquiry where the phenomena, events, people, processes, and institutions constitute the raw materials for inquiries of many kinds. The perspectives and research methods of many disciplines can be (add: and have been) brought to bear on the questions arising from education and inherent in education" (McMillan & Schumacher, 1989, p. 9). This is true largely because education is neither a science nor a discipline in the traditional senses of those terms (McMillan & Schumacher, 1989, p. 9).

<u>Inductive Reasoning and Inquiry</u> This type of reasoning and inquiry begins with the systematic collection and accumulation of observations. Over time, it may proceed toward the synthesis and interpretation of an ever growing set of observations. In turn, this may lead to the development of one or more generalizations regarding the phenomena under investigation. Attempts to accumulate, organize and pose relationships among a set of generalizations may be referred to as "theory building."

<u>Deductive Reasoning and Inquiry</u> This type of reasoning and inquiry begins with a theory or some form of theoretical framework. Statements

which serve as testable generalizations are abstracted from that theory. Questions and/or hypotheses may be posed relative to each generalization. These questions and/or hypotheses clearly identify those variables and variable relationships to be investigated. Observations are systematically collected on those variables and variable relationships. These observations are analyzed and interpreted in light of the original questions and/or hypotheses. This manner of inquiry may be referred to as "theory testing."

Theory is according to Kerlinger (1973), "a set of interrelated constructs (concepts), definitions, and propositions that present a systematic view of phenomena by specifying relationships among variables, with the purpose of (describing) ... predicting ... and explaining ... the phenomena" (p. 9). The power of a theory refers to the extent to which it will allow one to predict, control, and/or explain the phenomena of interest. The range of explanation of a theory commonly refers to the range of variable conditions or relationships it attempts to explain, and more concretely, to the range of situations to which those variable relationships apply.

B. A Model for Understanding and Interpreting Research

In addition to providing definitions for several key terms, I would like to introduce a heuristic device which serves as one way of looking at research (i.e., the design, conduct, reporting and interpretation of studies). This device is a modified and expanded view of a model developed by D. Bob Gowin called the 'Vee Heuristic' (Novak & Gowin, 1984, Ch. 3). Gowin refers to this model as "a tool for acquiring knowledge about knowledge, and how knowledge is constructed and used" (Novak & Gowin, 1984, p. 57). Since the primary purpose of research (inquiry) is the construction of knowledge, this model or heuristic should provide valuable insights into the (research) processes associated with knowledge construction. I would like to briefly present and describe Gowin's heuristic as a prerequisite to presenting a modified and expanded view of it (see Figure 1, p.33).

Gowin's knowledge Vee contains two axes, which are labeled as the Conceptual and Methodological axes. He refers to the conceptual axis as the 'thinking side', and to the methodological axis as the 'doing side' of the Vee. From a common point in the diagram (i.e., the phenomena of interest), these two axes move from simple to ever more complex and comprehensive levels of analysis. Gowin is careful to note that there should be an active interplay between these two axes:

In knowledge production or the interpretation of knowledge, all elements function interactively with each other to make sense out of the events or objects observed (Novak & Gowin, 1984, p. 56).

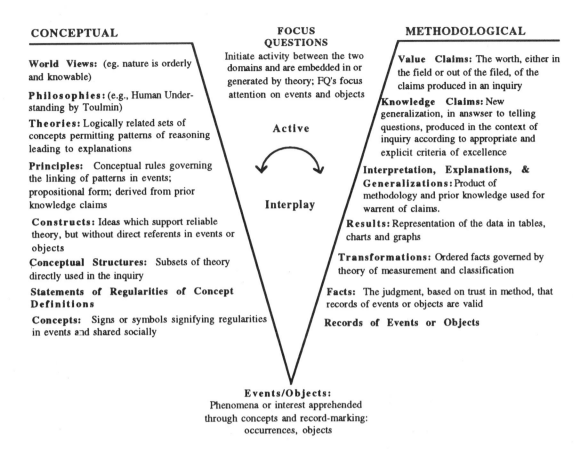

CONCEPTUAL

World Views: (eg. nature is orderly and knowable)

Philosophies: (e.g., Human Understanding by Toulmin)

Theories: Logically related sets of concepts permitting patterns of reasoning leading to explanations

Principles: Conceptual rules governing the linking of patterns in events; propositional form; derived from prior knowledge claims

Constructs: Ideas which support reliable theory, but without direct referents in events or objects

Conceptual Structures: Subsets of theory directly used in the inquiry

Statements of Regularities of Concept Definitions

Concepts: Signs or symbols signifying regularities in events and shared socially

FOCUS QUESTIONS
Initiate activity between the two domains and are embedded in or generated by theory; FQ's focus attention on events and objects

Active

Interplay

METHODOLOGICAL

Value Claims: The worth, either in the field or out of the filed, of the claims produced in an inquiry

Knowledge Claims: New generalization, in answser to telling questions, produced in the context of inquiry according to appropriate and explicit criteria of excellence

Interpretation, Explanations, & Generalizations: Product of methodology and prior knowledge used for warrent of claims.

Results: Representation of the data in tables, charts and graphs

Transformations: Ordered facts governed by theory of measurement and classification

Facts: The judgment, based on trust in method, that records of events or objects are valid

Records of Events or Objects

Events/Objects:
Phenomena or interest apprehended through concepts and record-marking: occurrences, objects

Figure 1.   A version of Gowin's 'Knowledge Vee,' with titles for and descriptions of key components (Novak & Gowin, 1984, p. 56).

From his uses of this heuristic, he offers the following insights:

> We have found that the Vee shape helps students recognize the tension and interplay between disciplinary knowledge constructed (and modified) over time and the knowledge an inquiry allows them to construct over time here and now. Although the conceptual elements on the left side of the Vee illuminate our inquiry, these are constructions (conceptions) that have developed over time, whereas the elements on the right are constructions from our immediate inquiry ... Another value of the Vee form is that because inquiries often go awry right at the bottom of the Vee, it is less easy to ignore relevant key events or objects or key concepts. (Novak & Gowin, 1984, pp. 57-58)

Gowin's knowledge Vee may be modified and expanded for use in scholarly research settings. Within these settings, there appear to be three key features to any study:

(a)   an explicit or implicit framework of substantive concepts employed in the design of a study;

(b)   a <u>framework of methodological concepts</u> employed in the design of a study; and

(c)   a <u>data organization, analysis and interpretation sequence</u> employed in generating knowledge and value claims.

If one accepts the proposition that these are key features of most, if not all educational research studies, then it follows that a modified version of Gowin's Vee should address all three. Since at present it does not, it may be expanded to include a third axis. The three axes would include two axes associated with the design of research, and a third which seeks to construct knowledge from collected data. A preliminary depiction of this three-dimensional heuristic is presented below.

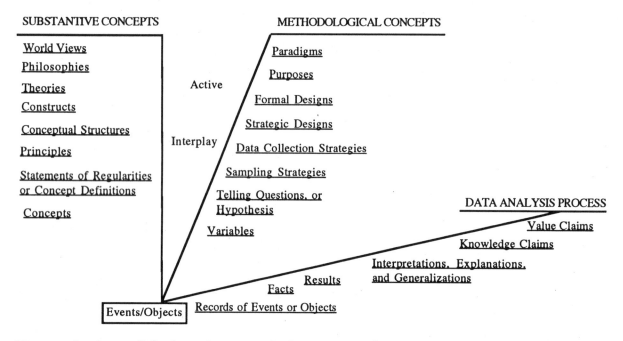

Figure 2. A modified and expanded version of Gowin's Vee heuristic, in which methodological concepts and the data analysis process become separate and explicit dimensions.

A comparison between Figures 1 and 2 will reveal at least two things. First, the ordering of components along Gowins' "Conceptual" axis has been altered in the modified version's "Substantive Concepts" axis (i.e., see the ordering of "Constructs," "Conceptual Structures," and "Principles"). Secondly, Figure 2 lacks descriptions for the newly added components along the "Methodological Concepts" axis. Descriptions for each may be found in Table 1 (next page).

Table 1
Descriptions for Components Found on the "Methodological Concepts" Axis *

Component	Description

<u>Paradigm</u>: An organized set of philosophical suppositions, including those about the nature of knowledge, which undergird the differing approaches to inquiry or research (e.g., multiple realities or images of reality may be socially constructed; there is no implicit need to dichotomize between fact and value statements);

<u>Purpose</u>: The nature of the knowledge contribution sought and/or made by each of the various research approaches or designs (e.g., exploration of phenomena, theory building, theory testing);

<u>Formal Design</u>: A pure or ideal form of the plan and structure of an investigation used to obtain evidence from identified sources for the purpose of responding to research questions. Such designs are prototypic of particular research paradigms and purposes, and have been developed and refined over time (e.g., true experimental designs, survey designs using stratified random sampling).

<u>Strategic Designs</u>: A pragmatic form of a formal design, which has been modified to fit conditions and/or constraints in the research setting, or to allow the researcher to respond to differing research purposes and questions.

<u>Data Collection Strategy</u>: A plan to use one or more techniques to collect desired observations/data in an organized manner (e.g., a plan to combine pencil-and-paper techniques with interview and unobtrusive observation techniques);

<u>Sampling Strategy</u>: A plan for selecting subjects and/or sources of data from a larger group of subjects/larger set of sources. In many though not all cases, this will be undertaken in a manner which allows the select group to somehow represent the larger group;

<u>Telling Questions or Hypotheses</u>: A question or statement (respectively) which clearly identifies the variable(s) and/or variable relationship(s) under investigation; and

<u>Variables</u>: Any class or category of object, behavior, or event, or specified attribute of such a class or category which observably varies from one circumstance to another, and which may be assigned differing values.

*Note: Sources consulted in developing these descriptions include Kerlinger (1973); Borg and Gall (1983); Isaac and Michael (1983); and McMillan and Schumacher (1989).

As with Gowin's initial model, there should be an active interplay between all three axes in the modified version of Gowin's Vee (see Figure 2, p. 34). For example, if a researcher chooses to design a study which focuses upon the kinds of environmental behavior individuals engage in, then s/he has a number of substantive and methodological design decisions to make. From a substantive design standpoint, sample decision questions are noted in Table 2 (next page).

Table 2
Sample Design Questions One Might Raise Along the Substantive Axis of the Heuristic in an Investigation of Responsible Environmental Behavior.

Axis Element	Sample Design Questions
Philosophy:	Should I offer any explicit philosophical statements about the intentionality of human actions from a given philosophical perspective (e.g., realism, pragmatism, existentialism)?
Theory:	Will I employ any theoretical framework for selecting and/or defining the kinds of behavior to be investigated (e.g., view behavior from the perspective of intention, social influence, conditioning or habit, circumstance, or means of coping)?
Construct:	Will I look at negative instances of environmental behavior (i.e., destructive ones), or only instances of responsible environmental behavior (REB)?
Conceptual Structures:	Is it better to select an organizing structure (e.g., Hungerford and Peyton's "Action Paradigm"), to generate one on my own, or to allow one to emerge from the data?
Principles:	Should I only look at repetitive (as opposed to one-time) behaviors?
Regularities /Definitions:	How should I define instances of environmentally positive/sound consumer actions?
Concepts:	Is it sufficient to study only instances of environmentally sound consumer purchases? What kinds of consumer purchases fall under this heading?

A similar set of questions may be generated which focus upon methodological design decisions. In continuing this example on responsible environmental behavior, a set of sample questions are presented in Table 3 (next page).

Table 3

Sample Design Questions One Might Raise Along the Methodological Axis of the Heuristic in an Investigation of Responsible Environmental Behavior.

Axis Element	Sample Design Questions
Paradigm:	Should this study be more of a quantitative or a qualitative study of REB?
Purpose:	Am I seeking to build, corroborate, or test any theoretical propositions about REB?
Formal Design:	Is there any reason for using a true as opposed to a quasi-experimental design?
Strategic Design:	Since there isn't an instrument for measuring one of the kinds of REB I want to investigate, should I collect anecdotal reports, even though this is a descriptive survey-type study?
Data Collection Strategy:	Should I use both self-reported paper-and-pencil and other reported direct observations, so that I can generate validity and reliability estimates?
Sampling Strategy:	Should I use a single sample population, or two sample populations to allow for comparisons?
Research Questions and/or Hypotheses:	Should I pose separate research questions for each of the types of REB I want to investigate
Variables:	How should I label and operationally define each of the types of REB I want to investigate?

With respect to Tables 2 and 3, responses to decision questions like these will probably be influenced by a variety of variables, including the status of relevant theory and research (i.e., the status of the knowledge bases the researcher may draw from), the researcher's own training and background (i.e., researcher's own strengths, limitations and biases with respect to substantive and/or methodological design), availability of funds and time, and accessibility to sample populations and subjects, among others. Consequently, it is often common for a researcher to have a constrained range of decision alternatives to choose from; i.e., s/he may (have to) make her/his decisions on some basis other than what would be an ideal (or formal) research strategy.

Despite such limitations, it should be clearly recognized that both types of design decisions have a bearing on the manner in which data are analyzed. For example, if a researcher begins a prediction study using the knowledge-attitude-behavior model as their conceptual structure, and their research questions only focus upon these variable relationships, then it is highly unlikely that they will generate any knowledge claims which pertain to environmental sensitivity or focus of control. Similarly, if the study employs an ethnographic or survey research design, it is highly unlikely that they will generate any firm knowledge or value claims of a cause-and-effect nature. Thus, there should be an active interplay between each of the two design axes (dimensions) and the data interpretation axis of the heuristic.

In closing, when professionals conduct analyses, reviews or syntheses of research studies, they tend to look at the kinds of features identified in this modified version of Gowin's Vee (see Roth & Hegelson, 1972; Voelker, A., et al., 1973; Bennett, 1974; Roth, 1976; Iozzi, 1981, 1984; Peyton, 1981; Lewis, 1981/2; Stewart, 1982; Hungerford, Tomera, & Wilson, 1983a, 1983b; Wilke & Leatherman, 1983; Hines, Hungerford, & Tomera, 1988; Iozzi, 1989a, 1989b; Marcinkowski, in development). Perhaps more importantly, such professionals also look for those types of active interplay or internal consistency within each study which are recommended by Gowin. When such interplay or consistency is lacking within studies, it has often been noted by the researcher or by reviewers of the study report. Thus, while this modified heuristic device can and will be used to probe the focal dilemma of interest here, it can also be used to help identify other research concerns or problems in the field.

C.   Identifying Dilemmas and Problems in EE Research

The dilemma which serves as the focus of this symposium is the apparent incompatibility between the older, more established research paradigm (i.e., the quantitative paradigm) and the younger, less established research paradigm (i.e., the qualitative paradigm). However, this dilemma is by no means the only, and is perhaps not even the most important problem facing those interested in research in environmental education (EE). I will not try to argue importance, as this is largely a function of professional perception and consensus. Rather, for the purposes of this discussion, it does appear to be important to identify other apparent research problems, and to discuss any relationship between each and the symposiums focal dilemma. Doing so may allow one to view a discussion of paradigms within a broader research context.

Based upon prior summaries, syntheses, and critical reviews of the EE research literature (Roth & Hegelson, 1972; Voelker, A., et al, 1973; Bennett, 1974; Roth, 1976; Iozzi, 1981, 1984; Peyton, 1981; Lewis, 1981/2; Stewart, 1982; Hungerford, Tomera, & Wilson 1983a, 1983b; Wilke & Leatherman, 1983; Hines, Hungerford, & Tomera, 1988; Iozzi, 1989a, 1989b; Marcinkowski, in development), the following have been identified in these documents as, and/or appear to me to be, research-related problems in EE:

1.   The methodological quality or rigor of much of the reported research, including designs and data collection procedures, has

been identified as sub-standard and in need of improvement.

2. The variables investigated in much of the reported research have largely been knowledge and/or attitudinal variables, despite the apparent limitations of this type of research and the calls for researchers to investigate a wider array of variables.

3. The substantive models or frameworks commonly employed in reported research have been weak. The most noteworthy example is a continuing reliance upon the knowledge-attitude-behavior model, which reflects the popular folklore that information input influences knowledge, which in turn positively influences attitudes, and that positive attitudes directly influence behavior (Hendee, 1972; Ramsey & Rickson, 1977, p. 10; Birch & Schwabb, 1983, p. 30; Marcinkowski, 1989, pp. 94-102; Hungerford & Volk, 1990, p. 9). Since empirically-based models/frameworks are available, they should be used to guide substantive design decisions.

4. Despite the appearance of the previously noted list of citations, there has been limited attention given to the synthesis and critical review of research in and relevant to the field. The area of research which has probably received the greatest attention has been that on responsible environmental behavior. On the other hand, there appear to be few, if any, separate, published attempts to do so for qualitative-type research.

5. A problem which appears to underlie #3 and build on #4 is the limited attention given to theory or model building in the field. While there are a number of ways of approaching model building, I would argue that empirical findings should be carefully considered. To date, there appear to be too few efforts which are grounded in research in the field, in part due to the absence of syntheses and critical reviews or research. Moreover, the resulting dearth of models leaves many researchers either to synthesize the relevant research on their own, to adapt existing models from other fields, or more simply, to rely upon either limited or uninspected popular models.

6. As in many fields, there appears to be a substantial 'gap' between what appears to be known via research, and what is commonly done in practice in the field. There are two sides to this problem, both of which are germane to this discussion: (a) in some cases, practice has advanced and research into such "good practice" is needed; and (b) in other cases, research has pointed out some fairly widespread limitations in practice, though these results often go unused. The latter is most apparent in surveys of formal programs (e.g., Childress, 1978), non-formal programs (e.g., Simmons, 1990), and teacher inservice programs (e.g., Wilson,

1988), for, among other things, these surveys indicate that there is widespread programatic inattention to important goals and objectives in the field.

7. In referring to the problems presented in #6, one of the underlying problems may have to do with program evaluation efforts. Studies of program evaluation (e.g., Childress, 1977; Disinger, 1981, 1989) indicate that few programs systematically collect observations/data on intended learning outcomes and on the program features which may contribute to or affect these. In turn, there appear to be a number of problems which underlie the dearth of systematic evaluation efforts. These include: (a) recognition of evaluation as a priority; (b) the time, costs, and effort involved in evaluation; (c) the limited expertise of administrators, teachers, and staff, as well as limited access to others with such expertise; and (d) the absence of a single collection or repository of the array of valid and reliable procedures/ instruments which might be useable for such purposes.

Those who work in research and evaluation in the field know how difficult it can be to gain access to funds which may be adequate for more than a single or small number of studies. The most common type of funded request is probably that which has been written into larger education grants for "evaluation;" (e.g., of training or development). And, few programs have the luxury of expending sizeable amounts of their own money on research or evaluation efforts. Further, those school systems that do have research and evaluation units tend to focus on areas other than EE, since EE is rarely a systemwide requirement. Moreover, few non-formal institutions are large enough to warrant even a single position for research and evaluation. In some cases, instructors have been trained to perform these functions. However, instructor training, available time, and available support services are often limited. In short, there tend to be many more pressing and immediate things to attend to than to design and/or conduct well thought out studies of practice.

8. Finally, many of these problems may, in part, be attributed to the pervading "culture of research." What I mean by this is that individual studies tend to be the rule (e.g., as in much of graduate level research), and cohesive programs of research the exception. A careful review of collections of research abstracts in the field (Iozzi, 1981, 1984) indicates that few members of the profession published more than two or three studies over the 1971-1982 period. And, while there are strands of research which have a programatic feel to them (e.g., key conservation and environmental concepts, investigation and action skills, community problem solving, and responsible environmental

behavior), these strands tend to be both few in number and circumscribed in nature. Under these conditions, one would have to overcome a number of barriers if they wished to develop a widespread, cohesive program of research on good practice, or on other educationally significant research variables of interest to the field.

While it is neither practical nor appropriate to address each of these apparent problems in this paper, it does seem appropriate to at least identify them. They are presented herein for several reasons. First, they broaden the context for discussing the symposium's focal dilemma. The list suggests that this dilemma is not the only research problem plaguing the field. And, given the nature of the symposium, it seems reasonable to infer that discussions would (and should) touch upon some of these other research problems. Second, a response to this dilemma should at least acknowledge the presence of other problems, and when possible, also seek to address them. An attempt will be made to do so in this paper when it appears appropriate.

D.   Closing Comments

Within this section of the paper, I have attempted to provide a broad context within which to view this discussion of the qualitative and quantitative paradigms. This has included communicating definitions for several key terms, presenting a modified version of Gowin's Knowledge Vee as a means for critically inspecting research decisions and reports, and a select list of research problems which confront the EE research community. These introductory comments allow, and perhaps encourage, many questions to be raised. These questions should be kept in mind, and probably aired for discussion as you review the main sections of this paper, as you review other papers, and as you participate in this symposium.

II. An Overview of Quantitative and Qualitative Research

A.   Three Levels of Analysis in Understanding this Dilemma

Rather than plunge into a review of the quantitative paradigm, I would rather begin with a comparative overview of the two paradigms. It is important to point out that an array of established educational researchers have written on this subject, and so, I will be drawing upon writings from a sizeable body of literature (e.g., Eisner, 1981; Isaac & Michael, 1981; Schulman, 1981; Borg & Gall, 1983; Smith, 1983; Smith & Heshusius, 1986; Firestone, 1987; Bryman, 1988; McMillan & Schumacher, 1989). Within this literature, there are differences of opinion as to how to conceptualize and organize a discussion of the two, for the manner in which one does so can show bias toward one paradigm or the other. Despite this, it is necessary to develop some means of organization so that analysis and discussion may proceed.

The framework I have chosen is taken from the modified version of Gowin's Vee presented in Figure 2 (p. 34). The methodological axis of that diagram contains a number of components which may serve as levels of analysis. Thus, a comparative overview could include analyses at the levels of: (1) paradigm; (2) purpose; (3) formal design; (4) strategic design; and (5) sampling and data collection strategy. The remaining parts of this section contain a comparative overview of the two paradigms using (1), (3), and (4) as levels of analysis, as each should offer some unique perspective to this discussion.

B.   The Two as Research Paradigms

Much has been written about quantitative and qualitative research as paradigms; i.e., as sets of philosophical assumptions about the nature of reality, truth, and knowledge. A broad review of the two as research paradigms is presented in Table 4 (below). At this level of analysis, researchers grapple with issues which "brings to the forefront the epistomological question of what is to count as knowledge. If researchers do not discuss this question, they are forfeiting any participation in determining the basis for the authority of their knowledge" (Smith, 1983, p. 13).

Table 4		
A Comparative Analysis of the Two as Paradigms *		
Features	Quantitative Paradigm	Qualitative Paradigm
Obvious Distinction	Presents results in numerical and more specifically, in statistical form	Presents results in narrative, and more specifically, in rich (thick) descriptive form
Origins	Derived from the natural and physical sciences, and reflects the tradition of scientific inquiry	Derived from the social sciences, including the fields of anthropology, sociology, psychology and history
Assumptions About the World (Reality)	Takes a logical positivist view, which assumes that there are social facts with a single objective reality apart from individuals' beliefs	Takes a naturalistic-phenomenological view, which assumes that multiple realities may be constructed through social processes

* Note: Sources consulted in developing this table include Kerlinger (1973); Eisner (1981), McMillan and Schumacher (1983), Smith (1983), and Firestone (1987)

Table 4: (contd)		
Features	Quantitative Paradigm	Qualitative Paradigm
Assumptions About Truth	Takes the position that truth consists of observable and verifiable (or objective) facts, and not of internal conditions, such as personal dispositions or values. This gives rise to a fact-value dichotomy.	Takes the position that there is no objective reality apart from the knower, and therefore truth consists of a complex of value-laden observations and interpretations. As a result, there is no a priori fact-value dichotomy.
Research Purpose	Seeks to establish patterns of, relationships between, and causes of social phenomena (description, prediction, and explanation)	Seeks to establish understanding of social phenomena from participants perspectives (exploration, description, grounded explanation)
Research Methods and Processes	Recognized procedures have been established for generating questions and designs before the study begins (i.e., a priori)	More flexible procedures have been established, and allow the questions and design to emerge or develop as a study progresses
Prototypical Designs	Survey, correlational and experimental designs	Ethnographic, historical and policy designs
Researchers Role	Researcher remains detached from the setting to avoid bias, and tends to rely upon instru- ments as an intermediary device for data collection purposes	Researcher becomes immersed in the setting, and tends to rely on disciplined subjectivity (Erickson, 1973) in order to cultivate understanding during and as part of data collection
Validity and Reliability Estimates	Validity and reliability are seen as characteristics of measurement devices. Estimates are obtained using known analysis procedures	Validity and reliability are seen as characteristics of the data themselves. Estimates are obtained through triangulation and audit trails
Methods of Data Analysis	Usually employs parametric and non-parametric statistical tests	Usually employs some form of content analysis (e.g., concept or theme analysis)
Importance of the Research Setting	Efforts are usually made to allow generalization of results beyond the particular setting of the study	Efforts are usually made to develop generalizations which are specific to the particular setting of the study
Importance of Theory	Theory building and testing (verification) serve as its basic aims	If any attention is given to theorizing, it tends to emphasize the generation of grounded theory

43

C.   The Two as Sets of "Pure" or Formal Designs

In Table 4, one of the key features on which the two paradigms are compared is labeled "Prototypical Designs." In research methods texts and manuals, authors commonly depict survey, correlational, and experimental type research designs as typical examples of quantitative designs. At the same time, they tend to depict ethnographic, historical and policy research designs as examples of qualitative designs (e.g., Borg & Gall, 1983; McMillan & Schumacher, 1989). One reason for doing so is that these types of designs have been developed and applied within the respective research traditions associated with the two paradigms. In simpler terms, Firestone (1987) suggests that "the purists assert that qualitative and quantitative methods are based in paradigms that make differing assumptions" (p. 16). Smith (1983) goes on to point out the potential danger in this:

> at the extreme, the methodology (designs) appropriate to one approach will be seen as irrelevant from the perspective of the other approach. In a milder sense, various elements and practices will be defined and interpreted differently, given the different perspectives. (p. 13)

Let us take a look at the manner in which survey, correlational, and experimental type designs are presented. Most methods texts present each as a distinctive type of quantitative design; i.e., each has its own chapter. Borg and Gall (1983) refer to survey research as "a distinctive research methodology" (p. 404). Within this type of design, they present a number sub-types, including cross-sectional, longitudinal, and delphi designs. With respect to correlational research, these authors go on the say that "the basic design in correlational research is very simple, involving nothing more than collecting data on two or more variables on the same group of subjects, and computing a correlation coefficient" (p. 573). Many research methods texts go on to present multivariate correlational studies and prediction studies as more sophisticated types of correlational designs, each marked by distinctive statistical analysis techniques (e.g., discriminant, regression, and path analyses). And, based upon the work of Campbell and Stanley (1963), experimental designs have tended to be presented as true experimental, quasi-experimental, or pre-experimental. Amongst these, the true experimental design evidences the most potent controls, and is therefore consistently noted as the most powerful and most valuable type of experimental design. On the other hand, pre-experimental designs, including many action research designs, are considered almost worthless due to the potential for internal and external validity threats which compromise the intent of this design, and any resulting cause-and-effect claims.

A review of methods texts and much of the literature on research design suggests that ethnographic, historical and policy research designs may also be seen as distinctive types of qualitative designs, as each often has a separate chapter devoted to it. However, there is one characteristic feature of qualitative designs which keeps them from sinking into the apparently rigid form of the various types of quantitative designs; i.e., they are fashioned in a more flexible or fluid manner. For example, Smiths (1982) assessment of enthnographic research is that it is "evolving and changing rapidly" (p. 588; as cited in McMillan & Schumacher, 1989, p. 383). McMillan and Schumacher go on to indicate that "accompanying the explosion of qualitative research is a proliferation of terms for over thirty variants of ethnography" (1989, p. 383). Borg and Gall (1983, pp. 804-5) present a somewhat similar view of historical research designs in stating "the search for historical facts and the interpretation of those facts are not necessarily discrete, sequential phases of a historical research project" (p. 803). While there are distinctive features comprising historical research designs, and some general sequence to them, the specific design tends to unfold in a manner not unlike that which occurs in ethnographic research. Lastly, policy research is akin to historical research in that both may be seen as forms of analytical research. "The (policy) analyst proceeds in a circular fashion because of the interrelationship of the research problem, sources, criticism, analysis, and explanation" (Macmillan & Schumacher, 1989, p. 442). Thus, by virtue of this tendency toward being flexible, qualitative designs tend to avoid much of the concretization we associate with "purity of design." Nonetheless, there still remains the tendency to define these various types of designs on the basis of sets of distinctive or distinguishing characteristics (Guba, 1981; Lincoln & Guba, 1982, 1988; Smith & Heshusius, 1986, p. 8).

If one only looked at research methods texts as the source of information about research designs, one might come away with two distinct ideas. The first is that the different types of quantitative and of qualitative designs have been developed with particular kinds of research purposes, problems and questions in mind. The importance of fitting design (or method) to purpose, problem and/or question is clearly recognized. In general, I take no argument with that idea. The second idea one may form is that each of these types and sub-types are used (more-or-less) just as they are presented. This may be reinforced by authors inclusion of segments from or synopses of studies which clearly and (hopefully) unambiguously reflect each distinctive type of design (e.g., Borg, 1987; McMillan & Schumacher, 1989; Fraenkel & Wallen, 1990). While this may serve as a useful textbook teaching device, it does tend to convey the message that studies tend to reflect features common to one and only one design. This second idea greatly over-simplifies how researchers construct, employ, and report research designs.

D.   The Notion of Research as Strategic Design

Professionals writing in the comparative analysis vein make the distinction between purist views and pragmatist views of research design. In seeking to counter the purist assertion that design reflects paradigm, ... Reichardt and Cook state:

    ... the pragmatists respond that many studies contradict the purists expectations about how method-types are supposed to be linked to paradigms. For instance, quantitative researchers use opinion polling to understand the perspectives of others and often immerse themselves in the situation during the planning and pre-testing phases of their studies. (Firestone, 1987, p. 17)

The point made by Firestone and others is reasonably apparent in Figure 2. In preparing a revised version of Gowins Vee, I have configured the hierarchy of "Methodological Concepts" such that formal designs are proximal to, and are more likely to reflect paradigm and purpose than would strategic designs. Similarly, strategic designs are more proximal to, and are more likely to reflect the research problems and questions one works with than would formal designs. In neither situation should these be considered hard and fast rules; rather they appear to be tendencies.

As is implied in Figure 2, the literature portrays pragmatists as being strategists; i.e., as arguing that research design is primarily a matter "of fitting research techniques to a problem" (Firestone, 1987, p. 20). There are two ways of viewing this tendency. On the one hand, Schulman (1981) suggests that we should base the selection of design (or method) on the basis of problem, rather than paradigm:

> We must avoid becoming educational researchers slavishly committed to some particular method ... We must first understand our problem, and decide what questions we are asking, then select the mode of disciplined inquiry most appropriate to those questions. If the proper methods are highly quantitative and objective, fine. If they are more subjective or qualitative, we can use them responsibly as well. (p. 12)

A second way of looking at this pragmatic or strategic approach to research design is to view research design as an active, construction process. Herein, a researcher pieces together those techniques which seem to enable her/him to best tackle the research problem of interest. Thus, pragmatists point to the potential for researchers to compromise the integrity of distinctive designs by choosing to incorporate features characteristic of other designs, including those associated with another paradigm, into their own. In this context, Smith and Heshusius (1986) indicate that,

> in this case one frequently sees questions such as, Can quantitative inquirers supplement their controlled instrumentation with open-ended observations in naturalistic settings? or, Can qualitative inquirers supplement naturalistic observation with the quantification of events? The answer to both questions is yes. In both cases, but especially for qualitative inquiry, the logic of justification does not impose detailed boundaries that determine every single aspect of (design or) practice. (p. 8)

The truth of the matter goes beyond this hypothetical point. A careful review of the literature will turn up studies which contain features considered distinctive of two or more formal designs, as well as of designs associated with both paradigms.

This tendency is not limited to bodies of research literature "out there." There is clear evidence that the EE research literature contains studies with features considered distinctive of <u>both</u> paradigms. For example, Tanners (1980) and Petersons (1982) early studies of "environmental sensitivity" employed lengthy, open-ended interviews for data collection purposes, and used content analysis procedures for data analysis purposes, as is common in qualitative research. In addition, both presented findings in the form of frequency distributions (i.e., quantitatively). Similarly, in experimental-type studies, both Ramsey (Ramsey, Hungerford & Tomera, 1981) and Horsley (1977) collected data on environmental behavior using pencil-and-paper instruments, and had others collect unobtrusive observations on the same individuals behavior (i.e., as is common in qualitative research). Further, in my dissertation, I used both pencil and paper instruments and open-ended interviews for data collection purposes. As a result, I employed traditional reliability estimatation procedures for several pencil-and-paper measures (i.e., using test-retest procedures), and less traditional triangulation procedures for estimating the dependability of my data (Marcinkowski, 1988). These examples could continue, and provide further evidence that many researchers do not feel restricted to techniques drawn from either one formal design or one paradigm. Observations of the state of the literature have led Miles and Huberman (1984) to assert that "epistemological purity does not get the job done" (p. 21).

E.   Remaining Points for Consideration

While there is some utility in having prepared a modified version of Gowins Vee heuristic to foreshadow this comparative overview of the two paradigms, others writing in the literature on this apparent dilemma are quick to point out underlying difficulties in this type of analysis. The concerns, insights and questions these writers offer are important ones to be considered in this context. I will try to illustrate them using brief quotes.

The first is raised by Smith and Heshusius (1986). "No discussion of qualitative and quantitative inquiry can stray very far from the challenge of objectivism and realism" (p. 10). They go on to point out that quantitative inquirys claim of "being capable of allowing us to describe social and educational life as it really is" (p. 10) has fallen on hard times. On the flip side of the coin, they note that "qualitative inquiry, in refuting that the rationality of inquiry must be derived from method (as paractices), must address the implications of its antifoundationalist assumptions" (p. 10).

A second point is raised by Firestone (1987). He suggests that:

> Choosing methods is not just a matter of coming at a single truth from differing directions. Nor is it soley a pragmatic question of fitting research techniques to a problem as the pragmatists suggest, although that does happen. On the other hand, ones method is not as rigorously determined by the choice of paradigm as the purists suggest. There are in fact a number of reasons for selecting a methodological approach, but ones decisions often express values about what the world is like, how one ought to understand it, and what the most important threats to that understanding are. (p. 20)

In terms relevant to the previous discussions, Firestone asserts while both paradigm and problem/question influence ones selection (or construction) of a research design, neither serves as the criterion for making design decisions. One might go further to assert that neither can, and neither should exert such influence.

A third point was raised by Smith (1983). He point out that on a day-to-day basis...

> ... Researchers must continually make judgements about that is good research as opposed to what is not - decisions which of course form the basis for the distribution of rewards within the profession. These judgements are played out in a variety of arenas... The problem this quantitative-qualitative debate underscores concerns the basis on which judgements are made: Is there a set of criteria for judging good and bad quantitative research and, independent of this, a set of criteria for judging good and bad qualitative research?... If the two approaches really do not differ... then only one set of standards may be needed to sort out the good from the bad. However, if these two approaches are felt to constitute distinct, yet equally appropriate perspectives, then different standards are needed, and it is unfair to judge qualitative efforts from a quantitative perspective and vice versa. (p. 13)

In response to this point, it is clear that some researchers have taken it upon themselves to develop guidelines for conducting, and standards for judging differing types of quantitative and qualitative research designs (e.g., Campbell & Stanley, 1963; Snow, 1974; Guba, 1981; Lincoln & Guba, 1982, 1988; McMillan & Schumacher, 1989). However, this fact neither ensures that there are sufficient sets of standards for all types of designs, nor that the existing sets of standards will be put to use within the profession.

A fourth point raised by Smith and Heshusius (1986) pertains to the manner in which "researchers resolve disagreements among themselves over the results on inquiry" (p. 11). He point out that, on the one hand, quantitative researchers "hold out the possibility that a return to the facts of the case will sort out the problem" when disagreements arise (p. 13). On the one hand, qualitative inquiry "has no independent or brute facts to appeal to since reality is mind-dependent. If people agree, it is because they share similar values, interests, and purposes - not because there are any givens that compel agreement" (p. 13). They go on to suggest that...

> ... if a quantitative inquirer disagrees with a qualitative inquirer,
> is it even possible for them to talk to each other? The answer,
> for the present anyway, is a qualified no. (p. 11)

While there may be an important Kernel of truth to these assertions (i.e., philosophical differences about reality and truth), the assertions overlook the fact that recognized qualitative researchers have responded to the expressed concern on this point by offering specific kinds of guidelines and criteria which may be appealed to when such disagreements arise. Guba (1981) clearly points out that he has done so since...

> ... both the novelty of the paradigm and the strangeness of the
> reporting format pose special problems for editors and referees
> of journals, peer review committees considering proposals, and
> naturalistic investigators themselves as they attempt to design
> and monitor their inquirers. (p. 75)

One may use Gubas points regarding the use of audit trails, triangulation, and similar procedures to argue that qualitative researchers should be able to respond, at least in part, to challenges of the type offered by Smith and Heshusius above; i.e., they should be able to confirm their data sources and defend the dependability of those data. If this much can be agreed upon, then researchers using quantitative and qualitative designs may be much closer to agreement on this point than Smith and Heshusius suggest.

The final point consists of a question, again raised by Smith and Heshusius (1986): "Given these differences (in the two paradigms), on what basis can researchers justify their work to the public, to educators, and for that matter, to themselves?" (p. 11). In other words, what do the results of studies using different designs associated with these differing paradigms mean? Those associated with the educational research enterprise come to understand the qualitative paradigm, designs, and techniques, and then to accept them on equal footing with the more traditional qualitative paradigm, designs, and techniques. With respect to the epistomological aspects of these questions, I would refer the reader to the discussion presented in Part IV.

III. An Introduction to Quantitative Research in Education and EE

A.   The Nature, Roots, and Intents of Quantitative Research

The chart presented in the previous section (Table 4) serves a general introduction to this section. To supplement this, I would like to begin with a quote from Bryman (1988):

> Quantitative research is, then, a genre which uses a special language which appears to exhibit some similarity to the ways in which scientists talk about how they investigate the natural order -- variables, control, measurement, experiment. This superficial imagery reflects the tendency for quantitative research to be underpinned by a natural science model, which means that the logic and procedures of the natural sciences are taken to provide an epistomological yardstick against which empirical research in the social sciences must be appraised before it can be treated as valid knowledge. (p. 12)

The philosophical tradition in which one finds Brymans "epistomological yardstick" is commonly referred to as "postivism". Smith (1983) identified a group of theorists, "which included among others Compte, Mill, and Durkheim" (p. 6), as the vanguard of this approach. However, he cautiously points out that "this group was working within an overall impiricist tradition as established by Newton, Locke, and others" (p. 6). From the writings of Bryman characteristics of this philosophical tradition can be identified as:

1. A belief that the methods and procedures of the natural sciences are appropriate to the social sciences. This view involves the acceptance of the premise that while the phenomena of interest in social science exhibit different properties or qualities than do the phenomena of interest to natural science, this does not serve as an obstacle to the use of the scientific methods in social science.

2. A belief that "only those phenomena which are observable, in the sense of being amenable to the senses, can validly be warranted as knowledge" (Bryman, 1988, p. 14). In effect, this means that any phenomena which cannot be directly experienced or observed, or observed with the aid of instruments (e.g., microscopes, telescopes are beyond the realm of science. In traditional terms, this is known as empiricism.

3. Accounts of positivism portray science as an inductive, constructive process: "scientific knowledge is arrived at through the accumulation of verified facts. These facts feed into the theoretical edifice pertaining to a particular domain of knowledge" (Bryman, 1988, p. 13).

4. Accounts of positivism also portray science as a deductive, applicative process: theories serve the backdrop to empirical research "in the sense that hypotheses are derived from them - usually in the form of postulated causal connections between entities - which are then submitted to empirical tests" (Bryman, 1988, p. 13).

5. Positivism reflects a particular posture with respect to the nature and role of values. Bryman clearly points out two distinct, though related aspects of this: (a) "the more obvious sense of needing to purge the scientist of values which may impair his or her objectivity and so undermine the validity of scientific knowledge" (p. 13); and (b) a denial of the "appropriateness of the spheres of the normative ... because normative statements cannot be verified in relation to experience" (p. 13).

Smith (1983) presents an analysis of the implications of these points for social science:

> this school of thought claimed that social investigation was a neutral activity in regard to values, and accordingly, social scientists conducting research should (1) eliminate all bias and preconceptions, (2) not be emotionally involved with or have a particular attitude toward the subject, and (3) move beyond common-sense beliefs. This last injunction meant that social science must develop a neutral scientific language that would rise above context-bound and value-laden everyday language. (p. 7)

There are two differing ways of viewing the "intentions" of quantitative research; i.e., by viewing intention at the level of paradigm, and at the level of formal design. At the level of paradigm, Bryman (1988, pp. 21-38) identifies four particular characteristics commonly associated with quantitative research:

(1) a need to establish clear linkages between the concepts (e.g., variables) rooted in research questions and hypotheses, and the phenomena to be observed (e.g., as in operational definitions);

(2) a frequent preoccupation with the establishment of <u>causal relationships</u>;

(3) a desire to establish that the results of a particular investigation can be <u>generalized</u> beyond a particular research setting; and

(4) a belief in the importance of the ability to <u>replicate</u> studies and their findings, and in the importance of doing so as a check on potential researcher bias.

In shifting to analysis at the level of design, McNeil, Kelly and McNeil (1975), Borg and Gall (1983, pp. 20-22), McMillan and Schumacher (1989), and others point out that the intentions of quantitative research may be generally organized into four categories: (a) to describe; (b) to predict; (c) to control; and (d) to explain. Authors of research texts usually view these categories of intention as differing types of knowledge. For example, the ability to accurately <u>describe</u> school drop-outs is qualitatively different than the ability to accurately <u>predict</u> who is likely and unlikely to drop-out. Moreover, the ability to <u>control</u> this situation (i.e., to reduce the rate of drop-outs) requires yet a third type of knowledge. And, these three type of knowledge are seen as qualitatively different from the ability to accurately <u>explain</u> how or why certain controlled improvements work in reducing the drop-out rate. This would require that other plausible explanations (rival hypotheses) have been identified, tested, and ruled out.

Within the arena quantitative research, these four types of knowledge may be seen as building on one another, and contributing, each in its own way, toward an understanding of causal relationships (Rosenshine & Furst, 1973; as cited in Borg & Gall, 1983, p. 632). For example, the ability to accurately predict is predicated upon a knowledge of apparent variable patterns and potential variable relations (i. e., descriptive knowledge). Further the ability to control may be based upon knowledge of potential causal or contributing factors (i.e., predictive knowledge). Finally, the ability to explain requires an understanding of the how causal variables have been operationally defined and manipulated.

Within the arena of quantitative research, it is also apparent that the differing types of knowledge one seeks to gain will require different types of research designs (or methods). For example, one would tend to make the following associations between type of knowledge and design:

(a) to describe: surveys, longitudinal and cross-sectional developmental studies, correlational studies;

(b) to predict: studies using correlation and multiple correlation statistical analyses (e.g., classification and discriminant analyses,

(c) to control and to explain: studies using experimental type designs.

This is not to say that quantitative methods are the only means for generating these types of knowledge. One may also view most qualitative methods from this perspective. Ethnographies and case studies tend to generally describe, while action research is oriented toward improvement, and analytical studies (e.g., historical, legal and policy studies) can be used to "interpret facts for causal explanations" (McMillan & Schumacher, 1989, p. 433). I will elaborate further on this point in Part IV of the paper.

B.   Overview of Quantitative Research Methods Used in Education

What influence have empiricism and positivism had on quantitative research in the social sciences and education?   These are terribly important questions, though a full response would require far more space than is available here.   Still, it is worth noting that it is terribly important because many believe that quantitative methods are positivistic in conception and orientation.   This is not only true of critics of quantitative methods.   Bryman (1988) points out that "the authors of textbooks on social science research methods give an account of the logic of quantitative research that bears a striking similarity to the positivist position (e.g., Goode and Hatt, 1952; Phillips, 1966)" (p. 18).   This is also apparent in more recent educational research texts (e.g., Campbell & Stanley, 1963; Kerlinger, 1973; Borg & Gall, 1983; McMillan & Schumacher, 1989), though in later versions, it is sometimes difficult to separate out a reliance upon science and empiricism from a reliance upon positivism per se.   Nonetheless, since many contemporary researchers have been schooled in the principles and methods of research using such texts, it is very likely that such texts have had a profound influence on their (our) conceptions of the research enterprise.

Probably the most distinctive example of a quantitative method which has been adapted from the postivistic tradition, and which is used in educational research is that of experimental research.   For this reason, I would like to present a very brief sketch to illustrate changes which have taken place regarding the use of experimental research in education.   The use of experimental research designs in education goes at least as far back as the early twentieth century (e.g., Thorndike & Woodworth, 1901).   Campbell and Stanley (1963) point out that "a wave of enthusiasm for experimentation dominated the field of education in the Thorndike era, perhaps reaching its apex in the 1920s" (p. 2).   They go on to point out that experimentation was included in a number of early research methods texts, notably those published by McCall (1923) and Fisher (1925, 1935).   In these cases, the emphasis tended to be upon one-variable-at-a-time research, without due attention to interactive effects among variables (Campbell & Stanley, 1963, p. 3).   Campbell and Stanley go on to relate the growing disillusionment in the 1930s with this approach to experimentation in education, largely due to disappointment over its resulting contributions.   They end their historical treatment as follows: "Undoubtedly, training educational researchers more thoroughly in modern experimental statistics should help raise the quality of educational experimentation" (p. 4).

Today, the use of experimental research in education is quite different than in its heyday in the 1920s.   These differences have been made by scholars such as Campbell and Stanley, who made a substantial contribution by systematically identifying threats to the internal validity and external validity of experimental-type studies (i.e., to its design and ability to generalize, respectively).   Perhaps of equal importance was their introduction of a system for classifying designs on the basis of such threats (i.e., as pre, quasi or true experiments). While true experiments reflect a research approach common to the natural sciences, Campbell and Stanley (1963) clearly pointed out that quasi-experiments have gained increasing acceptance in educational circles, since quasi-experiments were useful "in many natural social settings in which the person can introduce something like experimental design... even though he lacks full control over the experimental stimuli" (p. 35) and "for the educator who wishes to take his research out of the laboratory and into the operating setting" (pp. 34-35).

In furthering their work, Snow (1974) argued that "some rather unconventional additions and revisions in the design and analysis of educational experiments may be needed" (p. 265). He proposed that the term "representative" be introduced to refer to those experimental designs which seek to maximize the generalizability (external validity) of results. Thus, rather than simplify experimental conditions, researchers needed to account for the range of population, setting, treatment, and interactive conditions one would be likely to experience under natural conditions. His contention for offering such a proposal was as follows:

> we gain something and we lose something by imposing simple, strict, logical systems on natural phenomena. We also gain something and lose something by the looser, more probablistic and descriptive thinking derived from representative studies... There is a place for artificial laboratory research and for systematic experiments conducted in schools. There is also a place for quasi-representative experiments, quasi-representative-quasi-experiments, and for naturalistic case studies. (p. 288)

This prespective suggests that researchers have come a long way from the views originally offered by Thorndike and Woodworth in 1901, and by McCall in his 1923 text on the use of experimental design in education. While these changes have taken place, McMillan and Schumacher (1989) are still able to assert that experimental research exhibits...

> six distinguishing characteristics: statistical equivalence of subjects in different groups, usually achieved by random assignment of subjects; comparison of two or more groups or sets of conditions; direct manipulation of at least one independent variable; and a design that provides maximum control of extraneous variables. (p. 302)

In Table 4 (p. 12), I indicated that survey and correlational methods were also considered prototypical examples of quantitative research design. And, in the previous section, I included other descriptive and prediction-type studies as examples of quantitative design. I have briefly summarized the characteristics of these types of quantitative design in Table 5 (next page).

Table 5
Overview of Key Characteristics of Non-Experimental Quantitative Designs*

Type of Design	Key Characteristics
Surveys	(a) used to investigate the incidence, frequency, and/or distribution of characteristics in one or more identified and discrete populations;
	(b) use of established methods for selecting one or more samples from each population;
	(c) use of a standardized technique for collecting data from each member of each sample (e.g., pencil-and-paper instruments, interviews);
	(d) use of some procedure for tracking non-respondents, and for assessing whether the number and/or type of non-respondents are likely to influence the results; and
	(e) use of descriptive statistics to present sample characteristics and/or inferential statistics to allow generalizations about the population to be made.
Developmental	(a) used to investigate patterns and sequences of growth and/or change in a population as a function of time;
	(b) use of established methods for selecting one or more samples from that population;
	(c) use of standardized techniques for collecting data from each member of each sample (e.g., pencil-and-paper instruments, interviews, observations) over time;
	(d) translation of data to numeric form, as needed; and
	(e) use of descriptive and/or comparative statistics to analyze data for postulated patterns of difference and/or relationship.
Correlational	(a) used to investigate the nature and strength of relationships between two or more variables;
	(b) use of established methods for selecting one or more samples of subjects;
	(c) use of standardized techniques for collecting data from each member of each sample (e.g., pencil-and-paper instruments, interview protocols, observations);
	(d) translation of data to numeric form, as needed; and

* Note: Sources consulted in developing this Table include: Isaac and Michael (1981), Borg and Gall (1983), McMillan and Schumacher (1989)

Table 5: (continued)		
Type of Design	**Key Characteristics**	
Correlational (continued)	(e)	use of a correlational statistic, appropriate for the type of data collected, to analyze the data and generate a correlation coefficient; i.e., a numerical index of the relationship between each pair of variables investigated.
Prediction	(a)	used to investigate the extent to which one or more predictor variables are useful in predicting a specified criterion variable (i.e., usually a behavior, set of behaviors, or group membership); or to build theories about possible determinants of a criterion variable;
	(b)	use of established methods for selecting one or more samples of subjects;
	(c)	use of standardized techniques for collecting data from each member of each sample on predictor and criterion variables (e.g., pencil-and-paper instruments, interview protocols, observations);
	(d)	translation of data to numeric form, as needed; and
	(e)	use of a some form of correlation, partial correlation, and/or multiple correlation statistics (e.g., multiple regression) to provide a numerical index of the ability of predictor variables to account for or explain variability in the criterion variable.

Each of the types of design presented in Table 5 have been used extensively in educational research. This fact can be quickly ascertained from a review of the many research methods texts in education, reviews/summaries of educational research, and peer-review journals which publish educational research. Rather than dwell upon this, I would rather present an overview of the use of quantitative methods in our own field, environmental education.

C.   Trends in the Use of Quantitative Methods in EE

Given the relative longevity of quantitative methods, and the treatment of quantitative methods in graduate level research methods texts, it should come as no surprise that quantitative methods have tended to dominate research and evaluation efforts in the field. Thus, it should come as no surprise that descriptive research is the most common type of published EE research. The evidence for this assertion may be gleaned from the few sources which address this topic.

One of the earliest is the review of research conducted by Roth (1976). In Section VI he reports on evaluation instruments used in various studies. Of the 27 studies, at least 17 were doctoral dissertations. As one might expect under these circumstances, the vast majority (n=16) were reports of experimental-type studies. Of the remaining studies, six were instrument development studies, three were descriptive, and one was a correlational study. A second anecdote on this topic is found in Hungerford, Tomera and Wilsons (1983a) review of research reported in The Journal of Environmental Education (JEE), Volumes 3-12. In constrast to Roth's data, these authors note among their summary comments the following: "Experimental methods are employed infrequently in EE research. Descriptive methods predominate" (p. 172). These comments are relatively consistent with a review of ten years of experimental research report in JEE conducted by this writer (i.e., for Vols. 6-15, 1975-85). Over this period, only 33 experimental-type research or evaluation reports were located (i.e., when JEE contained between 20-30 research and non-research reports per year/volume over this period). One probable reason for the apparent discrepancy between Roths and these other two anecdotes is that differing segments of the research literature were reviewed (i.e., dissertations versus journal reports).

The most systematic sources of information about the relative frequency with which differing kinds of quantitative (and qualitative) research designs were used are the two reports from the North American Commission for Environmental Education Research (NCEER): Research in Environmental Education, 1971-1980 (Iozzi, 1981) and A Summary of Research in Environmental Education, 1971-1982 (Iozzi, 1984). When dissertations, journal reports and fugitive reports were abstracted, all studies (n=429) were also assigned a set of descriptors. One of the ten categories of descriptors was entitled "Research Methods" (Iozzi, 1981, p. xv). Since a methods descriptor was assigned to most studies, Iozzi was able to go back and identify the relative frequency of occurance of each research method. In reporting the results of his analyses, he offered the following conclusions:

> In this most revealing figure, there is no question as to the dominant type of research conducted in EE during 1971-1982 ... More than 70% of the research was classified as "descriptive" by NCEER. The fact that most of the studies conducted during that time period were "descriptive" in nature is most reasonable and logical, particularly when one considers that EE was really an emerging area of inquiry. (1984, p. 9)

This estimate suggests that of the 429 studies, over 300 were descriptive or correlational in nature. Of the remaining studies, Iozzi goes on to report that 18.1%, or approximately 77, were experimental studies, while 4.1%, or approximately 17, were pre-experimental studies. Finally, only 2.9%, or approximately 12 of the studies used ex post facto designs. His explanation for these figures was that most true/quasi-experimental studies had been conducted more recently, and served as a sign that the field had matured. Whether or not that was true is open to further analysis. Thus, he ended his discussion of designs employed by noting that "this issue merits further consideration and should be explored in future NCEER projects" (p. 13).

Before closing it should be noted that at least 90-92% of these 429 studies were primarily quantitative in nature. From that figure, one may draw at least two conclusions. As has been true for the field of education as a whole, quantitative designs have been the predominant type of design used in EE research circles (i.e., among graduate students and professional researchers). The research base in EE largely consists of the results of quantitative studies.

On the other hand there appear to be a number of plausible explanations for the dearth of qualitative studies. These include: (a) the relative recency of broader acceptance of qualitative designs in educational research circles when compared to the time period of research considered here; (b) researchers lack of awareness of or familiarity with these designs and techniques, leading to infrequent useage; (c) lack of funding for these types of studies, again leading to infrequent useage; (d) researchers failure to submit reports of qualitative studies (e.g., due to unfamiliarity with reporting processes, or fear of bias on the part of reviewers); and (e) failure to approve for publication reports of qualitative studies, since they may not have fit editors notions of what was good research. It is probable that several of these conditions have contributed in varying ways to the apparently low volume of qualitative research reports in EE. Nonetheless, as reports of qualitative studies grow in number and quality, as they should (Robottom, 1985), they should increasingly add to the knowledge and research base in the field.

D.   Apparent Contributions and Limitations of Quantitative Research

There are at least four ways of assessing apparent contributions and limitations of quantitative research. One may look at these aspects in broad, even global terms (i.e., at the level of paradigm), in terms of each type of quantative study, in terms of particular groups of studies, or in terms of individual studies. In a general sense, the comparative overview of the two paradigms pointed out some of the more apparent limitations of the quantitative methods in the global sense (e.g., reduction of complex social realities into numerical terms, difficulties with the notions of researcher objectivity and generalizability, and the tendency to impose theoretical frameworks a priori). Still, these limitations are not necessarily apparent in all types of quantitative studies, much less all studies. While it would be instructive to prepare a review of apparent contributions and limitations of quantitative studies by group or by study, that is a far larger task than is feasible in this context. Even though these analyses will not be undertaken here, it is worth noting that the modified version of Gowin's Vee (Figure 2) should be of use in such analyses. In this section, I will attempt to provide insights into several of the general contributions and limitations of the various types of quantitative studies in education.

I would like to begin with experimental-type research. The major contribution of experimental research is that it is the only type of research currently available which allows a researcher to test and offer very specific cause-and-effect claims. In quantitative circles, prediction and ex post facto designs may allow one to infer or hypothesize about cause-and-effect. However, as designs, they do not exhibit the controls needed to allow firm claims to be made. In educational experiments, researchers actually observe the effects of planned and controlled change.

This important contribution also belies the greatest limitations of experimental research. How one defines an independent variable may lead one to err on the side of over-simplifying the research setting (e.g., the old "one-variable-at-time" tendency). On the other extreme, a researcher may fail to fully define and delimit the complexities of a "treatment" in a way that allows her or him to determine which aspect(s) of the treatment may have been responsible for detected effects (i.e., whether desirable or otherwise). Researchers using experimental designs constantly walk a tightrope between the overly simple and overly complex. Beyond this, it can also be difficult to control the full range of non-treatment variables which may influence the selected dependent variable(s), again making it difficult to assess the impact of the treatment. Given these circumstances, researchers are admonished to repeat or replicate their experimental studies as a check on their results and on the generalizability of those results.

There are other potential limitations to this type of design. In most cases, it is difficult, if not impossible to insure that subjects will be randomly assigned to treatment groups. This is particularly true of classroom studies. And, while it is easier to randomly assign groups to treatments, this is often over-simplified by the small number of groups included (e.g., as a function of time, available resources). Statistical equivalence of groups is often used as an alternative to randomization in quasi-experimental studies. This too has its difficulties, for it is usually difficult to equate groups on more than one or two relevant variables. I will end this discussion of experimental research by noting that all of the internal and external validity threats identified by Campbell and Stanley (1963) and others (e.g., Borg & Gall, 1983; McMillan & Schumacher, 1989, pp. 308-309) can, and often do serve as limitations of experimental-type studies.

Correlational and prediction research also have made important contributions to education. They have allowed educators to develop insights into patterns of educational behaviors, events and processes, many of which are taken for granted (e.g., relationships between teaching for critical thinking or the use of positive reinforcement, and students' school performance). Further, the multivariate statistical techniques available to researchers now allow them to address many of the complexities of real-world patterns in their analyses. Hence, researchers need no longer look to or rely upon over-simplified models of behaviors, events, and so on. When used systematically, these types of research can serve as checks on intuitive assumptions about patterns or relationships associated with such phenomena.

As with experimental research, there are some limitations to correlation and prediction studies. While some may think of relationships in causal terms, these types of studies do not lead to causal claims. Rather they portray apparent relationships at one or more particular points in time. We may treat relationship claims as working hypotheses with respect to causality, though can rarely, if ever, test them using these methods. A second limitation has to do with the complex rules governing the various statistical analyses employed in correlational and prediction studies. Whether out of practicality or for some other reason, it is a fairly common occurrence that these rules are violated (e.g., a test requiring interval data is used on ordinal data sets). In some cases, these violations have relatively small effects upon statistical results. However, such violations can lead a researcher to misrepresent results, and thereby offer misleading or erroneous claims.

Descriptive type quantitative studies, such as surveys have also made important contributions to education. According to McMillan and Schumacher (1989), one of the greatest advantages of survey methods is that they are flexible and adaptable:

> Surveys are used in education for a wide variety of purposes. Many doctoral dissertations use surveys; state departments of education use surveys to determine levels of knowledge and to ascertain needs in order to plan programs; schools use surveys to evaluate aspects of the curriculum or administrative procedures; governmental agencies use surveys to form public policy; colleges of education use surveys to evaluate their courses and programs. Much of the use of surveys is for practical purposes and could be classified as evaluation research, although surveys are also used for basic and applied research. (pp. 293-294)

This adaptability should not be taken to mean that surveys are without limitation. I will present three. First, since surveys are often conducted using pencil-and-paper instruments, most surveys are only as useful as the quality of the instrumentation. It is very easy to develop "quick-and-dirty" survey instruments, making this any easy temptation to succumb to. Thus, it is a serious limitation that surveys often do not reflect the ideas and patterns of thinking of those to whom it will be administered. While there are procedures for attending to this (e.g., Dawes, 1972), there are no assurances that researchers will do so. A second, somewhat related limitation pertains to the quality of responses obtained from subjects to whom it has been administered. Even if surveys were carefully designed and administered, there is no assurance that the majority of subjects will self-report in an consistent manner. Again, to account for this, there are established procedures for generating validity and reliability estimates for survey instruments (e.g., Borg & Gall, 1983; McMillan & Schumacher, 1989), though again, there are no assurances that such concerns will be attended to by researchers. Weak instrumentation has been an ongoing criticism in survey, as well as in other types of quantitative research. A third limitation of surveys has already been noted in Table 5 (p. 55); i.e., the problem of potential bias when return rates are below desirable or proportional levels. The question here is as follows. Does this low response rate indicate that only certain type of subjects have completed and returned responses, thereby biasing my results? As noted in Table 5, there are established procedures for handling this potential through follow-ups, in data analyses, and in reporting. Nonetheless, this problems does crop up, and does serve as potential limitation in survey type studies.

This is a rather general overview of contributions or advantages, and of limitations of quantitative methods. It is far from being exhaustive. Readers interested in more detailed treatments are referred to any of the cited references. It is apparent that these methods exhibit a certain range of appropriate application when they are used with care. As with all educational research methods, they can be used for purposes beyond the bounds of appropriate application or employed in careless ways.

IV. Interpreting the Dilemma in Terms of Cooperation

A. The Status of the "Debate"

When I began to prepare this paper, I did so with certain inclinations. These inclinations had been informed both by my reading of research texts, my own research activities, and my teaching of research methods to classroom teachers. My personal and professional view was that any difference which existed between the two paradigms on a philosophical level had limited bearing on research activity, and that it was more appropriate to view the two sets of designs and techniques as complimentary rather than as competitive. As I read through the literature (i.e., at least that which is published or available in the U.S.), it became increasingly apparent that the great debate had moved in this direction (e.g., Smith & Heshusius, 1986; Firestone, 1987; Bryman, 1988).

In discussing the debate between the two paradigms, Bryman (1988) began with these introductory comments:

> Much of the discussion in the literature on these two research traditions has created a some-what exaggerated picture of their differences. These discussions reflect the tendency to treat quantitative and qualitative research as though they are mutually antagonistic ideal types of the research process ... While there are differences between the two research traditions ... there are also a number of points at which the differences are not as rigid as the programmatic statements imply. (p. 93)

Perhaps of greater importance is one of the closing statements Bryman offers on this debate:

One of the most unsatisfactory aspects of the epistomological version of the debate is that it is unclear whether its proponents are arguing that there is a link between epistomology and method of data collection or whether there ought to be such a bond. If the argument is that there is such a link, the epistomological argument runs into difficulties... (Further) it is not at all clear from the various writings on the debate about quantitative and qualitative research that the view exists that there ought to be a recognition of mutual interdependence of epistomology and method. The problem with the 'ought' position is that it fails to recognize that a whole cluster of considerations are likely to impinge on decisions about methods of data collection. (pp. 123-125)

Thus, given his analysis of the literature on the debate, Bryman moves on to a discussion of "Combining Quantitative and Qualitative Research" (Ch. 6).

The positions articulated by Bryman appear to be reasonably representative of the views currently held by many, if not most, within the educational research community. For example, Smith and Heshusius (1986) point out that this debate has moved through three relatively distinct phases over the last 25-30; i.e., from conflict to detente to cooperation. He cites Rist (1977) as sounding the bells of detente: "even though the two approaches had different epistomological traditions and tensions which remained, a set of accomodations is emerging whereby the various approaches ... are recognizing the right of peaceful coexistence" (p. 42, cited in Smith & Heshusius, 1986, p. 5). They go on to say that, "not suprisingly, detente has given way to the claim of compatibility and the call for cooperation" (p. 5). The positions these writers end up taking is basically this:

A recent trend in the literature concerning quantitative versus qualitative approaches to research indicate two things about the nature of this debate. First, many educational inquirers now accept the idea that there are two different, equally legitimate, approaches to inquiry. Second, many inquirers also feel that whatever differences may exist between the two perspectives, they do not, in the final analysis, really matter very much ... (Many) educational inquirers now seem to think that the profession has reached a stage of, if not synthesis, then certainly compatibility and cooperation between the two approaches. (p. 4)

It has been rather interesting to find that many in the educational research community have come to grips with and largely resolved the contentious aspects of this debate. Having found this, I would like to use the remaining sections of this part of the paper to look at these combinative, complimentary, and cooperative views, as I believe that will be of some benefit to the field.

B. Interpreting The Discussion in "Structuralist - Functionalist" Terms

Before I address the cooperative view in some detail, I would like to offer a brief anecdote. The setting from which the anecdote is taken should help tie it to this discussion. This past spring, I was one of five or six Americans asked to participate in a 'Working Seminar' on evaluation in EE held in Bordeaux, France. In addition, professionals in the field from Canada, England, Belgium, France, and Mozambique, were invited to participate. The general purpose of this short, six day meeting was to prepare a document on evaluation which Unesco would publish, and then use in other workshop or training settings. As the meeting progressed, those in attendance were asked to help edit the centerpiece of the document, to work in teams to fashion sections on differing aspects of evaluation (i.e., including program evaluation, evaluation of print materials, and assessment of learning outcomes), and to make a presentation to the entire group on some self-selected evaluation-related topic.

Over the course of the meeting, the Americans present had cause to discuss evaluation topics with their Canadian and European counterparts. Herein lies the anecdote. Following his presentation, one of the European participants was discussing some of the particulars of his presentation on student activities and learning. I found myself disagreeing with him, and eventually mentioned this to him. He could not understand why I was disagreeing with him. A few minutes later, one of the Canadians pulled me aside. He tried to explain to me the nature, or roots of this disagreement. Quite simply, he attributed it to a common difference in the way in which Europeans and Americans tended to approach many such discussions; i.e., the Europeans tended to take an approach which looked at structural patterns and relationships, while in his experience, Americans tended to take an approach which looked at what worked. He referred to the former as a "structural" approach and the latter as a "functional" one.

As I have reflected upon this, I began to realize that this anecdote provided one potentially useful way of looking at the qualitative-quantitative dialogue. It is apparent that many writers on educational research and evaluation outside the U.S. (e.g., England and Australia) have tended to take strong advocacy positions with respect to the qualitative paradigm. In some cases, it has been apparent that they also take anti-quantitative positions (e.g., Robottom, 1985). On the other hand, as is apparent in the previous section, I have observed many American researchers shift toward either a detente or a cooperation position with respect to the status of the two paradigms, regardless of which of the paradigms they tend to use and/or advocate. Thus, I have been left wondering if there might be any relationship between one's cultural view and the position one takes in this dialogue. For the sake of visual types (i.e., including myself), I have arranged this as a two-dimensional matrix (Figure 3, p. 64).

It is important to note that this writer clearly recognizes that this two dimensional analysis greatly oversimplifies the complexity of forces which shape views on and position in this dialogue. Due to this, I have tried to soften the language I have used (e.g., tends) to avoid construing apparent trends as stereotypical patterns. Still, this analysis does have its appeal. The attractive feature of this analysis is that it <u>would</u> seem appropriate for someone who thought in structural terms to affirm the is/ought relationship between paradigm and method (i.e., and take a debate position). On the other hand, it would also seem appropriate for some who thought in functional terms to reason at the strategic design level, and assume more of a cooperation position.

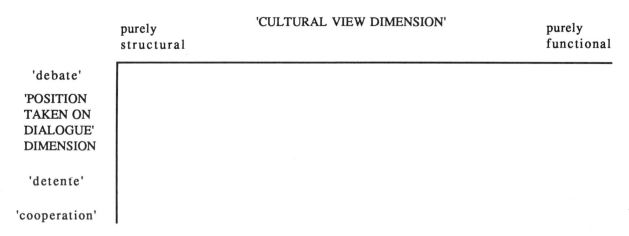

Figure 3. A two-dimensional matrix representing a continium of cultural views brought to the discussion of qualitative-quantitative research paradigms, and the continium of position taken in this discussion.

Despite its appeal, it is apparent that a host of other variables may influence a particular researcher's views on the quantitative-qualitative dialogue. For example, I would hypothesize that a number of research training variables (e.g., nature of the research methods course taken; research designs and techniques covered in methods courses taken; number of statistics courses completed with passing grades; the graduate advisor's philosophical views on research and research methods) could have a profound influence on the views a budding researcher will develop. Furthermore, I would hypothesize that a number of personality variables (e.g., ability to deal with ambiguity, flexibility, dogmatism, attention to detail) might also have some bearing on the position one might take in this dialogue. These are but two of the various types of variables which may tend to influence researchers' views.

C.   Cooperation within and across Single Studies

Within the writings of Smith and Heshusius (1986), Firestone (1987) and Bryman (1988), it is clear that some researchers have come to view the methods and techniques of the two paradigms as potentially complimentary, if not cooperative. After all, "researchers of a realist orientation are not prohibited from using a certain practice normally associated with qualitative inquiry" (Smith & Heshusius, 1986, p. 8) and "researchers already blend the two perspectives" (Miles & Huberman, 1984, p. 21, cited in Smith & Heshusius, 1986, p. 7). Both the possibility of doing so, and the fact that researchers in EE have already done so have been discussed in an earlier section of this paper on strategic design, and will not be repeated here (see pp. 16-17).

While the previous discussion on strategic design emphasized the potential and actual cooperative use of techniques associated with differing designs and paradigms within a single study, it did not address the notion of complimentarity; i.e., the view that studies of the same or related topics may yield results and insights which compliment one another. Firestone (1987) addresses this in his analysis of paradigm-derived methods. In this paper, he describes in some detail two studies which ...

> were chosen because I was directly involved in their production and could compare that process with the final product, because they address the same topic using qualitative and quantitative methods, and because the topic is of recurring interest to educational researchers. (p. 17)

In this case, the studies were of leadership influence upon organizational outcomes. After describing the rhetoric and design of these studies in some detail, he presents the conclusions under the heading of "Complimentarity":

> The differences presented above give qualitative and quantitative studies different descriptive strengths ... Used separately, qualitative and quantitative studies provide differing kinds of information. When focused upon the same issue, qualitative and quantitative studies can triangulate - that is, use differing methods to assess the robustness or stability of findings (Jick, 1979). Where studies using different methods have similar results, one can be more certain that the results are not influenced by the methodology. Where the results diverge more research is needed; but a comparison of studies can often suggest important lines of inquiry to pursue. In this case the two studies generally corroborate each other. (1988, pp. 19-20)

This example by Firestone serve as but one anecdote which attests to the potential complimentarity of methods or techniques across studies of the same problem. Bryman (1988) cites several others which reflect a triangulation view of complimentarity.

To further illustrate this form of complimentarity, I would prefer to do so using a clear example from the field of EE. In this example, three type of studies using distinctly different methods investigated the same variable, with each type of study building upon and corroborating the other. This example centers on the variable known to some as "environmental

Peterson (1982) employed in-depth interviews and a content analysis of transcripts. These studies may generally be considered qualitative in nature, though some may disagree (e.g., both researchers included frequency counts of influential life experiences in their results). Perhaps more importantly, the results from these studies were strikingly similar. Shortly after this, Scholl (1983) used a questionnaire format to collect data on the types influential life experiences identified by Tanner. Again, her results were strikingly similar to those reported by Tanner and Peterson. Subsequent to these three studies, and due to the recognition of the cohesiveness of their results, Sia (Sia, et al., 1985/86) conducted a prediction study. He included an environmental sensitivity scale constructed from Tanner's and Peterson's efforts as one of eight predictor variables. This scale was used in subsequent prediction studies by Marcinkowski (1989) and by Sivek (Sivek, et al., 1989/90).

This is a three tiered example of complimentarity. First, two qualitative studies were found to compliment one another. Second, the results from a third descriptive study using quantitative methods were found to compliment those obtained from the qualitative studies. Third, three quantitative prediction studies were able to include a scale on sensitivity due to the availability and cohesiveness of these previous studies' results, and further corroborated the results of the previous three studies. These descriptions and examples of complimentarity indicate that it is not only possible; it can be and has been used as an effective research strategy.

D.   Cooperation within and across Programs of Research

The example of complimentarity centered around environmental sensitivity leads nicely into a discussion of complimentarity within and across programs of research. If one looks more closely at this example, it is apparent that it exemplifies another form of complimentarity. In the example, two qualitative studies gave rise to a survey-type quantitative study, which, in turn, collectively gave rise to three prediction-type quantitative studies. Complimentarity did not end with the corroboration of results, since the variable environmental sensitivity turned out to be a significant entry-level predictor of the criterion variable used in all three studies; responsible environmental behavior. The results of two qualitative studies led to the identification of and instrumentation for a significant predictor of a desirable from of behavior.

Bryman (1988) refers to this as a "precursor" form of complimentarity: "There are a number of ways in which qualitative research can act as a precursor to the formulation of problems and the development of instruments for quantitative research" (p. 134). Again, Bryman goes on to present clear examples of this form of complimentarity (pp. 134-136). Bryman is careful to note that the reverse of this form of complimentarity may also occur; i.e., "investigations in which quantitative research precedes and provides an aid to the collection of quantitative data" (p. 136). While he does note that the number of examples of this are far fewer than of the reverse of this form, he does cite several examples of its occurrence.

This form of complimentarity was discussed in another context earlier in the paper (Section III.A. on "The Nature, Roots, and Intents of Quantitative Research"). In that section, I pointed out that research was best carried out when it built upon the results of prior investigations; i.e., when 'descriptive' research results were used in 'prediction' studies, and when these results were, in turn, used in experimental-type 'control' and 'explanation' studies. I also pointed out that this capacity for building knowledge across studies was not limited to quantitative studies, but was clearly possible in qualitative studies as well. This process of generating a body of knowledge from description up through explanation may be referred to as building a program of research. This is what Bryman (1988) refers to as that form of complimentarity in which "Qualitative and quantitative research are combined in order to produce a general picture" (p. 137). To more concretely illustrate this point, I have tried to fashion what I referred to earlier as 'formal research designs' into a framework which reflects, in concept, this notion of program of research (Table 6, p. 68).

When the idea of a program of research is applied in education, it means that the phenomena under investigation (e.g., individuals and objects, processes and events) are associated with the conduct of education, and that the <u>intent</u> of such research is to gain greater understanding of phenomena with which to improve the conduct of education in some dimension.

As noted in the first section of this paper, a brief review of the EE research literature reveals that there are few areas in which studies have been carried out across the various levels presented in Table 6 in any semblence of an organized fashion. One example which may be useful to consider here is the body of research on responsible environmental behavior. As the lists and summaries of research studies indicate, a very large number of studies have been conducted in this broad area (e.g., Ajzen & Fishbein, 1977; Lipsey, 1977; Van Liere & Dunlap, 1980; Cook & Berrenberg, 1981; McDougal, Claxton, Ritchie & Anderson, 1981; Geller, Winnett, & Everett, 1982; Hungerford, Tomera & Wilson, 1983a; Gray, Borden, & Weigel, 1985; Hines & Hungerford, 1984; Widman, Simmons, Kaplan, & DeYoung 1984; Marcinkowski, in development). The studies reviewed in these summaries utilized a wide variety of designs, including descriptive, correlational, prediction, experimental, evaluation, and action research designs. Some of the difficulties with this body of research are that studies have been conducted in a variety of fields, employed divergent theoretical frameworks, and, are reported in an array of publications as a review of associated references will indicate. This should be apparent in the sample decision questions presented in Table 2 (p.36).

Table 6
A Program of Research Framework Relating General Purpose to Formal Design *

A. <u>Theory Building Research: Problem Exploration or Data Generation Designs</u>
    1. Descriptive/Qualitative Research
        a. Survey Research
        b. Observational Research (Obtrusive and Unobtrusive)
        c. Descriptive Single-Subject Research
        d. Case and Field Studies (Ethnographic, Participant Observer)
        e. Developmental Research (Cross-Sectional, Longitudinal)
    2. Correlational Research (Simple Correlation and Prediction)
    3. Causal-Comparative and Ex Post Facto Research
    4. Historical Research

B. <u>Theory Building Research: Problem and/or Data Interpretation Designs</u>
    1. Case and Field Studies
    2. Historical, Legal and Policy Research
    3. Re-Analysis (e.g., with modified analysis procedures)
    4. Re-Interpretation (e.g., interpret data in terms of new hypotheses)

C. <u>Theory Building Research: Data Synthesis Designs</u>
    1. Trend Analysis
    2. Narrative or Qualitative Synthesis
    3. Vote-Counting
    4. Chi-Square Methods
    5. Meta-Analysis

D. <u>Theory Testing Research</u>
    1. Experimental Research
        a. True Experimental Research
        b. Quasi-Experimental Research
        c. Pre-Experimental Research
    2. Single Subject (Baseline-Treatment-Baseline-Treatment)

E. <u>Applied and Evaluation Research</u>
    1. Evaluation Research
        a. Needs Assessment
        b. Formative and Summative Evaluation
        c. Responsive Evaluation
    2. Action Research
    3. Educational Research and Development

---

* Note: Sources consulted in developing this Table include: Borg and Gall (1983); Isaac and Michael (1981); McMillan and Schumacher (1989). Philosophical, instrument development, and several other forms of research do not appear here as they do not fit within this framework.

Within this body of research, there appear to exist a number of programs of research, each of which reflects its own particular set of theoretical suppositions. A careful review of this literature indicates that the work of Fishbein, et al., Geller, et al., and Hungerford, et al., may each be considered a program of research in the area of responsible environmental behavior. Of these, the work of Hungerford, et al. appears to most closely reflect the structure of and interests within EE (e.g., Hungerford & Volk, 1990). Perhaps more importantly, their research and development efforts have regularly and systematically been informed by the results of research from other 'programs of research' in this area.

D.   Closing Comments

The notion of complimentarity and cooperation between qualitative and quantitative research designs and paradigms is more than a theoretical or hypothetical notion. It is very clear from the writings on this dialogue and from careful analyses of the EE research literature that a number of researchers have made complimentarity a reality. They have used techniques drawn from differing designs and paradigms in single studies, as well as in pairs and small groups of studies (i.e., in the form of triangulation). They have also used techniques to foster various ways of doing so within and across programs of research (e.g., in the form of precursor studies). It is very clear that a sizeable body of educational researchers do not feel constrained by philosophical or epistomological purity, but rather see great opportunities for designs and techniques from the two paradigms to be used in complimentary ways.

The forms and examples of complimentarity presented herein should not be construed as suggesting that it is easy to accomplish this. In closing the section on combining qualitative and quantitative research, Bryman (1988) indicates the following:

> There are a number of barriers to the integration of qualitative and quantitative research. One barrier has been a major theme of this book (add: and this paper) thus far - the view quantitative and qualitative research are based upon fundamentally incompatible epistomological positions. The suggestion that they derive from different views about how social reality ought to be studied has led some qualitative researchers to eschew survey procedures because of their positivistic taint ... Another obstacle is cost. The impact of resources on the conduct of social research is an underdeveloped topic. (p. 153)

To these, I would add the broad barriers discussed earlier in this paper; i.e., the influence of research traditions and of professional research training. From the review of textbook segments, it is apparent that many do not provide an even-handed treatment of designs and techniques associated with both paradigms. This may be explained from an historical viewpoint, where it is generally recognized that the tradition of quantitative methods was established long before qualitative methods were considered appropriate in educational inquiries. The upshot is that the historical character of the two traditions has tended to place qualitative research at a disadvantage in a number of ways, including adequate attention in methods texts and courses. There is evidence that research methods texts and courses are changing to more clearly address qualitative research. However, since the current generations of educational researchers have largely been schooled in quantitative methods, such changes are likely to come about slowly. Hopefully, professional discussions such as the one here will have some effect upon this (and other) barriers.

V. Recommendations for Resolving This and Other Identified Dilemmas

After preparing a paper of this scope, and on topics of such importance to the field, it seems appropriate to offer some suggestions or recommendations for addressing the focal dilemma (i.e., quantitative - qualitative research), and more generally, for addressing other apparent problems and needs identified throughout the paper. Thus, to the body of professional educators and researchers in the field of EE, I would like to offer the following set of recommendations.

1. <u>Familiarity with Allied Theory and Past Research</u>. There is no substitute for spending time getting to know the literature in the field of EE in particular, as well as in allied or closely related fields. This should subsume the literature consisting of research and evaluation reports, syntheses, critical reviews, and the like. It should also include the literature pertaining to social and educational theory, particularly as this body of literature relates to either the conduct or interpretation of research and evaluation. Therefore, opportunities available to faculty members, graduate students, and other professionals in the field should be expanded to actively support professional development in these areas.

2. <u>Familiarity with Research Methods and Strategies</u>. This serves as a corollary to the first recommendation. In this case, the emphasis is upon better understanding of the differing research paradigms, increasing one's familiarity with research designs and techniques which do and do not reflect these paradigms, and understanding how the principles undergirding these paradigms, designs and techniques relate to our understanding of and to the improvement of educational practices. This recommendation would again address expanding opportunities for professional development. This should include, but not be limited to research methods courses and seminars.

3. <u>Familiarity with the Research Setting(s)</u>. One common criticism of many educational researchers is that they are 'out of touch' with the world of practice extant in K-12 and other educational settings. If university faculty are to work collaboratively with school professionals on

research projects, it is critical that university faculty spend time getting to know their potential research setting on a more intimate basis. In a more general sense, this injunction implies that all researchers should get to know their research setting (i.e., if and when there is one).

4. Carefully Selecting and Defining Significant Research Problems and Questions. Bryman (1988) points out that one of the most fundamental of research activities is the identification and conceptualization of the problem under investigation. If done inadequately, it may impair design choices, and is likely to lead to flaws or limitations in a study. Perhaps of equal importance is the selection of significant research problems and questions. The editorship of The Journal of Environmental Education has frequently expressed their displeasure with many submitted manuscripts due to the 'trite' problems they address. A recommendation to improve in this area would also require adequate attention to Recommendations 1-3.

5. Constructing a Research Strategy. If anything, this paper should point out that a strategic approach to research design is not only possible; it can prove very effective. With due respect to those who take an advocacy position toward either paradigm, I would like to recommend that we begin to think of the techniques associated with various research designs as available tools, and that when we design studies, we make appropriate use of those tools. If this means using a pure design, so be it.

6. Attention to Questions of Validity and Reliability. One of the thorniest problems confronting both quantitative and qualitative researchers is the degree of attention given to generating estimates of the validity and reliability of our data. In quantitative circles, these procedures are well recognized, though often underutilized. The absence of such efforts is apparent in the abstracts of EE research reported between 1971-1980 (Iozzi, 1981). In qualitative circles, the procedures have been more-or-less established over the last ten years (e.g., Guba, 1981). Still, lack of attention to these details often leaves qualitative researchers open to criticism from within and without (LeCompte & Goetz, 1982; Bryman, 1988). Thus, I would recommend that increased attention be given to the various methods available to researchers to generate such estimates, and that researchers in the field try to make use of them.

7. Communicating Claims within the Context of Substantive and Methodological Concepts or Decisions. The initial criticism of researchers' lack of attention to the way in which claims are presented was offered by Stewart (1982). Subsequent critiques of research reported in The Journal of Environmental Education have often raised these types of questions. For this reason, I prepared a modified versions of Gowin's Knowledge Vee (Figure 2). I would like to encourage professional researchers and Journal editors to make use of this type of heuristic device as a check on the types of claims or criticisms offered by the writers of research reports.

8.   <u>Organizing, Interpreting, and Synthesizing Claims Across Studies</u>. As noted earlier, efforts to accomplish this in EE have been relatively few in number. It was relatively easy to do this when the field was small in size and studies far fewer in number (e.g., Roth & Hegelson, 1972; Roth, 1976). As the field has grown, there have been fewer and fewer holistic attempts to make sense of the research literature, primarily because of the effort required to accomplish that.   Another area of concern here pertains to the manner in which the findings of qualitative studies are organized and integrated.   Many such studies go unreported in the journal literature. And, by comparison, the methods for accomplishing the integration of qualitative studies still largely undeveloped (Bryman, 1988, Ch. 4). In this case, my recommendation goes out to those professionals who have an interest here, and that recommendation is to work collectively to develop ongoing funding to support this important work. Without it, we will continue building "'castles in the air".

9. <u>Applying Research</u>.   Some forms of research (e.g., action research, responsive evaluation) attempt to address the question of application of results within the design process. However, many studies do not do so, and so, researchers are left with perennial questions such as "Can educational research inform education practice?" (Eisner, 1984; Baker, 1984).   If we spend more time conceptualizing programs of studies which correspond better to questions or concerns of importance to practice in the field, we might avoid such questioning and criticism, and avoid having to defend our choice of problems. On the other hand, it also appears to be incumbent upon the research community to report summaries or reviews of research in easy-to-understand language, and to share these reports in various ways.   While this has been done over the last year through the NAAEE newsletter, <u>The Environmental Communicator</u>, it is an effort worth expanding.

These recommendations address a limited, though, I have argued, important set of research problems or dilemmas facing the field of EE. Still, these are not the only problems we face. Further, there is no attempt to argue that these recommendations represent the best way to address such problems. Rather, the manner in which the recommendations are stated is purposefully general in nature, leaving ample room for alternative strategies to be developed.   What is important is that a sufficient number of professionals in the field recognize the import of these and other research-related problems for the field.   Beyond that, we need to generate and exercise both the individual and the collective will which will enable us to resolve such problems.   If research is ever to make the kinds of contributions to EE theory and practice of which it is capable, "we" must both recognize and rise to the challenges before us.

References

Ajzen, I., & Fishbein, M. (1977). Attitude-behavior relationships: A theroetical analysis and review of empirical literature. Psychological Bulletin, 84(5), 888-918.

Baker, E. (1984). Can educational research inform educational practice? Yes! Phi Delta Kappan, 65(7), 453-455.

Bennett, D. (1974). A report on research and development in environmental education. Paper presented at the Fourty-Seventh Annual Meeting of the National Association for Research in Science Teaching, Chicago, IL, April, 1974. (ED # 091 218)

Best, J. (1981). Research in Education (4th ed.). Englewood Cliffs, NJ: Prentice-Hall, Inc.

Birch, S., & Schwaab, K. (1983). The effects of water conservation instruction on seventh-grade students. The Journal of Environmental Education, 14(4), 28-31.

Borg, W. (1987). Applying Educational Research: A Practical Guide for Teachers (2nd ed.). New York: Longman.

Borg, W., & Gall, M. (1983) Educational Research: An Introduction (4th ed.). New York: Longman Inc.

Bryman, A. (1988). Quantity and quality in social research. M. Blumer (Ed.), Contemporary Social Research Series, No. 18. London, England: Unwin Hyman.

Campbell, D., & Stanley, J. (1963). Experimental and Quasi-experimental Designs for Research. Boston, MA: Houghton Mifflin Co.

Childress, R. (1978). Public school environmental education curricula: A national profile. The Journal of Environmental Education, 9(3), 2-11.

Cook, S., & Berrenberg, J. (1981). Approaches to encouraging conservation behavior: A review and conceptual framework. Journal of Social Issues, 37(2), 73-107.

Dawes, R. (1972). Fundamentals of Attitudes Measurement. New York: J. Wiley and Sons, Inc.

Disinger, J. (1981). Environmental education in the K-12 schools: A national survey. In A. Sacks, et al. (Eds.), Current Issues VII. The Yearbook of Environmental Education and Environmental Studies (pp. 141-156). Columbus, OH: ERIC/SMEAC.

Disinger, J. (1989). The current status of environmental education in U.S. school curricula. Contemporary Education. 60(3), 126-136.

Eisner, E. (1981). On the differences between scientific and artistic approaches to qualitative research. Educational Researcher, 10(4), 5-9.

Eisner, E. (1984). Can educational research inform educational practice? Phi Delta Kappan, 65(7), 447-452.

Firestone, W. (1987). Meaning in method: The rhetoric of quantitative and qualitative research. Educational Researcher, 16(7), 16-21.

Fisher, R. A. (1925). Statistical Methods for Research Workers (1st ed.). London, England: Oliver and Boyd.

Fisher, R.A. (1935). The Design of Experiments (1st ed.). London, England: Oliver and Boyd.

Fraenkel, J., & Wallen, N. (1990). How to Design and Evaluate Research in Education. New York: McGraw-Hill Publishing Co.

Geller, S., Winnett, R., & Everett, P. (1982). Preserving the Environment: New Strategies for Behavioral Change. New York: Pergamon Press.

Gray, D., Borden, R., & Weigel, R. (1985). Ecological Beliefs and Behaviors: Assessment and Change. Westport, CN: Greenwood Press.

Guba, E. (1981). Criteria for assessing the trustworthiness of naturalistic inquiries. Education and Communications Technology Journal, 29(2), 75-91.

Hendee, J. (1972). Challenging the folklore of environmental education. Journal of Environmental Education, 3(3), 19-23.

Hines, J., & Hungerford, H. (1984). Environmental education research related to environmental action skills. In L. Iozzi (Ed.), A Summary of Research in Environmental Education, 1971-1982. The Second Report of the National Commission on Environmental Education Research. Monographs in Environmental Education and Environmental Studies, Volume II (pp. 113-129). Columbus, OH: ERIC/SMEAC.

Hines, J., Hungerford, H., & Tomera, A. (1988). An analysis and synthesis of research on responsible environmental behavior: A meta-analysis. Journal of Environmental Education, 18(2), 1-8.

Horsley, A. (1977). The effects of a social learning experiment on attitudes and behavior toward environmental conservation. Environment and Behavior, 9(3), 349-384.

Hungerford, H., Tomera, A., & Wilson, R. (1983a). Ten years of research in "The Journal of Environmental Education" - A brief analysis of Volumes 3-12. In A. Sacks, L. Iozzi, and R. Wilke (Eds.), Current Issues in Environmental Education and Environmental Studies, Volume VIII (pp. 163-181). Columbus, OH: ERIC/ SMEAC.

Hungerford, H., Tomera, A., & Wilson, R. (1983b). An analysis of the emphasis placed on overt environmental behavior (intervention) and allied variables in studies abstracted in "Research in Environmental Education, 1971-1980". In A. Sacks, L. Iozzi, and R. Wilke (Eds.), Current Issues in Environmental Education and Environmental Studies, Volume VIII (pp. 183-197). Columbus, OH: ERIC/SMEAC.

Hungerford, H., & Volk, T. (1990). Changing learner behavior through environmental education. Journal of Environmental Education, 21 (3), 8-22.

Iozzi, L. (Ed.). (1981). Research in Environmental Education, 1971-1980. Columbus, OH: ERIC/SMEAC. (ED # 214 762)

Iozzi, L. (Ed.). (1984). A Summary of Research in Environmental Education, 1971-1982. The Second Report of the National Commission on Environmental Education Research. Monographs in Environmental Education and Environmental Studies, Volume II. Columbus, OH: ERIC/SMEAC.

Iozzi, L. (1989a). What research says to the educator, Part One: Environmental Education and the Affective Domain. Journal of Environmental Education, 20(3), 3-9.

Iozzi, L. (1989b). What research says to the educator, Part Two: Environmental Education and the Affective Domain. Journal of Environmental Education, 20(4), 6-14.

Isaac, S., & Michael, W. (1981). Handbook in Research and Evaluation. San Duego, CA: EdITS Publishers.

Kerlinger, F. (1973). Foundations of Behavioral Research (2nd ed.). New York: Holt, Rinehart and Winston, Inc.

LeCompte, M., & Goetz, J. (1982). Problems of reliability and validity in ethnographic research. Review of Educational Research, 52(1), 31-60.

Lewis, G. (1981/82). A review of classroom methodologies for environmental education. Journal of Environmental Education, 13(2), 12-15.

Lincoln, Y., & Guba, E. (1982). Establishing dependability and confirmability in naturalistic inquiry through an audit. Paper presented at the Annual

Meeting of the American Educational Research Association, New York, NY, March, 1982.

Lincoln, Y., & Guba, E. (1988). Criteria for assessing naturalistic inquiries as reports. Paper presented at the Annual Meeting of the American Educational Research Association, New Orleans, LA, April, 1988.

Lipsey, M. (1977). Personal antecedents and consequences of ecologically responsible behavior: A review. Catalog of Selected Documents in Psychology, 7(4), 70. (Manuscript No. 1521).

Marcinkowski, T. (1989). An analysis of correlates and predictors of responsible environmental behavior. (Doctoral dissertation, Southern Illinois University at Carbondale, 1988). Dissertation Abstracts International, 49 (12), 3677-A.

Marcinkowski, T. (in development). The modeling, measurement, and prediction of responsible environmental behavior: A review of the research literature, with recommendations. Monographs in Environmental Education and Environmental Studies, Volume ____. Troy, OH: NAAEE.

McCall, W. (1923). How to Experiment in Education. New York: Macmillan.

McDougall, G., Claxton, J., Ritchie, B., & Anderson, C. (1981). Consumer energy research: A review. Journal of Consumer Research, 8(3), 343-354.

McMillan, J., & Schumacher, S. (1989). Research in Education: A Conceptual Introduction (2nd ed.). Glenview, IL: Scott, Foresman and Co.

McNeil, K., Kelly, F., & McNeil, J. (1975). Testing Research Hypotheses using Multiple Linear Regression. Carbondale, IL: Southern Illinois University Press.

Miles, M., & Huberman, A. (1984). Drawing valid meaning from qualitative data: Toward a shared craft. Educational Researcher, 12( ), 20-30.

Novak, J., & Gowin, D.B. (1984). Learning How to Learn. New York: Cambridge University Press.

Peterson, N. (1982). Developmental variables affecting environmental sensitivity in environmental educators. Unpublished masters thesis, Southern Illinois University at Carbondale.

Peyton, R. B. (1981). EE research update. Presentation at the Midwest Regional Environmental Education Conference, Wisconsin Dells, WI, Sept., 1981.

Ramsey, C., & Rickson, R. (1977). Environmental knowledge and attitudes. Journal of Environmental Education, 13(1), 24-29.

Ramsey, J., Hungerford, H., & Tomera, A. (1981). The effects of environmental action and environmental case study instruction on the overt environmental behavior of eighth-grade students. Journal of Environmental Education, 13(1), 24-30.

Rist, R. (1977). On the relations among educational research paradigms: From disdain to detente. Anthropology and Education Quarterly, 8, 42-49.

Robottom, I. (1985). Evaluation in environmental education: Time for a change in perspective. Journal of Environmental Education, 17(1), 31-36.

Roth, R. (1976). A Review of Research Related to Environmental Education, 1973-1976. Columbus, OH: ERIC/SMEAC. (ED # 135 647)

Roth, R., & Hegelson, S. (1972). A Review of Research Related to Environmental Education. Columbus, OH: ERIC/SMEAC. (ED # 068 359)

Scholl, M. (1983). A survey of significant childhood learning experiences of suburban/urban environmentalists. Paper presented at the 12th Annual Conference of the North American Association for Environmental Education, Ypsilanti, Michigan.

Schulman, L. (1981). Disciplines of inquiry in education. Educational Researcher, 10(6), 5-23.

Sia, A., Hungerford, H., & Tomera, A. (1985/86). Selected predictors of responsible environmental behavior: An analysis. Journal of Environmental Education, 17(2), 31-40.

Simmons, B. (1990). National survey of EE Center goals: Are we really practicing what we preach? In B. Simmons, C. Knapp, and C. Young, (Eds.), Setting the Agenda for the '90s: Selected Papers from the Nineteenth Annual Conference of the North American Association for Environmental Education (pp. 169-175). Troy, OH: NAAEE.

Sivek, D., & Hungerford, H. (1989/90). Predictors of responsible environmental behavior in members of three Wisconsin conservation organizations. Journal of Environmental Education, 21(2), 35-40.

Smith, J. (1983). Quantitative versus qualitative research: An attempt to clarify the issue. Educational Researcher, 12(3), 6-13.

Smith, J., & Heshusius, L. (1986). Closing down the conversation: The end of the quantitative-qualitative debate among educational inquirers. Educational Researcher, 15(1), 4-11.

Snow, R. (1974). Representative and quasi-representative designs for research on teaching. Educational Researcher, 44(3), 265-291.

Stewart, J. (1982). Opinion - Empirical research reported in "The Journal of Environmental Education": A critique. Journal of Environmental Education, 14(1), 42-44.

Tanner, R. T. (1980). Significant life experiences: A new research area in environmental education. Journal of Environmental Education, 11 (4), 20-24.

Thorndike, E., & Woodworth, R. (1901). The influence of improvement in one mental function upon the efficiency of other functions. Psychological Review, 8, 247-261, 384-395, 553-564.

Van Liere, K., & Dunlap, R. (1980). The social basis of environmental concern: A review of hypotheses, explanations, and empirical evidence. Public Opinion Quarterly, 44(2), 181-197.

Voelker, A., et al. (1973). Environmental Education-Related Research: 1969-1972. Columbus, OH: ERIC/SMEAC.

Widman, R., Simmons, B., Kaplan, R., & DeYoung, R. (1984). Behavioral Approaches to Energy Conservation in Organizations: A Selected Review of the Literature. (CPL Bibliography No. 143). Chicago, IL: Council of Planning Librarians.

Wilke, R., & Leatherman, J. (1983). Conclusions and generalizations drawn from "Research in Environmental Education, 1971-1980", regarding teacher training pre-service, teacher training in-service, community resource use, and field trips. In A. Sacks, L. Iozzi, and R. Wilke (Eds.), Current Issues in Environmental Education and Environmental Studies, Volume VIII (pp. 199-207). Columbus, OH: ERIC/SMEAC.

Wilson, T. (1988). A study into the attainment of goals for environmental education through the inservice teacher education efforts of a university-based network of centers for environmental education. Paper presented at the Annual Meeting of the North American Association for Environmental Education, Orlando, FL.

About the Author

Thomas Marcinkowski is an associate professor in the Science Education Department at the Florida Institute of Technology, 150 West University Boulevard, Melbourne, Florida 32901. He occupies the Acopian Position in Environmental Education, and his primary responsibility is to develop and administer the university's graduate programs in Environmental Education, Master's through Ph.D. Within NAAEE, he has served as chair of the North American Commission for Environmental Education Research (NACEER) since October, 1988. As chair, he has actively supported two symposia on research paradigms/methods in EE (San Antonio '90, Toronto '92). He serves as a consulting editor for *The Journal of Environmental Education* (1983 -), and as an associate research editor for *Legacy, The Journal of the National Association for Interpretation* (1991 -). Currently, he is working with several members of NACEER to complete the Commission's second abstracting project, to prepare for the Commission's field evaluation of *Project Learning Tree,* and to help Mexican members of NACEER develop plans to support EE research/researchers in Mexico and across Latin America.

ALTERNATIVE PARADIGMS IN ENVIRONMENTAL EDUCATION RESEARCH: THE INTERPRETIVE PERSPECTIVE

Diane C. Cantrell

Abstract

Assumptions underlying three distinctly different paradigms -- positivism, interpretivism, and critical science -- currently guide research. Although acceptance of interpretivism is increasing within education, positivism remains the dominant paradigm for both education and environmental education. In an effort to increase the potential for naturalistic inquiry, this paper 1) provides an understanding of the philosophical foundation underlying interpretivism, 2) argues that a distinction exists between methodology (positivism, interpretivism) and method (quantitative, qualitative), with the former more critical than the latter, 3) proposes that environmental education fits well with the interpretive paradigm and qualitative methods, and 4) outlines what this approach would look like in practice in terms of research design, data collection, data analysis, and rigor. The intent is to inform practice as well as to clarify criteria which are appropriate for assessing the merit of environmental education research based upon the interpretive model.

Introduction

Mark Twain once said that if the only tool one has is a hammer, then one tends to treat everything as if it is a nail. While a hammer remains functional, if not optimum, for driving a screw, it become less useful for a bolt and basically dysfunctional for paper staples, twist ties, tape or glue. What is used for "holding and fastening" requires different tools be they hammers, screwdrivers, wrenches, scissors, or human hands. In a similar way, using a hammer to kill an intruder or to prop open a door demonstrates uses not in keeping with the recognized intent of this tool.

Mark Twain's insight reflects practices in environmental education research. For years, inquirers have hammered with one research paradigm, positivism, as if all topics of inquiry were nails. Currently, the tools for realizing the full potential for environmental education research remain locked in the tool box.

A Look at the Tool Box -- Differing Perspectives

A key issue in the paradigm debate centers around the unity of the sciences. Are the natural and social sciences basically the same or are the subject matters inherently different? In his discussion of phenomenology, Bernstein (1976) poses the distinction in terms of how theorists account for "man-in-the-world," either through a "scientific image" or through a "manifest image." He states:

> Thus those who endorse the scientific image maintain that science will provide not a partial but a complete account which can in principle, if not yet in fact, explain even the "indispensable core" of human concepts, by showing how they are based on more fundamental scientific principles. And those who endorse the manifest declare not just that a scientific account of man is incomplete, but that, if we "subject science itself to rigorous scrutiny," we will see in it a second -order discipline based on a more fundamental understanding of man-in-the-world (p. 120).

The first view perceives human beings as complex physical systems differing from the rest of nature not in kind but perhaps in degree. Therefore, science can provide explanations for how the system works. Inadequate explanations appear as temporary setbacks rather than failures. The countering perspective argues that "scientific points of view. . . are always both naive and at the same time dishonest" and that failures in science indicate "deep conceptual or categorical confusions" (p. 121).

Friction between these two stances, based upon epistemological conceptions, has fired this debate for years. Wilhelm Dilthey, in the late nineteenth century, posited that knowledge is derived differently by the humanities and the natural sciences (Carr and Kemmis, 1983; Smith and Heshusius, 1986). "The former aims at "understanding" (Verstehen) and the latter at "explaining" (Erklaren) (Husen, 1988, p. 6). Smith (1989) summarizes the essence of the dispute by presenting the views of Comte along with Dilthey.

> Even though social science was behind the natural sciences in its development -- in part because it was the latest science to emerge -- in Comte's view social science, by adopting the forms of explanation, observation, and so on of the natural sciences, would eventually gain a similar intellectual and practical mastery of its subject matter . . .

> Dilthey, one of the principle exponents of this separation, claimed that the two areas required different approaches because they dealt with significantly different subject matters. . . according to this view, social objects and events, unlike physical objects and events, are constructed by human minds. And since

the meaning of social objects and events can only be understood by examining them within their contexts, the approach to the study of these "objectifications" of our minds must be hermeneutical or interpretive (p. 13).

This contrasting view of the nature of reality distinguishes a range of research perspectives, or paradigms, which includes positivism, interpretivism, and critical science. Each differs on basic underlying assumptions that ultimately guide choices about research methodologies and methods. The literature offers a variety of summary charts (Carr and Kemmis; 1983; Guba and Lincoln, 1981; Koetting, 1986; Lincoln and Guba, 1985; McCutcheon and Jung, 1990) and discussions (Bernstein, 1976; Comber, 1988; Eichelberger, 1989; Nielsen, 1990; Rist, 1977; Smith, 1989) which attempt to clarify the differences. Table 1 synthesizes these ideas by providing a comparison of five assumptions: purpose(s) of research, nature of reality, nature of knowledge, relationship between the knower and the known, and role of value(s) in research.

Table 1 Contrasting Views Underlying Alternative Paradigms			
Underlying Assumption and Beliefs About:	Positivism	Interpretivism	Critical Science
Purpose(s) of research	Discover laws and generalizations which explain reality and allow to predict and control	Understand and interpret daily occurrences and social structures as well as the meanings people give to the phenomena	Emancipate people through critique of ideologies that promote inequity and through change in personal understanding and action that lead to transformation of self-consciousness and social conditions
Nature of reality (ontology)	Single, givens, fragmentable, tangible, measurable, convergent	Multiple, constructed through human interaction, holistic, divergent	Multiple, constructed, holistic, divergent; social and economic; embedded in issues of equity and hegemony
Nature of knowledge (epistemology)	Events are explained based upon knowable facts, real causes or simultaneous effects; lawlike regularities exist	Events are understood through mental process of interpretation which is influenced by and interacts with social context -- mutual simultaneous shaping	Events are understood within social and economic context with emphasis on ideological critique and praxis

Table 1 (continued) Undelrying Assumption and Beliefs About:	Positivisim	Interpretivisim	Critical Science
Relationship between knower and the known	Independent, dualism	Interrelated, dialogic	Interrelated, influenced by society and commitment to emancipation
Role of value(s) in research	Value free	Value bounded	Value bounded; ideological critique and concern for inequities

Based upon these assumptions, general characteristics of interpretivism become evident. Researchers from this orientation seek to understand phenomena and to interpret meaning within the social and cultural context of the natural setting. Unlike positivist who believe that reality exists apart from the researcher and is knowable, interpretivist hold that reality is constructed. In fact, "inquiry is not a matter of offering interpretations of reality, but one of offering interpretations that become reality, to the extent they are agreed upon" (Smith, 1989, p. 171). Counter to positivists, interpretivist seek subjective perceptions of individuals. Carr and Kemmis (1983, p. 88) emphasize that to identify the actor's "motives and intentions correctly is to grasp the 'subjective meaning' the action has for the actor." In support of this idea, Fetterman (1988) indicates that researchers from the phenomenological perspective "argue that what people believe to be true is more important than any objective reality; people act on what they believe. Moreover, there are real consequences to their actions" (p. 18). In order to uncover what people believe and to render meaning about their actions and intentions, interpretive researchers interact dialogically with the participants. Within this interrelationship, values cannot be sidestepped. Unlike positivists who attempt to separate values from facts and offer explanations of reality which are empirically verifiable, interpretivists accept the inseparable bond between values and facts and attempt to understand reality, especially the behavior of people, within a social context. In general, interpretivism and critical science share many tenets in common, with one marked difference. The former focuses primarily on understanding and interpretation and the latter on emancipation and critique of ideologies.

When a Screwdriver Is Most Appropriate, Use It -- Methodology vs. Methods

In studying Table 1, a person can quickly recognize, perhaps, her or his orientation. The intent here is not to assist researchers in cementing their own philosophical entrenchments but to provide philosophical goggles which enlighten their view and, in turn, lead to an acceptance of the wider array of methodologies. Along with this acceptance, comes an issue of appropriateness.

The literature of the 1980s was replete with comparative discussions, variously referred to as debates, conversations, or wars, which examined different paradigms, quantitative versus qualitative research, and approaches most appropriate for education. Little overall consensus exists. Smith and Heshusius (1986), in tracing the evolution of concern, outline three historical phases: 1) conflict where proponents so strongly recognized the fundamental differences in assumptions, procedures and attitudes that they often approached mutual disdain; 2) detente in which proponents, while accepting paradigmatic differences, decreased their concern over underlying assumptions and increased their concern over issues of procedure; and 3) compatibility and cooperation where proponents' concerns over assumptions are minimal and those related to procedure are primary. While the authors suggest that the latter represents the current state of affairs, the other views or similar stances still exist.

For example, Miles and Huberman (1988) advocate the latter position when they state, "We contend that researchers should pursue their work, be open to an ecumenical blend of epistemologies and procedures, and leave the grand debate to those who care most about it" (p. 223). They support this position on the grounds that the debate is unlikely to be resolved during the researcher's lifetime and that epistemological purity does not get research done (p. 223-4). In addition, they believe that the differences represent a continuum rather than a dichotomy with both camps, in practise, sharing more and more similarities.

Patton (1990), in a similar discussion, raises a key issue. He states that his purpose is to:

> increase the options available to evaluators, not to replace one limited paradigm with another limited, but different, paradigm. . . Rather than believing that one must choose to align with one paradigm or the other, I advocate a paradigm of choices. A paradigm of choices rejects methodological orthodoxy in favor of methodological appropriateness as the primary criterion for judging methodological quality. The issue then becomes not whether one has uniformly adhered to prescribed canons of either logical-positivism or phenomenology but whether one has made sensible methods decisions given the purpose of the inquiry, the questions being investigated, and the resources available. The paradigm of choices recognizes that different methods are appropriate for different situations (pp. 38-39).

The role of the paradigm and the methods as well as the relationship between the two emerges as the most critical issue in the debate. In contrast to Miles and Huberman and Patton, Fetterman (1988) addresses the misleading nature of the terms "quantitative" and "qualitative" when he writes, "They are commonly accepted handles for both the contrasting paradigms and the methods associated with them. However, each paradigm employs both quantitative and qualitative methods . . . Focusing on methods, however, is like focusing on the symptoms rather than the disease" (p. 18). Bednarz (1985) offers another analogy. "Methods are neutral in the sense that a hammer is neutral to its use for building fine furniture or smashing ants; that is, they serve the purposes of the researcher. Philosophical orientations are not neutral" (p. 290).

Smith (1989) further clarifies the relationship between method and paradigm by offering a distinction between "method as technique" and "method as logic of justification." Researchers may apply techniques from one approach to the other with "no problems of consequence" (p. 170). However, in justifying each approach, the distinctions summarized in Table 1 are critical.

Perhaps the strongest champions for making this distinction are Lincoln and Guba (1988) who believe that the underlying assumptions not only take critical precedence, but also, in fact, dictate in large measure the methods to be used. They present a parallel analogy to that of Bednarz:

> It may very well be the case that there is no immediate connection discernible between the methods -- the tools and techniques -- that an investigator uses and the inquiry paradigm that guides him or her. On seeing a man using a hammer, we cannot tell whether he is operating as a carpenter, an electrician, or a plumber. What we can be quite sure of, however, is that the way the hammer is used will greatly depend on whether the user construes himself or herself as a carpenter, electrician, or plumber. The hammer may be a method, but using it in the service of carpentry is an instance of methodology. One can mix and match, or blend, hammers, saws, wrenches, levels, and the like, but one cannot mix and match or blend carpentry with, say, plumbing (p. 91).

While Lincoln and Guba can accept perhaps the blending of methods promoted by Miles and Huberman, they find the "mind sifts back and forth between paradigms" advocated by Patton as far more problematic (p. 90-1). In defending their position, they refer to the assumptions underlying the naturalistic (interpretive) paradigm and state, "These axioms represent fundamentally different ontological, epistemological, and axiological postures; a call to blend or accommodate them is logically equivalent to calling for a compromise between the view that the world is flat and the view that the world is round" (p. 93). Comber (1988) suggests that the 1980s catalyzed a new paradigm debate "between validating research according to how it is done and validating research according to why it is done" (p. 779). In this way, what is most appropriate for research in education, and, in turn, for environmental education, depends upon which paradigm fits most appropriately.

An Interpretive Tool Box for Environmental Education Research -- Methodological Appropriateness

While the positivist paradigm remains the dominant one in education, the interpretive perspective has gained much wider acceptance (Fetterman,

1988; Firestone and Dawson, 1988; Lather, 1986; Lincoln and Guba, 1985; Smith, 1987). Based upon the previously discussed underlying assumptions, the shift appears not only appropriate but long overdue. The complex nature of education -- entangled in interrelationships, replete with social, political, and economic context, and laden with values -- demands that an alternative paradigm drive educational research.

While the impetus for change exists for the field of education, environmental education in particular lags behind in the acceptance of postpositivistic paradigms (Robottom, 1985). This results, in large part, perhaps, from its subject matter connections. Rooted in the natural sciences and nature study, its allegiance may initially appear reasonable. But, with its emphasis on an interdisciplinary approach, environmental education subject matter encompasses the social sciences as well. In addition to the content and process of these areas, it utilizes the content and processes of education, carrying with it, in turn, the complexities of this arena. Words used in describing and defining environmental education -- knowledge, values, skills, holistic, interdisciplinary, biophysical, sociocultural, interdependence, integrated, motivated and committed, relationship with natural and built environments, and social responsibility, to name a few -- present the best case for why the field needs to accept an alternative paradigm. In fact, the way in which these phrases match, parallel and complement those listed in Table 1 under "interpretive" and "critical science", it may be more than reasonable to suggest that these perspectives are the most appropriate for environmental education. While much of the following discussion is relevant to both paradigms, the focus is on the former.

How the Interpretive Inquirer Uses the Tools in the Environmental Education Research Tool Box

As discussed previously, methodology (e.g., interpretive paradigm) guides choices concerning methods. An understanding of the appropriateness of qualitative research methods depends upon an understanding and valuing of the assumptions underlying the interpretive paradigm. While interpretive studies are not limited solely to the use of qualitative methods, they are recognized as the methods most typically used (Guba and Lincoln, 1981; Patton, 1990).

The term "qualitative research" is used synonymously for a number of research approaches associated with the interpretive and critical science perspectives. These include, for example, naturalistic, ethnographic, ethnomethodological, phenomenological, postpositivist, subjective, artistic, hermenuetics, case study, humanistic, ecological, action research, participatory, feminist, and emancipatory (Jacob, 1987, 1988; Lincoln and Guba, 1985; Patton, 1990; Peshkin, 1988; Smith, 1987). In this way, qualitative research is no more monolithic than quantitative research. Neither one reflects a single point or even a narrow perspective on the continuum but a range of possibilities tightly bound to the paradigm and the purpose of the inquiry. Yet, there are characteristics of interpretive research using qualitative methods that clearly distinguish it from positivist research using quantitative methods.

One of the major reasons these methods have not been seen as appropriate for environmental education is because they are viewed through positivist goggles. Arguments over "quality" or the perceived lack of quality in a study hinge upon the inherent philosophical differences discussed throughout this paper.

The following presents a brief overview of **research design**, **data collection**, **data analysis**, and **rigor** with an emphasis on the underlying assumptions of interpretivism and the use of qualitative methods. The purposes are twofold: 1) to translate the theoretical discussion into practice and 2) to provide interpretivist goggles for viewing and assessing the merit of research based upon this paradigm.

Research Design

The design of an interpretive inquiry differs substantively from that of a positivist (conventional) study. Lincoln and Guba (1985, p. 225) state, "The design specifications of the conventional paradigm form a procrustean bed of such a nature as to make it impossible for the naturalist to lie in it -- not only uncomfortably, but at all". The degree to which it differs, however, reflects the previously discussed lack of consensus regarding the blending and mixing of paradigms and methods. The following highlights the range of possibilities and clarifies their differences in an effort to depict and explain current practice. The discussion addresses six topics related to design: 1. degree of structure, 2. focus and research questions, 3. sampling, 4. instrumentation, 5. triangulation, and 6. initial plans for implementation.

1. <u>Degree of Structure</u>. In the classic sense, the research design for an interpretive study begins as a broad outline of contingency plans open to change throughout the study. An emphasis on an emergent design and researcher flexibility characterize this approach. Plans, research questions, theories, data collection strategies, and analysis all evolve from the beginning point as the researcher learns more about the people, places, events and processes which are the focus of the study. Rather than describing in advance every aspect of the design, interpretive researchers elaborate upon these details and their evolution as part of the final report. Based upon the underlying assumptions, Lincoln and Guba (1985, p. 225) argue that the "design of a naturalistic inquiry . . . <u>cannot</u> be given in advance; it must emerge, develop, unfold." Researchers, from Bogdan and Biklen's perspective (1982, p. 55), "proceed as if they know very little about the people and places they will visit . . . avoid going into the study with hypotheses to test . . . , believing that finding the questions should be one of the products of data collection rather than <u>a prior</u>."

However, those who accept a blending of methods perceive a wider range of possibilities. Miles and Huberman (1984, 1988), who describe themselves as "right-winged qualitative researchers" or "soft-nosed positivists," build a case for both the emergent design and a more systematic and structured approach. They state:

> Highly inductive and loosely designed studies make good sense when researchers have plenty of time and are exploring exotic cultures, understudied phenomena, or very complex social realities. But when one is interested in some better-understood social phenomena within a familiar culture or sub-culture, a loose, highly inductive design is a waste of time (1984, p. 27).

The following continuum identifies the characteristics of the different possibilities for interpretive research designs. It is important to note that the positivist design would still fall to the left of this continuum and that even a prestructured design would evolve and change throughout the study.

Prestructured

    tight
    deductive
    linear
    conceptual   framework
    focused and bounded
    theory   predetermined

Emergent

    loose
    inductive
    cyclic
    as if know little
    no   blinders
    grounded   theory

In determining the appropriate degree of structure for a study, the researcher needs to consider what is being studied, the purpose of the study, and underlying assumptions.

2. <u>Focus and Research Questions</u>. These decisions concerning structure are reflected in different elements of the overall design beginning with the focus and research questions. While the researcher needs an initial focus, it inevitably changes over time. Viewed positively, these changes "signal movement to a more sophisticated and insightful level of inquiry (Lincoln and Guba, 1985, p. 229). The focus establishes the boundaries of the study (what will be studied) as well as inclusion-exclusion criteria (relevancy of new information) (pp. 228-29). From a similar stance, Miles and Huberman (1984, p. 28) suggest, "Focusing and bounding data collection can be seen usefully as anticipatory <u>data reduction</u>; it is a form of pre-analysis, ruling out certain variables and relationships, and attending to others." Finally, Patton (1990, p. 166) points to the nebulous nature of inquiry and to real world constraints in stating, "There is no rule of thumb that tells a researcher how to focus a study. The extent to which a research question is broad or narrow depends on purpose, the resources available, the time available, and the interests of those involved. In brief, these are not choices between good and bad, but choices among alternatives, all of which have merit."

3. <u>Sampling</u>. Issues surrounding sampling as well as the logic that guides sampling decisions highlight one of the major differences between qualitative and quantitative methods. The quantitative approach involves representative samples selected <u>randomly</u> to allow the researcher to generalize to a larger population. The qualitative approach uses small, information-rich samples selected <u>purposefully</u> to allow the researcher to focus in depth on issues important to the study. For the former, once established, the same sample is used for the duration of the study. For the latter, samples change throughout the study through serial selection (one sample leads to another) in order to extend, test and fill in information (Lincoln and Guba, 1985, p. 201).

Initial sampling decisions center on what to sample (the unit of analysis) and are based upon the focus of the study and the context. Possibilities may include, for example, one or more of the following: individuals, groups, programs, objects, events, occurrences, settings, processes, and different times. Determining who, what and when to sample evolves from the initial knowledge, understanding and experience of the researcher; from recommendations given by gatekeepers, informants and experts; and form progressive understanding of the phenomena under study. Patton (1990, pp. 182-183) identifies and describes a number of purposeful sampling strategies which interpretive researcher may use:

- extreme or deviant case sampling
- intensity sampling
- maximum variations sampling
- homogeneous sampling
- typical case sampling
- stratified purposeful sampling
- critical case sampling
- snowball or chain sampling
- criterion sampling
- theory based or operational construct sampling
- confirming and disconfirming cases
- opportunistic sampling
- random purposeful sampling (still sample small size)
- sampling politically important cases
- convenience sampling
- combination or mixed purposeful sampling

Maximum variation sampling, for Lincoln and Guba (1985, p. 201) is the sampling mode of choice because it is used "to detail the many specifics that give the context its unique flavor . . . to generate the information upon which the emergent design and grounded theory can be based."

Sample size represents another marked difference. For qualitative methods, it is based upon the purpose of the study, not on specific rules. The researcher looks at what she or he wants to know, what will be useful, what will be credible, and what can be done within the constraints of time and resources (Patton, 1990, p. 184).

In the absence of definite rules for sample size, the interpretive inquirer must also decide at what point enough is enough, a state commonly referred to as data saturation or redundancy (Bogdan and Biklen, 1982; Lincoln and Guba, 1985; Patton, 1990). When no new information is forthcoming, or the inquirer reaches a point of diminishing return, sampling is complete. Since the research design is flexible, a common pit fall is to redefine the focus or goal as new and interesting data is collected, thus prolonging and expanding the study. The researcher needs to constantly find the balance between recognizing new information relevant to the focus of the study at hand and finding new information relevant to the focus of another or secondary study, albeit equally important and interesting. Identifying a realistic ending point, based upon redundancy, becomes a critical issue for the interpretive inquirer.

Along with this comes the issue of describing, explaining and justifying the sample strategies and size in such a way that peer reviewers and others using the research information fully understand the context within which to judge the sample. Patton (1990, pp. 185-6) elaborates upon this point:

> The validity, meaningfulness, and insights generated from qualitative inquiry have more to do with the information-richness of the cases selected and the observational/analytical capabilities of the researcher than with sample size....The researcher or evaluator is absolutely obligated to discuss how the sample affected the findings, the strengths and weaknesses of the sampling procedures, and any other design decisions that are relevant for interpreting and understanding the reported results. Exercising care not to overgeneralize from purposeful samples, while maximizing to the full the advantages of indepth, purposeful sampling, will do much to alleviate concerns about small sample size.

4. <u>Instrumentation</u>. Decisions concerning any instruments are also tied to the purpose of the study and the structure of the design. The primary instrument for qualitative methods is the inquirer himself or herself. For Lincoln and Guba (1981, 1985, 1988), the human instrument is the instrument of choice, regardless of any imperfections, because its adaptability best meets the research requirements tied to the interpretive paradigm. However, the human instrument may use other instruments to collect qualitative data such as a list of interview questions, observational checklist, or traditional paper-pencil instrument. Design decisions concerning instrumentation focus on if and when to develop an instrument (before or during data collection) and on the degree of structure. For example, does the researcher want to avoid blinders or pursue specific data? Emphasize context or be able to generalize to some degree? Not miss important information or reduce extraneous data (Miles and Huberman,

1984, pp. 42-3)?

5. <u>Triangulation</u>. The strength of the design, and in turn the merit and credibility of the study, is increased through the use of triangulation. Simply stated, this means that the researcher can corroborate information in one or more ways: <u>data triangulation</u> by using different data sources, <u>investigator triangulation</u> by using two or more researchers, <u>theory triangulation</u> by using different perspectives to interpret data, and <u>methodological triangulation</u> by using multiple methods to gather data (Guba and Lincoln; 1985; Miles and Huberman, 1984; Patton, 1990). Triangulation is not the only strategy for heightening robustness; however, by initially planning for it as part of the design, the researcher increases the likelihood that credibility can be substantiated.

6. <u>Initial Plans for Implementation</u>. While emphasizing that designs appropriate for interpretive studies remain highly flexible, several other decisions are important in the beginning. These include choices pertaining to: logistics (e.g., budget, time schedule, entry into field, concluding study) data collection (e.g., multimethods, recording devices, field notes), data analysis (e.g., procedures during and after data collection), and rigor.

Data Collection

With the malleable design as a guide, the research enters the field to begin data collection. The type of data, the role of the researcher in data gathering, as well as the specific methods for collecting data further delineate the nature of qualitative methods. In general, qualitative data consists primarily of words in the form of interview transcripts, field notes, and documents. It comes from fieldwork in which the investigator spends time in a natural setting gathering data first hand, typically through interviews, observations, and documentation. While these three forms are typically accepted as the primary modes for collection, Lincoln and Guba (1985) specify two other types of data: nonverbal cues which pertain to nonverbal communications (p. 276) and unobtrusive information residues which involve physical traces that can be collected in the absence of the respondents who provided them (pp. 279-80). In this discussion, both of these are subsumed under the other three categories.

As previously discussed, the researcher is the primary instrument of data collection. As with sampling issues, this distinction between quantitative and qualitative methods raises concerns within the minds of positivists. Based upon paradigm assumptions, Lincoln and Guba (1985, pp. 39-40) summarize why the human instrument is crucial to interpretive research. In comparison to paper-and-pencil instruments, the naturalistic inquirer chooses to gather data through humans:

> ...because it would be virtually impossible to devise a prior a nonhuman instrument with sufficient adaptability to encompass and adjust to the variety of realities that will be encountered;

because of the understanding that all instruments interact with respondents and objects but that only the human instrument is capable of grasping and evaluating the meaning of that differential interaction; because the intrusion of instruments intervenes in the mutual shaping of other elements and that shaping can be appreciated and evaluated only by a human; and because all instruments are value-based and interact with local values but only the human is in a position to identify and take into account (to some extent) those resulting biases.

Because the human instrument is responsive, is flexible, sees social organization as holistic entities, relies on propositional and tacit knowledge, and sees the unusual, Guba and Lincoln (1981) believe that its strengths outweigh its weaknesses. While the weaknesses cannot be ignored, they can be alleviated. People do have selective perceptions which must be taken into account during observation and interviewing. However, individuals can learn how to observe and interview as well as learn how to improve specific skills related to these tasks through education, preparation, and practice (Lincoln and Guba, 1985; Patton, 1990). Patton emphasizes that "to become a skilled observer is a no less rigorous process than the training necessary to become a skilled statistician. People don't 'naturally' know statistics--and people do not 'naturally' know how to do systematic research observations" (p. 201). Through education, inquirers can learn how to observe and interview as well as what to look for and what to ask. Through preparation, they can become physically, mentally and emotionally ready to make observations and conduct interviews. Finally, through simulations and apprenticeships, novice inquirers can practice their new skills and receive valuable feedback aimed at improving their observational and interviewing abilities.

The following sections present an overview of the three major methods of data collection--observation, interviews, documentation. These snapshots of data gathering describe for each method the purpose, the general nature of the strategy, the form of the data, helpful tools, and strengths and weaknesses. It is emphasized again that by using a combination of data collection techniques, the researcher capitalizes on the strengths of each and minimizes weaknesses inherent in single strategies (i.e., triangulation).

1. Observation. The purpose of observation is to give the researcher direct, first-hand experiences with the phenomena under study--to "walk in the shoes" so to speak. It is interpreted by many to mean participant observation and actually represents a continuum ranging from the "pure" observer to the "pure" participant (Bogdan and Biklen, 1982, Guba and Lincoln, 1981; Schatzman and Strauss, 1973). Either extreme is difficult to achieve. The first represents a type of one-way mirror look at the setting with no interference by the researcher and the latter completely involves the researcher in the setting to the point of "going native" and forgetting the original goal. Between the two extremes, the researcher functions as both participant and observer, but in two distinctly different roles — one as an

insider participating as a group member and the other as an outsider observing (Guba and Lincoln, 1981). The degree which one or the other role dominates depends on the research purpose and stage of research (beginning, middle, end).

Pure	Participant	Observer	Pure
Participant	as	as	Observer
	Observer	Participant	

In addition to deciding to what extent the inquirer will function as a participant or as an observer, she or he makes other decisions related to gathering data through observation: who will know the role of the researcher, who will know the purpose of the study, how often and for how long will the researcher observe, and what will be the focus of the study. These questions pertaining to the nature of the observation are tied, again, to the design and purpose of the study. Patton (1990) represents these issues as continua.

Overt	Covert
Full explanation of real purpose	False explanation of real purpose
Single observation, limited duration	Multiple, longterm observation
Narrow focus	Broad focus

For observation, the <u>data</u> appear in the form of field notes. While in one sense, all data collected can be consider field notes, a more specific definition describes them as "the mainstay of qualitative research...a written account of what the researcher hears, sees, experiences, and thinks in the course of collecting and reflecting on the data in a qualitative study" (Bogdan and Biklen, 1982, p. 74). The quality of the data and, consequently, the quality of the study depend upon the detail, accuracy, depth and thoroughness of the field notes. Field notes, while typically associated with observation, are also important in interviewing. They begin as rough notes jotted down in the field and end as expanded notes fleshed out after the field. Each of these is comprised of two elements: description and reflection (Bogdan and Biklen, 1982; Patton, 1990). The **descriptive** part contains a recording of the details of the observation with an effort to give as full and objective a rendering as possible of the subjects, dialogue, non-verbal communication, behavior, physical setting, events and activities. Recognizing that subjectivity exists, for example, in terms of what to include and word choices, the emphasis is on capturing through detailed, accurate, "thick" descriptions as much as possible of the setting. Descriptive rather than interpretive words depict what was observed.

The **reflective** part, clearly indicated within the notes or as separate notes, focuses on both the observer and on the researcher. For the observer, this includes, for example, feelings, reactions, biases, prejudices, physical or emotional state, and personal meaning. For the researcher, this may include reflection on initial analysis, methodology, insights, interpretations, clarifications, corrections, and ethical issues. Bogdan and Biklen (1982, p. 87) summarize the critical nature of field notes and their role in an emergent design:

> Because a researcher is so central to the collection of the data and its analysis, and because neither instruments nor machines nor carefully codified procedures exist, the qualitative researcher must be extremely self-conscious about his or her own relationship to the setting and about the evolution of the design and analysis. In order to do a good study, the researcher must be self-reflective, and keep an accurate record of methods, procedures, and evolving analysis.

Several tools can prove useful as an aid in data collection; however, their technological limitations must be kept in mind. Examples of mechanical devices include: tape recorder, dictating machine, typewriter, computer, steno mask, camera, and video or movie camera. Murphy's Law often plays a prominent role when using these tools--break downs, dead batteries, operator error. In addition, other concerns arise--obtrusive nature of device, selective recording capabilities, over dependence upon the tool rather than human instrument.

Observation as a data gathering technique offers both advantages and disadvantages. In terms of strengths, observation 1) provides the context for study, 2) allows for an inductive approach, 3) gives the researcher direct, first-hand experience with events while they occur, 4) serves as a check against bias, prejudice, and selective perceptions, 5) builds on the researcher's knowledge and/or enhances understanding, and 6) allows the inquirer to see the "whole" in a way that members cannot. In terms of weaknesses, observation may 1) alter the setting through the presence of the researcher, 2) not clearly differentiate between objective and subjective information, 3) become very time consuming and produce volumes of data, 4) result in too much involvement by the researcher (e.g., time, task, emotions, go native), 5) not adequately address the researcher's perceptions and biases, and 6) not sufficiently capture the setting because it is impossible to observe everything or have access to everything (Bogdan and

Biklen, 1982; Guba and Lincoln; 1981; Lofland, 1971; Patton, 1990; Schatzman & Strauss, 1973).

2. <u>Interviews</u>. The <u>purpose</u> of the interview, the second type of data gathering, is to allow the researcher to gather descriptive data in the subject's own words and to access the unobservable--to walk in the head, so to speak. This enables the inquirer to develop insights into how the participants interpret and make meaning of the world. While Bogdan and Biklen (1982) consider field notes and observation as the mainstay of qualitative research, Guba and Lincoln (1981) describe interviewing as the backbone.

As with participant observation, <u>interview formats vary along a continuum</u>, ranging from structured to unstructured (Bogdan and Biklen, 1982; Guba and Lincoln; 1981; Lofland, 1971; Patton, 1990). In **structured interviews**, the interviewer formulates questions ahead of time based upon a preconceived framework and definition of the problem. In **unstructured interviews**, the interviewer converses with the respondent who provides the content of the interview as well as the structure and definition of the problem. Guba and Lincoln (1981) believe that the nonstandardized interview best supports the purposes of naturalistic research. They propose that open-ended questions are most appropriate when, "the issue is complex, the relevant dimensions are unknown, or the interest of the research lies in the description of a phenomena, the exploration of a process, or the individual's formulation of an issue" (pp. 177-8). Bogdan and Biklen (1982) believe that the purpose or goal of the research dictates the type of interview. They state:

> Even when an interview guide is employed, qualitative interviews offer the interviewer considerable latitude to pursue a range of topics and offer the subject a chance to shape the content of the interview....Some people debate which approach is more effective, the structured or the unstructured. With semi-structured interviews you are confident of getting comparable data across <u>subjects</u>, but you lose the opportunity to understand how the subjects themselves structure the topic at hand....From our perspective you do not have to choose sides. You choose a particular type to employ depending on your research goal" (p. 136).

Patton (1990, p. 357) bases interview decisions on the particular situation, the needs of the interviewee, and the personal style of researcher.

Interview <u>data</u> includes the written responses by the interviewee, often in the form of transcripts typed from audio tapes, as well as descriptive and reflective field notes. While it is possible and in some cases preferable to collect this data by hand, the accuracy of data may be enhanced through <u>technical innovations</u> such as tape recorders, movie cameras, and video cameras. However, as with observations, these are not without their mechanical and logistical problems.

As with observation, interviewing as a method has several <u>strengths</u>. The researcher can 1) move back and forth in time to construct the past, construct the present, and predict the future, 2) access the otherwise inaccessible, 3) check observational information, reflections, and emerging theories with members of the setting, 4) gather information somewhat systematically, and 5) gain new insights and perceptions. <u>Weaknesses</u> also exist. Information and responses from interviews 1) are highly reflective of interviewee's perceptions and biases, 2) depend upon the respondent's ability to recall, 3) can be affected by interviewee's physical and emotional state, 4) can be effected by reactions to and interaction with the interviewee, and 5) depend in large part upon the interviewing skills of the researcher (Lincoln and Guba, 1985; Patton, 1990).

3. <u>Documentation</u>. The <u>purpose</u> of the third major method, documentation, is to provide additional information as well as to clarify or verify other data. <u>Documentation refers to "paper" data</u> and includes, for example, records, files, internal and external communications, agendas, policy documents, forms, reports, news articles, journals, textbooks, speeches, lists, and other similar items. It may also include photographs not taken by the researcher. The <u>data</u> comes in the form of original documents. These may be originals or copies reproduced through <u>copy machines or photocopy equipment</u>.

The use of documentation also suffers from <u>strengths and weaknesses</u>. On the one hand, documents 1) can provide a wealth of information, some of which is not accessible through observation or interviewing, 2) provide highly reliable information if records are legal or official in nature, 3) are easy and cost effective to duplicate, 4) are often readily accessible, 5) confirm information from other sources, 6) provide different perspectives on similar information, and 7) retain the context of the setting. On the other hand, they 1) may be of poor or variable quality (inaccurate, incomplete) and 2) can still reflect perceptions and biases of participants (Bogdan and Biklen, 1982; Guba and Lincoln; 1981; Patton, 1990).

Data Analysis

As with data collection, the procedures for analysis are unique and specific to qualitative research. "Analysis involves working with data, organizing it, breaking it down, synthesizing it, searching for patterns, discovering what is important and what is to be learned, and deciding what you will tell others" (Bogdan and Biklen 1982, 154). An inherent problem with qualitative analysis is well summarized by Patton (1990, p. 372):

> ...there are no absolute rules except to do the very best with your full intellect to fairly represent the data and communicate what the data reveals given the purpose of the study....This does not mean that there are no guidelines to assist in analyzing data. But guidelines and procedural suggestions are not rules....Because

qualitative inquiry depends, at every stage, on the skills, training, insights, and capabilities of the researcher, qualitative analysis ultimately depends on the analytical intellect and style of the analyst. The human factor is the great strength and the fundamental weakness of qualitative inquiry and analysis.

The human inquirer serves not only as the instrument of data collection but also as the tool for data analysis. The two remain intertwined because data analysis begins during data collection. The following provides a brief synopsis of strategies used for analysis during and after data collection.

1. <u>Analysis During Data Collection</u>. Analysis of the data begins during data collection to let "the field worker cycle back and forth between thinking about the existing data and generating strategies for collecting new--often better quality--data" (Miles and Huberman, 1984 p. 49). The inquirer, as if in pursuit of a suspect, ferrets out new information, checks leads, and tests fledgling hypotheses. The evidence begins to build a prima facie case for the emergent theory while the researcher plays both prosecutor and defense.

Several strategies facilitate the process. Field notes serve as the backbone for analysis in the field because they contain both the straight forward "objective" accounting of what occurred and the reflective comments. The latter are further elaborated upon during analysis through the technique of "memoing." In the form of theoretical and conceptual note writing, memoing is used to flesh out ideas and tie them together, specifically as they pertain to emerging theories and patterns (Miles and Huberman, 1984; Schatzman and Strauss, 1973). As the researcher develops initial insights and interpretations in the field, he or she can bounce some of these ideas off participants as a way to "test" ideas. This technique, known as member check, can confirm, modify or correct initial premises. Finally, the researcher begins to organize and manage data through strategies such as summary sheets and codes.

2. <u>Analysis of Data After Collection</u>. With no rules of thumb, several approaches to analysis exist in practice and are supported by the field. Perhaps the most typical and widely used method is the development of a <u>coding through content analysis</u>--identifying categories or themes based upon patterns and ideas that emerge from the data. The researcher reads through the data looking for primary patterns (e.g., words, phrases, behaviors, thoughts, events) which repeat and stand out. After assigning initial labels to these patterns, she or he begins to apply these labels to the different kinds of data. Through sorting, comparing and contrasting, a system for classification emerges (Patton, 1990). While these codes remain data specific, Bogdan and Biklen (1982) suggest the following list of families of codes as examples of some of the coding possibilities: setting/context codes, definitions of the situation codes, perspectives held by subjects, process codes, event codes, strategy codes, relationship and social structure codes, methods codes, and preassigned codes.

The development of a coding system is the foundation for the <u>constant comparative method</u>, an approach credited to Glaser and Strauss (1967). Originally developed as a means for deriving (grounding) theory, Lincoln and Guba (1985) have adapted it as primarily a data processing procedure. It involves four phases: 1) comparing incidents applicable to each category (i.e., develop categories, intuitively assign incidents to categories, compare new incidents to previous incidents in same and different groups coded in the same category, write memos on ideas concerning categories and the fit of incidents, write rules for assigning categories), 2) integrating categories and their properties (shift from comparing incidents to incidents to comparing incidents to rules), 3) delimiting the theory (codes require fewer modifications,   number of categories are reduced and categories become saturated), and 4) writing the theory.

The most systematically and <u>procedurally oriented approach</u> to analysis comes from Miles and Huberman (1984, 1988).   These "soft nosed positivists" propose that "analysis consists of three concurrent flows of activity: data reduction, data display, and conclusion drawing/verification" (1984, p. 21). The first, **data reduction**, involves the "process of selecting, focusing, simplifying, abstracting and transforming the raw data that appear in field notes" (1988, p. 229). Before data collection, anticipatory data reduction occurs through design decisions which focus and bound the study. During collection, interim data reduction is accomplished through summary sheets, coding, memoing, site analysis meetings, interim site summaries, and post data collection reduction. **Data displays**, the second flow activity, provides a means of dealing with the cumbersome nature of the narrative text (field notes). They are "designed to assemble organized information in an immediately accessible, compact form, so that the analyst can see what is happening and either draw justified conclusions or move on to the next-step analysis the display suggests may be useful" (1984, 21-2).   Miles and Huberman (1988, p. 234) identify two types of graphic representations: descriptive figures (context charts, growth gradients) and explanatory figures (scatterplots, event-state flow charts, casual networks).   Finally, **conclusion drawing/verification** deals with the emerging meanings that have to be tested for their plausibility. Numerous tactics are suggested by Miles and Huberman (1988) for these two processes. Conclusion drawing includes counting, noting patterns or themes, seeing plausibility, making metaphors, splitting variables, subsuming particulars into the general, factoring, noting relationships between variables, finding intervening variables, building a logical chain of evidence, and making conceptual/theoretical coherence (p. 237). Verification includes checking for representativeness, checking for researcher effects, triangulation, weighing the evidence,   making contrasts/comparisons, checking the meaning of outliers, using extreme cases, ruling out spurious relations, replicating a finding, checking out rival explanations, looking for negative evidence, and getting feedback from informants.

This overview of tactics on verification leads into the fourth and final topic under this discussion of how to apply in practice the interpretive paradigm and qualitative methods to environmental education research.

Assuring the Rigor and Trustworthiness of the Findings

While researchers strive for results that others would consider rigorous and trustworthy, criteria for assessing these qualities for a non-experimental study differ from those of an experimental study. This phase perhaps is the most critical point at which consumers of research must wear the appropriate goggles--interpretive ones for interpretive studies, positivist ones for positivist studies. Wearing positivist goggles to assess the rigor of an interpretive study leads to inappropriate questions concerning, for example, sample size, generalizability, and objectivity.

Positivists typically speak of validity, reliability and objectivity when assessing the worth of a study. Based upon the underlying assumptions of the paradigms, these concepts do not transfer directly to interpretive inquiry. Some authors retain the terms of validity and reliability while proposing conceptually different means for judging merit (LeCompte and Goetz, 1982; Patton, 1990; Rist, 1977). Others use different terminology to convey the requisite criteria (Phillips, 1987; Zelditch, 1962). Lincoln and Guba (1985) offer parallel terms which may be more applicable. They suggest that naturalistic researchers are concerned with the: 1) credibility (internal validity) of their findings, 2) transferability or how well their working hypotheses would "fit" in another context (external validity), 3) dependability (reliability) or testing for consistency by a second evaluator, and 4) confirmability of the data (objectivity).

Although researchers vary in the terms they use, they agree that adequate procedures exist to assure the quality of the research and the findings. The following briefly discusses some of the strategies which can help assure the rigor, worth, and trustworthiness of interpretive studies (Borman, LeCompte and Goetz, 1986; Eisner, 1981; Lincoln and Guba, 1985; Miles and Huberman, 1984; Patton, 1990). Triangulation involves cross-checking data and interpretations by drawing upon different data sources, methods, and perspectives. Prolonged and repeated observations reduce researcher effect and identify typical as well as atypical characteristics. This goes along with representativeness, in which the researcher strives to investigate the widest range and diversity of events and people possible within the study. Member checks and peer debriefing are two methods which entail asking others if the data are accurate and if the interpretations are plausible. Testing rival explanations and seeking negative cases places the researcher in somewhat of a devil's advocate role, trying in essence to disprove working hypotheses. Intersubjective understanding makes explicit the subjective aspects of interaction with participants. Thick description depicts in detail and depth all elements of the context in a way that allows a reader to then determine the "fit" with another context. A clear description of the design and procedures enables others to reconstruct and corroborate the study.

Finally, Patton (1990) argues that the issue of credibility centers on three interrelated elements: rigorous techniques and methods, the credibility of the researcher, and the philosophical belief in the interpretive paradigm and qualitative methods. He suggests that Miles and Huberman emphasize the first and Guba and Lincoln the third. He asserts that all three are critical. As long as inappropriate goggles cloud the view, interpretive studies will not be seen as credible. Techniques and methods must be clearly described and delineated to enable others to envision the study and judge its worth. Perceptions of the researcher's qualifications and experience lie at the heart of credibility since this individual serves as both the instrument of data collection and the tool for data analysis.

Everything Is Not a Nail--A Final Look at Environmental Education Research

Environmental education, in general, has been limited in two ways by the hammer of positivism. First, it chips away at environmental education research, inadequately addressing the highly complex, interactive, holistic nature of the settings and issues under study. While the pieces that fall contribute to the accumulating pile of knowledge and understanding, they do so in a more or less piecemeal fashion. The interpretive paradigm strives to investigate the pieces as well as the whole with an emphasis on understanding and interpreting the complex interrelations. It too is perhaps only chipping away at this monumental task, but its product may be more appropriate for understanding environmental education phenomena. Secondly, as the dominant research paradigm, positivism has served as a research gatekeeper, effectively screening out what is perceived to be "sloppy" research. Interpretive research is criticized "for not being something it never intended to be, and is not given credit for its strengths" (Borman, LeCompte, and Goetz, 1986, p. 42).

Regardless of research perspectives, experts in the field of environmental education generally recognize that there is room for improvement. The interpretive paradigm and qualitative methods provide much promise--if given a chance. In an effort to increase the potential for naturalistic inquiry, this paper 1) provides an understanding of the philosophical foundation underlying interpretivism, 2) argues that a distinction exists between methodology (positivism, interpretivism) and method (quantitative, qualitative), with the former more critical than the latter, 3) proposes that environmental education fits well with the interpretive paradigm and qualitative methods, and 4) outlines what this approach would look like in practice in terms of research design, data collection, data analysis, and rigor. The intent is to inform practice as well as clarify criteria which are appropriate for assessing the merit of environmental education research based upon the interpretive model. Because most naturalistic inquirers have been raised in a positivist culture, they know better than to ask a quantitative researcher, "Why is your sample size so large?" The hope here is that the quantitative researchers will stop asking the qualitative researcher, "How can you generalize with such a small sample?"

References

Borman, K. M., LeCompte, M. D., & Goetz, J. P. (1986). Ethnographic and qualitative research design and why it doesn't work. American Behavioral Scientist, 30(1), 43-57.

Bednarz, D. (1985). Quantity and quality in evaluation research: A divergent view. Evaluation and Program Planning, 8, 289-306.

Bernstein, R. J. (1976). The restructuring of social and political theory. Philadelphia: University of Pennsylvania Press.

Bogdan, R. C., & Biklen, S. K. (1982). Qualitative research for education: An introduction to theory and methods. Boston: Allyn and Bacon.

Carr, W., & Kemmis, S. (1983). Becoming Critical: Knowing through action research. Victoria: Deakin University.

Comber, B. (1988). The continuing conversation: choices in educational research. Language Arts, 65, 776-786.

Eichelberger, T. (1989). Disciplined inquiry: Understanding and doing social research. NY: Longman.

Eisner, E. W. (1981). On the differences between scientific and artistic approaches to qualitative research. Educational Researcher, 10(4), 5-9.

Fetterman, D. M. (1988). Qualitative approaches to evaluating education. Educational Researcher, 17(8), 17-23.

Firestone, W. A., & Dawson, J. A. (1988). Approaches to qualitative data analysis: Intuitive, procedural, and intersubjective. In D. M. Fetterman (Ed.), Qualitative approaches to evaluation in education: The silent scientific revolution (pp. 88-115). NY: Praeger.

Glaser, B. & Strauss, A. L. (1967). The discovery of grounded theory: Strategies for qualitative research. Chicago: Aldine.

Guba, E. G., & Lincoln, Y. S. (1988). Do inquiry paradigms imply inquiry methodologies? In D. M. Fetterman (Ed.), Qualitative approaches to evaluation in education: The silent scientific revolution (pp. 88-115). NY: Praeger.

Guba, E. G., & Lincoln Y. S. (1981). Effective evaluation. San Francisco: Jossey-Bass Publishers.

Husen, T. (1988). Research Paradigms in education. Interchange, 19(1), 2-13.

Jacob, E. (1988). Clarifying qualitative research: A focus on traditions. Educational Researcher, 17(1), 16-24.

Jacob, E. (1987). Qualitative research traditions: A review. Review of Educational Research, 57(1), 1-50.

Koetting, J. R. (1986). Foundations of naturalistic inquiry: Developing a theory base for understanding individual interpretations of reality. (ERIC Document Reproduction Service No. ED 263 426)

Lather, P. (1986). Issues of validity in openly ideological research: Between a rock and a soft place. Interchange, 17(4), 63-84.

LeCompte, M. D., & Goetz, J. P. (1982). Problems of reliability and validity in ethnographic research. Review of Educational Research, 52(1), 31-60.

Lofland, J. (1971). Analyzing social settings. Belmont, CA: Wadsworth Publishing Company.

Lincoln, Y. S., & Guba, E. G. (1985). Naturalistic inquiry. Newbury Park, CA: Sage Publications.

McCutcheon, G. & Jung, B. (1990). Alternative perspectives on a action research. Theory Into Practice., 29, 144-151.

Miles, M. B., & Huberman, A. M. (1988). Drawing valid meaning from qualitative data: Toward a shared craft. In D. M. Fetterman (Ed.), Qualitative approaches to evaluation in education: The silent scientific revolution (pp. 222-244). NY: Praeger.

Miles, M. B., & Huberman, A. M. (1984). Qualitative data analysis: A sourcebook of new methods. Beverly Hills, CA: Sage Publications.

Nielsen, J. M. (Ed.). (1990). Feminist research methods. Boulder: Westview Press.

Patton, M. Q. (1990). Qualitative evaluation and research methods (2nd ed.). Newbury Park, CA: Sage Publications.

Patton, M. Q. (1988). Paradigms and pragmatism. In D. M. Fetterman (Ed.), Qualitative approaches to evaluation in education: The silent scientific revolution. (pp. 116-137). NY: Praeger.

Peshkin, A. (1988). Understanding Complexity: A gift of qualitative inquiry. Anthropology and Educational Quarterly, 19, 416-424.

Phillips, D. C. (1987). Validity in qualitative research: Why the worry about warrant will not wane. Education and Urban Society, 20(1), 9-24.

Rist, R. C. (1977). On the relations among educational research paradigms: From disdain to detente. Anthropology and Educational Quarterly, 8(2), 42-49.

Robottom, I. (1985). Evaluation in environmental education: Time for a change in perspective. The Journal of Environmental Education. 17(1), 31-6.

Schatzman, L. & Strauss, A. L. (1973). Field Research. Englewood Cliffs, NJ: Prentice-Hall, Inc.

Smith, J. K. (1989). The nature of social and educational inquiry: Empiricism versus interpretation. Norwood, NJ: Ablex Publishing Corporation.

Smith, J. K., & Heshusius, L. (1986). Closing down the conversation: The end of the quantitative-qualitative debate among educational inquirers. Educational Researcher, 15(1), 4-12.

Smith, M. L. (1987). Publishing qualitative research. American Educational Research Journal, 24, 173-183.

Zelditch, M., Jr. (1962). Some methodological problems of field studies. The American Journal of Sociology, 67, 566-576.

About the Author

Dianne Cantrell is the assistant chief for the Office of Public Information and Education for the Ohio Department of Natural Resources. In this capacity, she coordinates environmental education programs for the department including staff development, teacher and adult education, and partnering with schools. She currently serves on the advisory committee for the state science model course of study.

As a former faculty member at The Ohio State University at Newark, she taught graduate and undergraduate courses in early and middle childhood education, mostly in the areas of science, social studies and environmental education. Through her research, she has studied issues related to inservice education and staff development, curriculum implementation, and teacher education. She has extensive experience in conducting and evaluating inservice programs including statewide implementation of Project WILD and Project Learning Tree. She has also taught at the middle school level.

She received her Ph.D. in curriculum, instruction and development and her M.S. in environmental education from OSU. She is past president of the Ohio Conservation and Outdoor Education Association and serves on the Research Commission and Publication Committee for NAAEE.

ALTERNATIVE PERSPECTIVES IN ENVIRONMENTAL EDUCATION RESEARCH: PARADIGM OF CRITICALLY REFLECTIVE INQUIRY

Paul Hart

Abstract

The purpose of this research symposium was to engage the environmental education community in critical thought and discussion about the nature, purposes, and outcomes of research in environmental education. The purpose of this paper was to raise issues around one of three distinguishable paradigms in educational research, that of critically reflective inquiry, and to stimulate discussion on implications of research methods appropriate to this form of research as a means of improving the theory and practice of environmental education.

Context

According to Shulman (1988), education is a field of study rather than a discipline and as such has applied the research methodologies of other disciplines to the study of its problems rather than develop its own unique forms of inquiry. This inadequacy has created debates within educational research that may be recognized in terms of deeper historical methodological debates within and between social and natural science disciplines; especially within and between anthropology, sociology, and psychology; over what counts as educational research. By the 1970s, these debates about research were as evident in education as in other fields of social inquiry (Schon, 1983) in struggles within and between educational psychology, philosophy, and sociology. These struggles have more recently manifested themselves in methodological debates over the relative strengths and weaknesses of approaches to ethnography, case study and, most recently, action research as against the traditions of experimental psychology, the paragon of positivism within the social sciences (Carr & Kemmis, 1986)[1].

---

[1]Part of this status problem of the field of education within the academic community is due, it seems to me, to the view that education is regarded as an applied science whose theoretical knowledge is always knowledge about one or more of its underlying disciplines (for example, the psychology of learning or the sociology of schools). According to Kemmis (1989), this derivative status of the field of education is particularly galling because it implies that education is without distinctive theoretical content and hence that there can be no distinctive understanding of education as subject matter or method.

Different approaches to educational research are underpinned by different theories of educational change. It is because of different theoretical assumptions that different ideas about the aims of educational research have given rise to some friction and disagreement within the educational research community. Within the last decade, issues surrounding different approaches to educational research have been brought into sharp relief by important changes in social science research and within the philosophy of science. The notion of paradigms (in the Kuhnian sense) has been used to ground methodological debate which arose initially around questions of legitimacy of qualitative research methods and evolved into the quantitative-qualitative debate (Howe & Eisenhart, 1990).

Within the social sciences, many of the changes in thinking that can be applied to research have evolved from an infusion of European thought containing concepts such as poststructuralism, hermeneutics, deconstruction theory, interpretivism, and critical theory. Associated with this new thinking about educational problems has been a closing of the gap between methods of the social sciences and the humanities, an attack on "traditional" quantitative technical educational research methods, and the recognition of research as a political process.

Also associated with the rise of alternative views of education and educational research has been a movement within the philosophy of science toward a post- or nonpositivistic era in which positivism is no longer considered to be a tenable epistemological position (Garrison, 1986; Howe, 1985, 1988; Phillips, 1983, 1987). According to this position, positivism, which failed as a reconstruction of the logic of natural science and was largely ignored by natural scientists, was, ironically, regarded as the logic of natural science by social scientists, especially psychologists, who embraced positivism as an accurate portrayal of the scientific method - the method of behaviorism (see Mackenzie, 1977). Within the philosophy of science, the positivist picture of empirical science, where observation (means) is strictly separated from purpose (ends), has been replaced by the notion that all scientific investigation is theory laden (i.e., as an outgrowth of human purposes and constructions). It is, broadly speaking, inherently interpretive (see Bernstein, 1983; Rorty, 1982). Thus, claim Howe and Eisenhart (1990), there is no reason to attempt to legitimate qualitative educational research using quantitative criteria of validity and reliability. This stance, should not imply abandoning educational standards, merely understanding them within an alternative paradigm where methods are judged in terms of purposes.

According to Philip Jackson (1990) in his recent address to the American Educational Research Association (AERA), these developments in paradigmatic thinking about educational questions have occasioned discord in some quarters - the way rapid and significant change is bound to do. Vigorous debate over the relative merits of qualitative and quantitative approaches has enlivened the discourse of the educational research community, once devoted almost exclusively to issues of tests and measurement, reliability and validity, and the search for universal rules for education, for generalization as theory. The current trend in education is to use methods for a practice-based research that is context specific, "trying to figure out what's happening here and now", using descriptive strategies, with heavy dependence upon naturalistic observation and narration, to join researchers, with practitioners so results are practical and at the same time contribute to understanding (i.e., theory). We need to learn "how to look", said the president of AERA. This takes time and patience accompanied by a certain frame of mind, sharing different perceptions (as opposed to looking for interrater reliability). We must begin to appreciate the <u>complexity</u> of classrooms, learn to <u>see</u> them better, as teachers and researchers, in a new light; to pry beneath the surface, to try to figure out what is going on by scratching around at the ordinary. We need to search for <u>deeper meaning</u> and how it emerges from our encounters with complex systems and at the same time be self reflective about our research purposes <u>and</u> methods.

This trend toward the practical has been accompanied by a corresponding decline of interest in the discovery of universal rules and principles of the teaching and running of schools. Although the idea is not uncontested, some have called this a paradigm shift.

The success of new paradigms depends upon meaning. If meaningful, new paradigms and associated methods will attract support. There will be recommendations for journals and funding agencies to broaden their focus, to diversify the range of studies accepted by choosing broadly educated reviewers to make the decisions. We still need well-crafted studies, rigorous in their own way according to their own criteria. We all want work to be done thoroughly and rigorously. But we also need to learn to ask different questions - to devise distinctly educational ways of answering these questions, and to be open to changing lenses, alternative angles of vision.

Intentions: The Intentionality of the Critical Inquiry Paradigm

Schwab (1970) distinguished the notion of the practical from the technical as a purpose in educational research. Technical (instrumental, means-ends, hypothetico-deductive) reasoning presupposes given ends (e.g., uncontested goals of environmental education) and following known, established methods (proven statistical techniques) to test preconceived hypotheses. Practical reasoning, by contrast, does not assume given ends or follow imposed rules of theory in resolving educational questions which confront educators in their day-to-day lives.

According to Habermas (1972), empirical-analytic science serves a <u>technical</u> interest, whereas hermeneutical sciences (some forms of sociology, anthropology, psychology) serve a <u>practical</u> interest (an interest in guiding, informing, educating by interpreting our understandings of the world, by distilling experience. Following a critical theory tradition Habermas (1984, 1987) constructed the notion of <u>emancipatory</u> interest (based on notions of rationality, justice, and freedom). This critical theory goes beyond the demonstration of connections between thought and action, as in the notion of the reflective practitioner developed by Schon (1983) to a socially critical interest which aims at ideology critique (conscientization), deliberative inquiry, and action aimed at improving both the practice and theoretical understanding of education. That is, individual enlightenment (personal theory) is predicated on collaborative action in the form of a theory-practice interaction (dialectic).

Kemmis (1989) distinguishes the major features of these different approaches to education research, distinguishing between empirical analytical (positivist), interpretive, and critical approaches to research (see Appendix 1), based on arguments in Carr and Kemmis (1986). According to Kemmis (1989), the paradigm debate on education research has raised important epistemological and ontological questions about the intentions of this research. It has offered new perspectives on the connections between thought and action, between theory and practice, between technical and practical theories within a broader emancipatory framework. Adopting a critical perspective entails not only the interpretation of our understanding of the theory and practice of education but also the transformation of these relationships through participatory action research wherein collaborative groups of supporting practitioners develop and carry out proposals for action based on their transformed perspectives.

New developments in educational research methods have resulted from these differences in intents and purposes. Although they share characteristics with interpretive research (in the sense that they aim to create the conditions for educational change by changing the ways in which educational practitioners and policy makers understand themselves and their actions), these "activist" forms of educational research such as critical inquiry (see Berlak & Berlak, 1981); participatory research (see Hall, 1979; McTaggart & Kemmis, 1988); and action research (Carr & Kemmis, 1986; Winter, 1987) cannot be other than participatory research, requiring collaborative inquiry as a means of educational reconstruction (i.e., practical transformation of personal and educational levels).

According to Kemmis (1988), critical social scientific research, including emancipatory action research, employs a practical form of reasoning (like that of interpretive research) which at the same time is critical (it is shaped by the emancipatory intent to transform educational practices through ultimately ideology critique - the critique of educational ideologies which serve the interests of specific groups at the expense of others). Critical inquiry in the form of action research requires the development of self-reflective communities of teacher researchers committed to critically examining their own practices and improving them. Whereas applied science and interpretive research artificially separate researchers (theorists) and practitioners by employing a theory of change which seeks to bring practitioners in line with researchers' theories (explicitly in applied science research and implicitly in interpretive research) participatory, action research practitioners develop their own practical theories of action (i.e., presuppositions, values, assumptions) through acting and thinking about acting as part of the process of change.

Actions: The Action Methodology of the Critical Inquiry Paradigm

Educational action research is a form of educational research which places control over process of educational reform in the hands of practitioners in collaboration with their critical friends (whether teachers, administrators, researchers, parents, or students). Grundy and Kemmis (1982) have described a diversity of views about the character of action research in education: British action research tends to emphasize interpretive inquiry (Elliott, 1984); the Australian tends to be more critical, more politically aware (Carr & Kemmis, 1986); American versions had tended to be more technical (for the best examples, see Cohen & Finch, 1987; Evans, Stubbs, Duckworth, & Davis, 1981). Oja and Smulyan (1989) describe all collaborative action research in terms of the following characteristics:

- provides a methodology which engages teachers in all aspects of the research process as they study their classrooms and schools

- combines goals of improved practice, greater theoretical understanding, and professional development

- unites teachers and university researchers in the "naming and framing" of problems of practice (see also, Schon, 1983)

- focuses on the process of individual professional development through involvement in collaborative groups

- provides teachers with supports and challenges needed for personal and professional growth

- offers several new lenses for analyzing what contributes to or impedes personal and professional development, improved practice, and improved theoretical understanding

Action research is not a new concept. Kurt Lewin coined the phrase "action research" about 1944 and presaged three important characteristics: its participatory character; its democratic impulse, and its view of social change. In the United States, Teachers College, Columbia University became a center for action research with advocates such as Stephen Corey (1953) and Hilda Taba (Taba & Noel, 1957). However, between 1954 and 1972, after a decade of growth, action research went into decline. Federal funding agencies in the U.S. began to employ the applied science model for educational research where scholars applied for federal funding, did the research using quantitative methods geared to criteria of statistical validity and reliability, and reported to the funding agency within strict guidelines. There was no real provision for linking research to change in educational practice. After 1972, with the establishment of the National Institute of Education a more sophisticated model of research-development-diffusion-adoption (RDDA) evolved to translate "what research says" to the teacher. Problems arose in the late 1970s when researchers and practitioners began to question the applicability of quantitative, experimental (applied science) methodologies to educational settings and problems. Traditional research methods tended to restrict the researcher's focus to short-run events, isolated variables, and a limited range of meanings, creating an oversimplified picture of a complex educational reality (Hall, 1975; Mishler, 1979; Nixon, 1981).

In the 1970s a growing number of researchers began to articulate the value of more qualitative research methods which sought a deeper understanding of both educational practice and underlying educational processes by attempting to theoretically ground critical accounts of "what happens". Action research focused on helping teachers become self-reflective practitioners who could examine their own practice, critically and systematically. An early example was documented by Stenhouse (1975); later examples include the Ford Teaching Project (Elliott, 1977) and the Cambridge Action Research Network (CARN) (Nixon, 1981). This resurgence of action research activity reflected researcher dissatisfaction with traditional research methodology and teacher dissatisfaction with results that could not help them improve their practices (Ward & Tikunoff, 1982).

Whereas earlier studies of action research focused on project outcomes, action researchers of the 1980s advocated advanced notions of group decision making at the level of principle rather than technique and focus on both needs of practitioners and the demands of educational research, that is, to improve both professional practice and our understanding of educational theory (Ebbutt, 1985; Elliott, 1985; Kelly, 1985; Whyte, 1986). Nixon (1981), Burgess (1984, 1985a,b,c) and Hustler, Cassidy, and Cuff (1986) attempt to establish the basis for action research as a valid, rigorous, and productive form of educational research by advocating critical examination of their own action research process as a means of improving the process of action research. However, . . .

> The rigour of action research does not derive from the use of particular techniques of observation or analysis (for example, measuring instruments or statistical analyses) or the use of particular metatechniques (for example, techniques for establishing the reliability or validity of measures, or for ascertaining the power of tests). Rigour derives from the logical, empirical, and political coherence of interpretations in the reconstructive moments of the self-reflective spiral (observing and reflecting) and the logical, empirical, and political coherence of justifications of proposed action in its constructive or prospective moments (planning and acting) (Kemmis, 1988, p. 46).

Action research has been assisted by a rise of new wave methods in educational research and evaluation (interpretive approaches, illuminative evaluation, case study methods, ethnography, and so forth) with their emphasis on participant perspectives and categories as important and influential in shaping educational policy and practice. Action research also provides a response to the accountability movement in education in that practitioners can adopt a self-monitoring role as a proper means of justifying practice and generating sensitive critiques of the working conditions in which they practice. The organization of support networks of concerned professionals who have successfully applied action research strategies have increased general awareness among teachers of an understandable, workable approach to the improvement of practice through critical self-reflection.

The characterization of "the action research approach" has been consolidated, recently, by Oja and Smulyan (1989) who describe four basic elements of contemporary action research method as follows:

1. **Action research is <u>collaborative</u>**

   - entails mutual <u>understanding</u> and decision making (democratic) and common <u>action</u> (Street, 1986)

   - entails cooperation - agreement to proceed individually toward self-defined goals through deliberative inquiry (i.e., working together in all phases) (Hord, 1981)

   - entails teachers and researchers setting common purposes, mutually planning research design, data collection, and report writing so both theory and practice are "designed in" together (Little, 1984; Oja & Pine, 1981)

   - assumes equal responsibility to identify, inquire, and resolve problems and concerns of teachers in classrooms

   - recognizes unique insights and skills of each participant (Tikunoff, Ward, & Griffin, 1979)

   - assumes teachers and researchers communicate as peers, frequently and openly throughout the process, to avoid possible conflicting perceptions and assumptions resulting from different positions in the field (Cummings & Hustler, 1986; Threadgold, 1985)

2. **Action research is <u>practical</u>**

   - focuses on informed, committed action (i.e., praxis), that is, action informed by "practical theory" and which may, in turn, inform and transform the theory which informed it

- focuses on educational practices, not as phenomena or treatments or even as expressions of teacher intentions and perspectives. Practice is not to be understood as behavior but as strategic action in response to contextual problems and dilemmas - their solution is only found in doing something. Since only the practitioner has access to personal practical theory, action research, as a study of praxis, entails research into one's own practice (Kemmis, 1988). Action researchers deliberately plan actions strategically designed as an experiment simultaneously to improve practice, to more deeply understand that practice and the situation in which the practice occurs; to monitor those actions and their consequences; and, retrospectively to reconstruct an interpretation of the action in context as a basis for future action. According to McTaggart and Kemmis (1988), the action research method may be conceptualized as a self-reflective spiral of cycles of planning, acting, observing, and reflecting (see Appendix 2)

- focuses on changing and improving a situation on the basis of teacher problems and concerns (Cummings & Hustler, 1986; Ebbutt, 1985)

3. Action research entails professional development

- assumes that educational change depends on commitment and understanding and action of those involved

- assumes that if teachers work together on a common problem, clarifying and negotiating ideas and concerns, they will be more likely to change attitudes and behaviors, if their own research indicates it necessary (Anning, 1986; Cassidy, 1986; Hall, 1975)

- assumes that collaborative action groups are absolutely necessary for the support and impetus required to seriously and systematically explore practice and professional problems (Smulyan, 1984; Enright, 1981; Evans, et al., 1981). Groups can provide many perspectives and through a collaborative action research process groups can be encouraged to develop increased flexibility in thinking about issues and concerns, to be more receptive to new ideas, and to address problems more divergently (Groarke, Ovens, & Hargreaves, 1986; Pine, 1981)

- focuses on teacher thinking about their practices which, according to Noffke and Zeichner (1987) has been associated with an increased sense of professionalism in terms of increasing feelings of self worth and confidence; increasing awareness of personal beliefs, assumptions, biases and predispositions; increasing congruence between beliefs (personal theories of action) and practices (personal actions); and broadening teacher views on schooling, education, and society

4. Action research entails creating conditions for project structure (time and support)

- assumes the need for planning for frequent opportunities for communication among participants, for democratic leadership and for spiral cyclings of planning, acting, observing, reflecting, and revising

- assumes the need for clear goals, for a shared frame of reference, a sense of commitment, for mutual understanding using appropriate language

- assumes that the development of understanding is recursive rather than linear, allowing teachers to engage in discourse about successive improvements that have evolved and to use their own reflections, understandings, and developing theories to inform their own practice and research

- assumes a school climate that encourages and facilitates communication and experimentation (Cohen & Finch, 1987; Whyte, 1986), an administration that operates on collegial decision making, and participants who are equally motivated by their interest in improving their practices and willing to devote the time and energy needed

- assumes a community base where teachers are encouraged to pursue improvements that may include school (district) and community concerns (a sympathetic public)

To this basic set of essential action research elements, there are a number of action research advocates who would add a critical, or socially critical, dimension (see Gough & Robottom, 1990). This dimension adds the provision that action research participants should engage in critical thinking and action with a view to social reconstructive action ultimately. According to the socially critical orientation, education must:

- engage society and social structures immediately, not merely prepare students for alter participation

- engage social issues and give students experience in working on them - experience in critical reflection, social negotiation and the organization of action

- develop the power of constructively critical thinking, not just in individuals but also in group processes

- emphasize social and critically reflective processes

Reflections on the Nature of Action Research as a Methodology for Critical Inquiry Within Environmental Education

The nature of action research may be characterized in terms of epistemology, ontology, and worldview. It is at these levels of discussion that the relationship to environmental education becomes meaningful. According to Kemmis (1988), knowledge is constructed from an action research process in a way that redefines both planning for future practice and the practitioners's general practical theories. The interpretations of others in the situation will be relevant in the process of reconstruction (see also Driver & Easley, 1978 for a constructivist interpretation of learning). The crucial point is that only the practitioner can have access to the perspectives and commitments that inform a particular action as praxis, thus praxis can only be researched by the practitioner him/herself. The interaction of action and understanding (personal practical theory) is a uniquely personal process of rational reconstruction and construction (Kemmis 1988, p. 45).

That this created knowledge is subjective, and thus may be systematically distorted by ideology, is an illusion created by the image of value-free "objective" social science (Kemmis, 1988). The purpose of critical self-reflection is to discover previously unrecognized distortions of interpretation and action (for example, the taken-for-granted assumptions of habit, custom, precedent and the limitations on action that these assumptions produce. This interactive process of construction/reconstruction of knowledge is a key aspect of the epistemology of action research.

Evaluation of the meaningfulness of action research does not derive from criteria of validity or reliability but from the logical/empirical/political interpretations and justifications of the ideas and actions involved in construction/reconstruction. Although typically the action research processes are evaluated by practitioner/researchers in terms of the 'sense' it makes, in relation to their experience and understanding[2], Kemmis (1988) postulates formal evaluative criteria at levels of scientific discourse (preconditions of discourse, validity in terms of truth [accuracy]); enlightenment (preconditions of open communication aimed at mutual understanding [ethically in terms of respect, honesty, integrity, sensitivity, confidentiality] and authenticity of insight [grounded in participants own circumstances and experience]); and organization of action (prudent responsible decisions in the selection of strategies resolution of tactical questions and conduct of experiments in classrooms and schools). Evaluation on the quality of research requires analysis at each of these levels

---

[2]The relationship between outside "facilitators" and action researchers can have profound effects on the character of the research. To varying degrees they can influence the agenda of issues to be addressed and the ownership (authenticity) of the questions and the interpretation of findings. Some of what passes for action research today is merely a species of field experimentation or applied science research carried out by the academy "on" or "for" teachers, not "by" teachers. Forgetting the preconditions necessary some researchers have conducted studies in the name of action research but paradigmatically opposed to the nature and spirit of action research conveyed here.

of discourse, the organization of enlightenment, and the organization of action.

Ultimately, action research as a methodology must be evaluated within the paradigmatic orientations that appear to characterize the field of education. Gough (1987b, 1989) contrasts the traditional education paradigm, concerned with distribution of propositional knowledge, with an ecological (ecopolitical) paradigm concerned with construction of knowledge. This is of interest to environmental educators because the ecological paradigm described by Gough represents an environmentalist worldview and raises the issue of the nature of education envisioned within such a worldview. According to Stevenson (1987, p. 73) while the goals of nature study and conservation could be relatively easily accommodated within the existing organization of schools, the more recent critical and action orientation of environmental education creates a far more challenging task for schools.

The rhetoric of environmental education focuses on improving the quality of life on the planet. Therefore, environmental education has a revolutionary purpose of transforming the values that underlie our decision making from those that aid and abet environmental degradation to those that support a sustainable planet in which all organisms can live with dignity. This contrasts with the traditional purpose of schools which have been charged with preserving the existing social order by reproducing the norms and values that currently dominate political, hence environmental, decision making. These contradictions between environmental education and schooling have not been seriously engaged by environment educators.

The guiding principles and key characteristics of environmental education establish particular kinds of pedagogical practices as being necessary to achieve the stated goals. For example, learners should work toward the resolution of environmental problems; teaching and learning are intended to be cooperative processes involving inquiry into and action on environmental issues; the development of knowledge, skills, and values is not only directed towards action, but emerges in the context of preparing for (i.e., the inquiry) and taking action; curriculum and pedagogical planning need to be highly flexible. However, common knowledge indicates that in most classrooms there is a markedly different, yet consistent, pattern to current pedagogical practices than the guiding principles of environmental education advocate. Typically teachers act as dispensers of factual information, students respond to teachers' questions, and knowledge is acquired individually for future use (i.e., in later life). The teacher is frequently the only participant who actively engages in high order thinking processes.

Observable surface-level discrepancies between theory and practice betray deeper, more fundamental pedagogical contradictions between environmental education and schooling as follows:

- While an environmental education curriculum should be interdisciplinary and focus on real practical problems, school curricula, especially in science, are discipline-based and emphasize abstract theoretical problems.

- Whereas a curriculum in environmental education is emergent and problematic in that the content arises as students are involved in specific environmental problems, most school curricula are predefined since they are designed to serve predetermined behaviorally specific ends (that is, ends whose attainment can be readily assessed).

- Whereas pedagogy in environmental education ought to be problematic in the sense that the way for students (and teachers) to solve environmental problems is uncertain, most school programs embrace an unproblematic pedagogy of information dissemination. This results from instructional means being clearly defined by the criterion of the efficient achievement of the desired ends.

- Whereas a function of knowledge in environmental education is immediate use for the social value of a sustainable and emancipated quality of life, the major function of school knowledge is storage for future use and the enhancement of individual status and economic well-being.

- Whereas environmental education advocates learning that is holistic and cooperative, school learning tends to be atomistic and individual.

- Whereas in environmental education rhetoric, students are active thinkers and generators of knowledge, in schools students are usually in the passive position of spectators and recipients of other people's knowledge and thinking.

- Whereas learning and action should proceed hand in hand according to environmental education theory, the acquisition of knowledge precedes its application in most school practices.

- Whereas the mastery of relevant knowledge and skills is demonstrated in environmental education by students' actions in real situations (that is, their performance in exerting influence on environmental decision making), in schools students write about theory in artificial situations (that is, their performance in "influencing" the teacher). (Stevenson, 1987, p. 75-76)

Given these issues that reflect the "gap" between schooling and the goals and advocated processes of environmental education, how can environmental education be organized for reconstruction of school curriculum?

Recently, McClaren (1987) has argued for the importance of participation of the teacher in improving environmental education.

> The implementation of curriculum ultimately depends on teacher support and commitment. The classroom teacher is at the center of the transaction of public schooling. No matter how much curriculum theorists and developers may believe in the value of the importance of their programs, and no matter how elegant their designs may be on paper, in the final analysis no curriculum can be (or should be, in my opinion) teacher-proof. The proponents of mandated curriculum, whether in environmental education or arithmetic, all too often forget this. To them, the curriculum is simply a technology to serve their purposes, and teachers are merely cogs in the machinery (McClaren, 1987, p. 53).

It is apparent that environmental educators have focused their attention on the development of environment-related goals and have neglected to probe deeply enough into pedagogy, particularly at the level of the teacher. The process problem remains in environmental education because environmental educators have not focused on the real-life working conditions of teachers, their perceptions about change, and the support system needed to facilitate change in teaching method demanded by these new curriculum materials.

In my view, the key issue in efforts to organize for more and better environmental education is not simply one of producing more or better curriculum project materials, but one of creating the conditions for participatory action research as a prerequisite to curriculum planning and professional development. The central problem in environmental education change is lack of teacher involvement. It is a problem because educational change has pedagogical and political dimensions. Our failure to recognize the importance of the political nature of the process of educational decision making has resulted in a dismal record in past attempts to stimulate change. The process issue of whether to integrate or segregate will absolve itself in the larger process of resolution of conflicts surrounding the process of teacher change. And a key aspect of teacher change is teacher participation. Rather than being mere "cogs in the machinery" teachers have influential theories and values about environment and education which guide their actions in environmental education. The real life working conditions of teachers need to be taken into account both in research (theorizing) and in curriculum development (practice). Authentic teacher participation in curriculum research and development must be supported.

Posch (1988) has argued for a "participatory research" role for teachers in environmental education curriculum development.

> Teachers who take on this (curriculum development in environmental education) duty need to communicate with each

other and need external support . . This, however, is not enough
. . When a teacher no longer contents himself [herself] with
imparting systematic knowledge, but exceeds the limits set by
the school and accepts to cope with unstructured situations, he
[she] increasingly needs to be aware of what he [she] does, a
kind of systematic reflection on his[her] own actions, in order to
keep a check on the risks connected with environmental
projects, and in order to facilitate communication on his [her]
actions and further development. Therefore, we want to
encourage teachers to evaluate their work with the pupils
themselves and to write about it . . .

I think that this aspect of "research" as a sort of systematic
reflection on one's own actions will become increasingly
important and is not only apt to contribute to the building up of
a stock of practical professional knowledge, but will also improve
the social status and the autonomy of the teaching profession.

As regards the further development of environmental project
instruction, I personally attach particular importance to three
perspectives:

- The improvement of teacher-teacher communication and the
  integration of a greater number of teachers/schools into this
  exchange of experiences,

- The production of knowledge on environmental project
  instruction by the teachers themselves, and

- A more dynamic and innovative design of infrastructural
  conditions for this sphere of work (Posch, 1988).

An Example of Participatory Action Research Within a Paradigm of Critical Inquiry

The question naturally arises: What specific forms would participatory
action research take in "real-life" situations? The example of a project
currently in progress in southeastern Australia illustrates some apparent
correspondences between an action research project in environmental
education and socially critical education (Gough & Robottom, 1990).

Seven schools along the southeast coast of Australia engaged in developing
environmental education curricula focusing on water quality in nearby
streams, lakes and ponds, and in the sea off local swimming beaches. The
schools were linked with each other and with Deakin University by
electronic mail.

There were three dimensions to teacher activities in the overall project: engagement in scientific study with students, participation in an international computer conference, and involvement in a form of participant research focusing on educational issues.

Some features of the project illustrate its alignment with the participant research approach to curriculum development in environmental education:

1. The project engaged critical environmental education. The environmental education engaged in by the school was interested in environmental accountability - it was environmental education for environmental responsibility.

2. The project attracted significant support from the local community. As the school developed environmental education programs in response to perceived local environmental concerns, community interest and support were forthcoming. In one instance, the local Water Board provided assistance with water sampling and the local press provided public visibility to the role of the schools in addressing this environmental issue of concern to the community.

3. The project was consistent with principles of participation and responsiveness. Teachers were involved in the study of the project itself through data collection (diaries, computer logs, field notes, and photography) and in processes of identification of technical, teaching, and curriculum issues of interest and concern to themselves.

4. The project embodied a range of structures for enhancing communication between participants. Individual visits by university personnel, project newsletters, computer conferences, and project workshops were all part of the project and supported the views of Posch (1988) that in environmental education it is important to work towards the improvement of teacher-teacher communication.

Gough and Robottom (1990) describe characteristics of this participatory action research project that suggest a common ground between environmental education and the critical inquiry paradigm. For example, in relation to epistemology of practice, the project embodied a constructivist view of knowledge simply by exhibiting fidelity to the key principles of the rhetoric of environmental education, albeit with a distinctive critical orientation. That is, the substantive knowledge of the programs engaged in by the schools was "working knowledge" generated by the participants themselves. The environmental critique in this case was an action-based, community-embedded form of inquiry yielding "working knowledge" that was transactional rather than transmissive, generative/emergent rather than preordinate, opportunistic rather than systematic, and idiosyncratic rather than generalizable . . . . School activities were exemplified as interactive involvement in socially significant politically-relevant participant-negotiated tasks focused on student participation in community change, and employing consultants as required for communication and methodological problem solving (Gough & Robottom, 1990, p. 9-12).

Gough and Robottom (1990) acknowledge that, although classes were conducted in the spirit of collaborative research communities, some conditions for critical self reflection aimed at improving the relationships of teacher/student practices, understandings and situation were lacking. Nevertheless, the project illustrates the practicality of participatory action research as a natural method for environmental education.

The restructuring and reconstructing of environmental education, as illustrated by the Australian action research project, can help to bring about the changes needed to make society more actively and effectively environmentally responsible. The forms that this reconstruction takes will need to involve concentration on teachers' reflection on their own practice and active participation in new curriculum development. Not only must curriculum development in environmental education be considered in terms of the materials and methods that are really the "product" but also in terms of the process whereby the teacher becomes the "researcher".

Environmentalism has evolved to the point where conflicting messages could lead to a confusion of environmental education goals and directions Gough (1987). If environmental educators are able to get beyond the dictates of environmentalist contradictions and focus on the pedagogical process by involving teachers in reflective practice and curriculum reconstruction as a means of professional development, environmental education may yet provide a crucial core in the education of an environmentally responsible citizenry. The key element in all this is the process - get that right and the product will take care of itself. This paper contends that teacher involvement is a key element in the process of environmental education renewal in the field of education.

Conclusion: Environmental Education as Critical Inquiry - Aligning Theory and Practice

Gough (1987b) describes how education must change in order to align with an ecological worldview. As a foundation for educational inquiry, it is the critical action research paradigm that most closely aligns with the ecological worldview that underlies mainstream environmental education rhetoric but does not align with environmental education activity. For example, the influential and widely accepted environmental education policy statements that emerged from international conferences at Belgrade in 1975 and Tbilisi in 1977 established goals for environmental education that include the intellectual tasks of critical appraisal of environmental issues and the formulation of a moral code concerning such issues, as well as the development of a commitment to act on one's values by providing opportunities to participate actively in environmental improvement (Stevenson, 1987). In addition to prescribing the development of critical thinking, problem-solving, and decision-making skills within the context of quality-of-life issues, the Tbilisi Declaration emphasized that students should be actively involved in all levels of working toward resolution of environmental problems (UNESCO, 1978, p. 18). However, there appear to be few examples of environmental education practice that authentically enact this educational philosophy policy.

Admittedly, environmental education is a product of both the older and the emerging worldviews and to some extent reflects the contradictions and conflicts that accompany a major paradigm shift. This mixture of environmental ideologies is particularly evident in the variety of courses variously labeled environmental science or environmental studies, which often embody uncritical assumptions about scientific and applied science research methods in resolving problems of environmental "management". Even when intentionally labeled environmental education, many of these courses have preserved teaching practices and learning experiences that embody an earth-centered ontology based on a scientific worldview (Zais, 1976). For example, environmental education in schools tends to reproduce the industrial model of schooling dominated by the authority of teachers, textbooks and timetables, by trivial pursuits of memorizing information and routinely performing technical tasks. In the 1960s educational philosophers and curriculum theorists such as Schwab and Bruner attempted to broaden this rather narrow epistemology base to include an epistemology of discovery. What appears to be happening in the 1980s and 1990s in environmental education is a shift in the epistemological base to an epistemology of constructed knowledge based on a man-centered ontology. Current arguments in the field of science education (especially within the science-technology-society-environment movement) reflect this tension of competing worldviews as seen in arguments for the extension of the science curriculum base to include values, morals, ethics, and aesthetics as legitimate components of the real (authentic) world of science.

Whereas historically schools were not intended to develop critical thinkers, social inquirers, and problem solvers, or active participants in environmental/social decision making, contemporary environmental education imposes a revolutionary purpose on schools - one which intends to transform the values that underlie our decision making through educational practices that can only be described as action research. For example, there is a distinct alignment between the principles of action research described earlier and the following pedagogical and curriculum practices which Stevenson (1987) embeds within guiding principles (UNESCO, 1978) and key characteristics (Fensham, 1978; Hart, 1979, 1987) of environmental education.

> Teaching and learning are intended to be co-operative processes of inquiry into and action on real environmental issues. Such an inquiry process demands that students actively engage in critical

or complex thinking about real problems. The development of knowledge, skills and values is not only directed towards action, but emerges in the context of preparing for (i.e., the inquiry) and taking action. Consequently, curriculum and pedagogical planning need to be highly flexible. For example, as well as adapting to students' own social constructs, the teacher should be amenable to students' decisions in relation to both their learning and their actions. (Stevenson, 1987, p. 75)

Clearly, action research methods recommended for practitioner-researchers align with a pragmatic epistemology of constructed knowledge, based on a man-centered ontology (Zais, 1976) and an ecological (as opposed to applied science) worldview (Gough, 1987a). Although this worldview also aligns with environmental education rhetoric, it unfortunately does not yet characterize environmental education activity in schools. Perhaps it is only when practitioners themselves decide to practice education within an action research (critically social) paradigm that environmental education activity in schools can finally align with its now aging rhetoric.

References

Anning, A. (1986). Curriculum in action. In Hustler, D., Cassidy, T., & Cuff, T. (Eds.), Action research in classrooms and schools. London: Allen & Unwin.

Berlak, A. & Berlak, H. (1981). Dilemmas of schooling: Teaching and social change. London: Methuen.

Bernstein, R. (1983). Beyond objectivism and relativism. Philadelphia: University of Pennsylvania Press.

Burgess, R. (Ed.). (1984). The research process in educational settings: Ten case studies. Lewes: Falmer.

Burgess, R. (Ed.). (1985a). Field methods in the study of education. Lewes: Falmer.

Burgess, R. (Ed.). (1985b). Issues in educational research: Qualitative methods. Lewes: Falmer.

Burgess, R. (Ed.). (1985c). Strategies of educational research: Qualitative methods. Lewes: Falmer.

Cassidy, T. (1986). Initiating and encouraging action research in comprehensive schools. In Hustler, D., Cassidy, T., and Cuff, T. (Eds.), Action research in classrooms and schools. London: Allen & Unwin.

Carr, W. & Kemmis, S. (1986). Becoming critical: Education, knowledge and action research. London: Falmer.

Cohen, M. & Finch, M. (1987). Teacher leadership and collaboration: Key concepts and issues in school change. Paper presented at the annual meeting of the American Educational Research Association, Washington, DC.

Corey, S. M. (1953). Action research to improve school practices. New York: Teachers College, Columbia University.

Cummings, C. & Hustler, D. (1986). Teachers' professional knowledge. In Hustler, D., Cassidy, T., & Cuff, T. (Eds.), Issues in education research: Qualitative methods. Lewes: Falmer.

Driver, R. & Easley, J. Jr. (1978). Pupils and paradigms: A review of literature related to concept development in adolescent science students. Studies in Science Education, 5, 61-84.

Ebbutt, D. (1985). Educational action research: Some general concerns and specific quibbles. In Burgess, R. (Ed.), <u>Issues in educational research: Qualitative methods</u>. Lewes: Falmer.

Elliott, J. (1977). Developing hypotheses about classrooms from teachers' practical constructs: An account of the work of the Ford Teaching Project. <u>Interchange, 7</u> (2), 2-22.

Elliott, J. (1984). Improving the quality of teaching through action research. <u>Forum,</u> 74-77.

Elliott, J. (1985). Facilitating action research in schools: Some dilemmas. In Burgess, R. (Ed.), <u>Field methods in the study of education</u>. Lewes: Falmer.

Enright, L. (1981). The diary of a classroom. In Nixon, J. (Ed.), <u>A teacher's guide to action research</u>. London: Grant-McIntyre.

Evans, C., Stubbs, M., Duckworth, E., & Davis, C. (1981). <u>Teacher initiated research: Professional development for teachers and a method for designing research based on practice.</u> Cambridge, MA: Technical Education Research Center.

Fensham, P. (1978). Stockholm to Tbilisi - the evolution of environmental education. <u>Prospects, 8</u> (4); 446-55.

Garrison, J. (1986). Some principles of postpositivistic philosophy of science. <u>Educational Researcher, 15</u> (9), 12-18.

Gough, A. & Robottom, I. (1990). Environmental education and the socially critical school. Paper submitted to <u>Journal of Curriculum Studies.</u>

Gough, N. (1987a). Greening education. In Hutton, D. (Ed.), <u>Green politics in Australia</u>. Sydney: Angus & Robertson.

Gough, N. (1987b). Learning with environments: Towards an ecological paradigm for education. In Robottom, I. (Ed.), <u>Environmental education: Practice and possibility.</u> Victoria, Australia: Deakin University Press.

Gough, N. (1989). From epistemology to ecopolitics: Renewing a paradigm for curriculum. <u>Journal of Curriculum Studies, 21</u> (3), 225-241.

Groarke, J., Ovens, P., & Hargreaves, M. (1986). Towards a more open classroom. In Hustler, D., Cassidy, T., & Cuff, T. (Eds.), <u>Action research in classrooms and schools</u>. London: Allen & Unwin.

Grundy, S. & Kemmis, S. (1982). Educational action research in Australia: The state of the art. <u>The action research reader</u>. Victoria, Australia: Deakin University Press.

Habermas, J. (1972). Knowledge and human interests (trans. J. J. Shapiro). London: Heinemann.

Habermas, J. (1984). The theory of communicative action, vol. I: Reason and the rationalization of society (trans. T. McCarthy). Boston: Beacon.

Habermas, J. (1987). The theory of communicative action, vol. II: Lifeworld and system: A critique of functionalist reason (trans. T. McCarthy). Boston: Beacon.

Hall, B. L. (1975). Participatory research: An approach for change. Convergence, 8 (2), 24-31.

Hall, B. L. (1979). Knowledge as a commodity and participatory research. Prospects, 9 (4), 393-408.

Hart, P. (1979). Environmental Education: Identification of Key Characteristics and a Design for Curriculum Organization. Unpublished doctoral dissertation. Burnaby, Canada: Simon Fraser University.

Hart, P. (1987). Science for Saskatchewan schools: A review of research literature, analysis and recommendations. Regina, Canada: Saskatchewan Instructional Development and Research Unit.

Hord, S. M. (1981). Working together: Cooperation or collaboration. Austin, TX: University of Texas at Austin, Research and Development Center for Teacher Education.

Howe, K. (1985). Two dogmas of educational research. Educational Researcher, 14 (8), 10-18.

Howe, K. (1988). Against the quantitative-qualitative incompatibility thesis (or, dogmas die hard). Educational Researcher, 17 (8), 10-16.

Howe, K. & Eisenhart, M. (1990). Standards for qualitative (and quantitative research: A prolegomenon. Educational Researcher, 19 (4), 2-9.

Hustler, D., Cassidy, T., & Cuff, T. (Eds.). (1986). Action research in classrooms and schools. London: Allen & Unwin.

Jackson, P. W. (1990). The functions of educational research. Educational Researcher, 19 (7), 3-9.

Kelly, A. (1985). Action research: What is it and what can it do? In Burgess, R. (Ed.), Issues in educational research: Qualitative methods. Lewes: Falmer.

Kemmis, S. (1988). Action research. In J. P. Keeves (Ed.), <u>Educational research methodology, and measurement: An international handbook.</u> New York: Pergamon Press.

Kemmis, S. (1989). <u>Metatheory and metapractice in educational theorising and research</u>. Unpublished paper. Victoria, Australia: Deakin University.

Little, J. W. (1984). Seductive images and organizational realities in professional development. <u>Teachers College Record</u>, <u>86</u> (1), 84-102.

Mackenzie, B. (1977). <u>Behaviorism and the limits of scientific method.</u> Atlantic Highlands, NJ: Humanities Press.

McClaren, M. (1987). The problem of curriculum infusion in environmental education. In Disinger, J. (Ed.), <u>Trends and issues in environmental education: Environmental education in school curricula</u>. Columbus, OH: ERIC/NAEE.

McTaggart, R. & Kemmis, S. (Eds.). (1988). <u>The action research reader, third edition</u>. Victoria, Australia: Deakin University Press.

Mishler, E. G. (1979). Meaning in context: Is there any other kind? <u>Harvard Educational Review</u>, <u>49</u> (1), 1-19.

Nixon, J. (1981). <u>A teachers' guide to action research</u>. London: Grant-McIntyre.

Noffke, S. & Zeichner, K. (1987). <u>Action research and teacher thinking: The first phase of the AR on Ar project at the University of Wisconsin, Madison</u>. Paper presented at the annual meeting of the American Educational Research Association, Washington, DC.

Oja, S. & Pine, G. (1981). <u>A two year study of teacher stages of development in relation to collaborative action research on schools</u>. Washington, DC: National Institute of Education Research Proposal.

Oja, S. & Smulyan, L. (1989). <u>Collaborative action research: A developmental approach</u>. London: Falmer.

Phillips, D. (1983). Postpositivistic educational thought. <u>Educational Researcher</u>. <u>12</u> (5), 4-12.

Phillips, D. (1987). <u>Philosophy, science, and social inquiry</u>. New York: Pergamon Press.

Pine, G. (1981). <u>Collaborative action research: The integration of research and service.</u> Paper presented at the American Association of College Teachers of Education, Detroit.

Posch, P. (1988). The project "environment and school initiatives". In OECD/CERI, <u>Environment and school initiatives. Report of the international conference on the teaching and learning of environmental issues in primary and secondary schools</u>. Linz, Austria: Organization for Economic Cooperation and Development, Centre for Educational Research and Innovation.

Rorty, R. (1982). <u>Philosophy and the mirror of nature</u>. Princeton, NJ: Princeton University Press.

Schwab, J. J. (1970). <u>The practical: A language for curriculum.</u> Washington, DC: National Education Association.

Schon, D. A. (1983). <u>The reflective practitioner</u>. New York, NY: Basic Books.

Shulman, L. (1988). Disciplines of inquiry in education: An overview. In R. Jaeger (Ed.), <u>Complementary methods for research in education</u> (pp. 3-17). Washington, DC: American Educational Research Association.

Smulyan, L. (1984). <u>The collaborative process in action research: A case study</u>. Unpublished dissertation, Harvard University.

Stenhouse, L. (1975). <u>An introduction to curriculum research and development</u>. London: Heinemann.

Stevenson, R. (1987). Schooling and environmental education: Contradictions in purpose and practice. In Robottom, I. (Ed.), <u>Environmental education: Practice and possibility.</u> Victoria, Australia: Deakin University Press.

Street, L. (1986). Mathematics, teachers, and an action research course. In Hustler,, D., Cassidy, T., & Cuff, T. (Eds.), <u>Action research in classrooms and schools</u>. London: Allen & Unwin.

Taba, H. & Noel, E. (1957). <u>Action research: A case study</u>. Alexandria, VA: Association for Supervision and Curriculum Development.

Threadgold, M. (1985). Bridging the gap between teachers and researchers. In Burgess, R. (Ed.), <u>Issues in educational research: Qualitative methods</u>. Lewes: Falmer.

Tikunoff, W., Ward, B., & Griffin, G. (1979). <u>Interactive research and development on teaching study: Final report.</u> San Francisco, CA: Far West Regional Laboratory for Educational Research and Development.

UNESCO. (1978). <u>Intergovernmental conference on environmental education, Tbilisi, USSR, 14-26 October 1977: Final report</u>. Paris: UNESCO.

Ward, B. & Tikunoff, W. (1982). <u>Collaborative research</u>. Paper presented at the National Institute of Education sponsored conference, The Implications of Research on Teaching for Practice.

Whyte, J. (1986). <u>Girls into science and technology: The story of a project.</u> London: Routledge & Kegan Paul.

Winter, R. (1987). <u>Action-research and the nature of social inquiry: Professional innovation and educational work</u>. Aldershot, UK: Avebury.

Zais, R. (1976). <u>Curriculum: Principles and foundations</u>. New York: Harper & Row.

About the Author

Paul Hart is a professor in the Faculty of Education at the University of Regina, Canada. He received his Ph.D. in Curriculum and Instruction (Environmental Education) in 1979 and teaches science and environmental education as well as curriculum and research methods courses at undergraduate and graduate levels.

Dr. Hart is a board member of the North American Association for Environmental Education and a member of UNESCO - Canada, Man and the Biosphere Network (MAB-Net). He is also a member of the Saskatchewan Outdoor and Environmental Education Association. He has written a number of papers in the area of environmental and science education for journals such as <u>Science Education, Journal of Research in Science Teaching</u> and for the <u>Journal of Environmental Education</u> of which he is a consulting editor.

Since 1987, Dr. Hart has served as Director of the Saskatchewan Instructional Development & Research Unit (SIDRU) a provincial research and development center active in developing instructional strategies materials for teachers. He has been a visiting scholar in Australia and represented Canada at a UNESCO seminar on environmental education in Malta. His current interest concerns the nature of research in education, particularly science and environmental education.

RAISING QUESTIONS: REACTIONS TO AND BUILDING ON THE SYMPOSIUM

BEYOND BEHAVIOURISM: MAKING EE RESEARCH EDUCATIONAL

Ian   Robottom

Abstract

Environmental education concepts need be contested and critically debated. Quantitative research is not the be all and end all. Alternatively there are three kinds: positivist, interpretivist, and critical. Arguably a fourth is philosophical research. This contribution delves into the issue.

Introduction

The title of this symposium ("Contesting Paradigms in Environmental Education Research") is significant. Choice of the term "Contesting" (rather than "alternative", for example) relates to the idea in the more general educational field of curriculum studies of "essentially contested concepts" (Gallie, 1964; Shaw, 1976; Robottom, 1987). This idea suggests that there are some educational concepts which are <u>necessarily contested</u> -- that is, that there are some concepts which ought to be the subject of continuing critical discourse and debate. The idea of essentially contested concepts suggests that for some concepts, their proper use inevitably involves disputation on the part of educators, rather than the assumption and perhaps persuasion of lasting consensus. I see the issue of the relative adequacy of different paradigms of environmental education research as an essentially contested concept. Not incidentally, I think there are good reasons for thinking that the very visible and very North American "Goals of Environmental Education" ought to be the subject of "contestation" -- as necessarily the subject of continuing debate by participants at all levels of environmental education practice.

To describe the debate at this symposium as concerned with an ongoing dialogue about "qualitative and quantitative approaches to environmental education research" is, in my view, inaccurate and misleading. It is inaccurate because it suggests that the debate is about *two alternative* kinds of research, while the structure of the symposium clearly admits three kinds (positivist; interpretivist; critical), and ought arguably to admit consideration of a fourth kind -- that of philosophical research. And perhaps more importantly, it is misleading because to use the language of "alternative approaches" is to suggest a complementarity and even-handed eclecticism that in fact the symposium wishes to treat as problematic.

It seems to me that for this reason, the term "paradigms" was also an advised choice. The use of the term is to suggest that the debate ought to progress beyond a consideration of alternative forms of data collection -- beyond a mere appraisal of quantitative and qualitative "methods" within an overall positivist framework. To equate "paradigm" with "method" or "technique" (see Marcinkowski, 1990a: pp. 2, 42) is to deny the issue of ideology and to make facile the treatment of different research paradigms as merely different tools in the researcher's toolbox. This is like claiming that the essential differences between social life in Moscow and New York reside in these cities' different geographical locations. The purpose behind the symposium's use of the term is to suggest that there are distinct genres of educational research -- genres whose distinctiveness lies not in their main forms of data collection (qualitative; quantitative), but in the assumptions which prefigure what is to count as appropriate research topics, appropriate research questions, appropriate methodologies and even appropriate research outcomes (see Kuhn, 1962). In short, what is distinctive about research paradigms is not their forms of data collection but their "political theory" or their "ideology" (Robottom, 1985).

It is the intention in this paper to consider the paradigms of environmental education research presented by Marcinkowski (1990a), Cantrell (1990) and Hart (1990) in terms of the political theory that accompanies them. In particular, the relationship of the three paradigms of research with (what seems to me to be) the main _educational_ aspiration of environmental education -- the development of independent critical thinking in relation to environmental issues -- will be considered. Given the obvious and excessive dominance of positivist research in environmental education, the larger part of this paper will be taken up with addressing tensions emanating from the positivist paradigm. [In this reaction paper, my own "biases" will be evident. Like it or not, we are all "biased" and I do not wish to deny my own strongly held perspective on this issue. Perhaps that is why I was chosen to be a reactor!]

The Behaviourism of Positivist Research in Environmental Education

Positivist research in environmental education is based essentially on an applied science model, assuming that the allegedly objectivist genre of scientific research applied in respect of the physical/natural world is also the most adequate for application in respect of the social/political world of environmental education. Marcinkowski, Cantrell and Hart point out some of the details of the close relationship between positivist EE research and traditional natural scientific research. My main concern here, however, is with an obvious feature of the political theory of positivist research as expressed in the North American Association for Environmental Education -- its strongly _behaviourist_ perspective. Behaviourism has become the ideology of positivist EE research: it prefigures decisions about research focus, design, data collection, and importantly it prefigures our perceptions of the relationships between teachers, pupils, subject matters, and educational settings:

- as Marcinkowski (1990a: p.4, 23) correctly points out, advocates of positivist EE research see its power as "the extent to which it will allow one to predict, control, and/or explain the phenomena of interest";
- the task of research is seen as understanding, predicting, and modifying "responsible problem solving behaviour" (as if this were unitary and consensual);
- the ultimate achievement of research is perceived as a situation in which it is possible to fully predict environmental behaviour;
- teachers and pupils are seen as essentially manipulable by the researchers: it is considered proper to apply "behavioural intervention strategies" and to "manipulate situational factors in order to produce desired behavioural changes" even if the individuals (whom it must be remembered are members of a democracy interested in independent critical thinking) do not necessarily want to change in this way:

> Thus, in situations in which individuals do not possess those personality characteristics which would lead to the development of a desire to help alleviate environmental problems, these individuals may be enticed into behaving responsibly toward the environment by the application of behavioural intervention strategies. (Hines, Hungerford and Tomera, 1986-87, p.7)

> It is not known at what point a person will forego economic and other personal benefits to do what preserves the integrity and stability of the environment ... it may be more efficacious, in the case of certain environmental problems, to manipulate situational factors in order to produce the desired behaviour changes. (Hines, Hungerford and Tomera, 1986-87, p.8)

Thus the behaviourism of positivist EE research has a strong deterministic character; it seeks to control (through prediction and reinforcement) certain ways of thinking and acting valued by the researchers. The language of behaviour modification thinly conceals its interest in influencing (shaping and constraining) how we conduct ourselves in our environments. This deterministic character is a point I wish to return to later.

The Role of the Goals

One of the most common expressions of positivist research in environmental education is an attempt to ascertain the extent to which programs (the focus could be on pupil, teacher, or syllabus) achieve certain goals. In this instrumental kind of research, program practices are seen as assessible means to taken-for-granted ends. A significant and consistent feature of this research is this taken-for-granted character of educational ends, which in North American environmental education seems to equate to the "Goals for Curriculum Development in Environmental Education" composed by Hungerford, Peyton and Wilke in 1980. The lofty status which researchers themselves continually award these goals is significant because it tends to be reflected in the professional roles ascribed to participants in the research -- pupils, teachers, subject matters, and the researchers themselves.

I need to make clear at this point that I have nothing but respect for the sustained, imaginative and committed efforts of the workers (for example: Stapp, 1969; Harvey, 1976; Hungerford, Peyton and Wilke, 1980) responsible for the development of the now oft-cited "Goals of Environmental Education". The points I now wish to make relate only to the continuing status accorded those goals (particularly by the community of researchers themselves), not to the people or processes involved in their initial formulation some ten or more years ago.

As an outside observer, one gains the impression that these goals are seen and treated as the source or embodiment of all worthwhile theory in environmental education. Recommendations have been published (Volk, Hungerford and Tomera, 1984) suggesting that:

- instruments be developed which could assess <u>student accomplishment</u> relative to the goals for EE;
- <u>teachers</u> could also be directly assessed regarding their ability to identify, teach, and implement EE goals;
- <u>existing programs and projects</u> ... should be analyzed in respect to the goal levels which they address;
- such research ... serve as a vehicle toward providing <u>the direction for a coordinated thrust</u> within the field of EE.

In this research, any differences between the objectives utilised in existing environmental education curricula and those recommended by "leaders in the field" are viewed as "inconsistencies", "weaknesses", or "deficiencies".

There is an important point here. If we are serious that teachers and pupils should exercise independent critical thinking in respect of environmental education, in what sense is it justifiable to appraise their practices in terms of the theories of <u>others</u>? Isn't it possible, and desirable, that "existing programs and projects", for example, are informed by <u>their developers' own</u> well thought out theory of environmental education? Furthermore, what right does one sector of the academy have to make pejorative moral judgements of "weakness" and "deficiency" about an existing program just because it doesn't comply with that sector's statement of goals? The higher intellectual and even moral ground assumed for the goals and their originators by the authors themselves is clear in such judgements.

The goals continue to be cited as the theoretical referent in such diverse activities as evaluation of instruction (Ramsay, Hungerford and Volk, 1989), teachers (Champeau, Gross and Wilke, 1980), software (Wilson, 1990), and curriculum development (Gardella, 1986). They loom large in the most recently reported research in the <u>Journal of Environmental Education</u> and in contributions to UNESCO (Hungerford *et al*, 1990).

Of course, it could be argued that such a heavy and sustained emphasis on a single set of "Goals of Environmental Education" is acceptable practice, but only if we could be assured that the goals have been and continue to be the subject of critical appraisal and reappraisal by practitioners in terms of their (the goals') social, political, cultural, historical (in short, their ideological) appropriateness. Unfortunately, it seems, the goals have not been the subject of critical appraisal and debate in the decade of the 80's.

Part of the problem is that instrumental research of the kind that has dominated NAAEE research literature in the decade of the 80's is incompetent to do this task, precisely because in such research, the ideological appropriateness of the goals (their value in every sense) is taken for granted. All that is being evaluated in such instrumental research is the ability of programs (pupils; teachers; subject matters) to achieve these goals. Every instance of instrumental research in which the goals are presented as given reference points amounts to a not-so-tacit reinforcement of the status of the goals and their advocates.

Yet this is only part of the problem. Attempts to pursue research design issues at the 1990 national conference have tended to be dismissed as in some sense insulting to the researcher or to the authors of the criteria. Yet if we are to be able to make an informed judgement about how seriously to take the outcomes of this research, such questions must be asked and answered (and answered in terms other than mere recourse to authority). Even more worrying than this would be public attempts (for example: Hungerford, Peyton and Wilke, 1983) to foreclose debate about the goals and to impose upon the rest of us a rationalist theory of action in which definitional questions are petulantly and almost forcibly put aside in favor of getting on with the job of goal implementation (Jickling, 1990; Robottom, 1987).

So the situation as I see it, and within which I am responding to the debate about the relative adequacy of different paradigms of EE research, is that there exists a public statement of "Goals for Environmental Education" which we are told should direct our activities in environmental education on a broad front, and which despite being a social construction imagined within a particular social, cultural, political and historical context ten years ago, now tends to be reified and objectified and itself placed beyond critique. There appears to be an irony here in light of admonitions that researchers should grapple with issues which:

> brings to the forefront the epistemological question of what is to count as knowledge. If researchers do not discuss this question, they are forfeiting any participation in determining the basis for the authority of their knowledge (Smith, 1983, cited in Marcinkowski, 1990a).

Control and Critical Thinking: A Contradiction?

The behaviourist paradigm within which this instrumental research and uncritical reinforcement of the goals of environmental education is taking place gives rise to a contradiction. Within a behaviourist paradigm, the problem of improvement of environmental education is seen as a matter of identifying and controlling the variables associated with (for example) "responsible environmental behaviour". This is a deterministic framework: not only does behaviourism assume and seek to identify and explain certain relationships, it makes no in-principle distinction between these activities and those of control and enforcement by application of behavioural intervention strategies and manipulation of situational factors.

Within this deterministic framework, control over the goals represents immense power in social control. To the extent that this behavioural research succeeds, it not only creates and sustains a division of labor between researchers and practitioners, but also imposes the researchers' environmental, educational and social values (those values embedded in the goals that the research takes for granted) onto pupils and teachers in a way that is fundamentally disempowering. While to some this may be seen as the strength of the approach, in a democratic world interested in independent critical thinking about a range of social, political and (not least) environmental issues, such determinism is contradictory and self-defeating. Put at its simplest, the determinism of behaviourism is anathema to independent critical thinking (or ... "it doesn't make sense to try to _force_ people to be independent and critical"). Clifford Knapp (1990) seemed to put his finger on the problem when he recently posed the question, "Teaching for Responsible Environmental Action: Are we brainwashing or educating our students?". The main point I wish to make in this paper is to suggest that we would do well to think about which label best describes the interests of behaviourist research.

This would appear to be a self-evident educational aim. But ironically environmental education researchers do not, in one important sense, seem to be a very _educational_ lot: in seeking guidance in their professional activities they are not very outward-looking to the more general educational field, where the most recent educational thinking tends to be articulated. Rather, recourse tends to be made to applied science fields like psychometrics, behaviour analysis, natural resources, human ecology and statistics. This dependence on the authority of natural science is demonstrated in the bibliographies of some reviews of environmental education research. For example, in a recent discussion of research on "responsible environmental behavior", Marcinkowski (1990b) cited "a listing of prominent fields, periodicals, and approaches" to demonstrate the "diverse sources of and frameworks for REB research". While the list was only a sample, the word "education" appeared only once in the titles of 25 periodicals, and _not one serious educational journal was cited_.

The Promise of Non-Behaviourist Research in Environmental Education.

Perhaps the most obvious difference between behaviourist and non-behaviourist paradigms of research in environmental education is the difference in what counts as educational theory -- or, put more simply, whose goals are the focus of the research. In both interpretive (Cantrell, 1990) and critical (Hart 1990) paradigms of research in environmental education, there is a prime interest in explicating the "interpretive categories of practitioners" -- the aspirations, presuppositions, assumptions and values held tacitly or consciously by practitioners, and in terms of which their educational actions can be made intelligible. By focusing on these interpretive categories, the research addresses issues of interest and concern to practitioners themselves. Such research is concerned with the generation of knowledge within and for the context in which is used and has meaning, and only within which its consequences can be evaluated. There is little or no interest in generalisability as a measure of the success of the research -- research success is judged by its helpfulness in improving the educational self-understanding of practitioners in particular educational settings. Far from in some sense sullying the research (tainting its claims to "objectivity"), a concern with the explication of practitioners' interpretive categories is the only way that the research can actually address the educational character of the issues it is focusing on. To be educational at all, research must engage (value; explicate -- certainly not ignore) the aspirations, assumptions, presuppositions and values actually held by the practitioner, because it is only in terms of these categories that educational practices can be made intelligible. Educational practices are enacted not because of the existence of some external set of goals prepared by members of the academy many years ago (romantic as this notion may seem); they are enacted because they are informed by and cohere with certain "internal" aspirations, assumptions, presuppositions and values held dear by the practitioner. The proper purpose of non-behaviourist research is to make public these categories for appraisal. In the case of interpretive research, this nearly always entails a role for the researcher as explicating these categories for the practitioner's "enlightenment" and self-appraisal. In terms of the political theory of interpretive research, this act is based on the assumption that the practitioner him/herself is an independent, critically thinking individual for whom enlightenment in this fashion will likely lead to improved practice. In my judgement, this assumption is more consistent with the fundamental interest of environmental education (that of encouraging independent critical thinking) than the deterministic impulse of behaviourist EE research.

As stated, in interpretive research, the researcher is nearly always an outsider. In the "critically reflective inquiry" discussed by Hart (1990), the researcher is the practitioner him/herself. This is an even more empowering condition than interpretive research -- it entails action beyond enlightenment. The critical reflection paradigm of research seeks through its own processes to reconceive the role of the practitioner in research and to reconceptualise the politics of educational research. As in interpretive research, credence is given to the interpretive categories of practitioners, but unlike interpretive research, the practitioner has the capacity to directly influence the direction that the research takes. This means that in critical research, the practitioner has the opportunity (in fact, the responsibility) to "co-opt" the research to address and redress some of the contradictions, inequities and injustices that act to limit attempts to improve (environmental) educational situations. Critical research exceeds the "enlightenment" of interpretive research and aspires to "empowerment through action". The impulse in critical research in environmental education is for self-determined environmental, educational and social improvement (see Greenall Gough and Robottom, 1990). Thus critical reflective inquiry, as the name suggests, creates the conditions for the environmental education practitioner to actually enact some of the principles held dear to environmental education -- in particular, the principle of independent critical thinking. I concur[1] with the view of Willis that:

> The radical or reconceptualist form [of educational research] is superior, expressly because it includes consideration of both human consciousness and political action and thus can answer moral and social questions about curricula which the dominant form cannot. It encourages individuals to be intelligent, autonomous agents, taking responsibility for their own actions and encouraging the intelligent, autonomous actions of others within a mutually interdependent and evolving social situation (Willis, 1981).

Some Questions

In response to an invitation from the chairperson of this symposium, and in the interests of further debate, I pose the following questions for consideration at this or other research forums:

• to what extent do pupils have an opportunity to critically appraise the goals of environmental education in NAAEE research activities?

• what would life actually be like for teachers and pupils if, within the behaviourist paradigm, we were able to approach a situation of accounting for 100% of the variance in respect of "responsible environmental behaviour"?

• in what sense do NAAEE's processes of reporting EE research (the Journal of Environmental Education, commissioned reviews of research, programs and software, contributions to Unesco) reinforce the behaviourist paradigm of research?

---

[1] For a more argued personal position on this debate see Greenall Gough and Robottom, 1990; Robottom, 1985, 1987a, 1987b, and 1987c.

- in the interpretive paradigm, how can interpretive researchers' interpretive reconstructions of practitioners' reality serve as a useful guide to further action?

- in the critical paradigm, what claims are made about ways of overcoming the inherent relativism of interpretive accounts?

References

Cantrell, D. (1990) Alternative Paradigms in Environmental Education: The Interpretive Perspective. Paper presented as part of a symposium entitled **Contesting Paradigms of Environmental Education Research** at the annual conference of the North American Association for Environmental Education , San Antonio, Texas, USA: 1-7 November.

Champeau, R,; Gross, M.; and Wilke, R. (1980) An assessment of teachers' understanding and use of Goals for Curriculum Development in Environmental Education. In Sacks, A.B.; Burrus-Brummel, L.L.; Davis, C.B.; and Iozzi, L. (Eds) Current Issues VI: The yearbook of Environmental Education and Environmental Studies. Columbus, Ohio: ERIC/SMEAC Information Centre.

Gallie, W. (1964) Philosophy and the Historical Understanding. London: Chatto and Windus.

Greenall Gough, A. and Robottom, I. (1990) Environmental Education and the Socially Critical School. Submitted to the Journal of Curriculum Studies 1990/91.

Hart, P. (1990) Alternative Perspectives in Environmental Education Research: Paradigm of Critically Reflective Enquiry. Paper presented as part of a symposium entitled **Contesting Paradigms of Environmental Education Research** at the annual conference of the North American Association for Environmental Education , San Antonio, Texas, USA: 1-7 November.

Harvey (1976) Environmental Education: A delineation of substantive structure. Doctoral Dissertation, Southern Illinois University, Carbondale, University Microfilms, 77-16622.

Hines, J., Hungerford, H., and Tomera, A. (1986-87) Analysis and Synthesis of Research and Responsible Environmental Behavior: A Meta-Analysis. Journal Of Environmental Education 18 (2), 1-8.

Hungerford, H.; Peyton, R.; and Wilke, R. (1980). Goals for Curriculum Development in Environmental Education. Journal of Environmental Education 11 (3), 42-47.

Hungerford, H.; Peyton, R.; and Wilke, R. (1983). Yes, EE does have definition and structure. Journal of Environmental Education 14 (3), 1-2.

Hungerford, H., Volk, T., Dixon, B., Marcinkowski, T., and Sia, A. (1990) An Environmental Education Approach to the Training of Elementary Teachers: A Teacher Education Program. Paris: UNESCO-UNEP International Environmental Education Programme (Environmental Education Series 27).

Jickling, B. (1990) Environmental Education, Problem Solving and Some Humility Please. Paper presented at the annual conference of the North American Association for Environmental Education, San Antonio, Texas, USA: 1-7 November, 1990.

Kuhn, T. (1962) The Structure of Scientific Revolutions. University of Chicago Press.

Marcinkowski, T. (1990a) A Conceptual Review of the 'Quantitative Paradigm' in EE Research. Paper presented as part of a symposium entitled **Contesting Paradigms of Environmental Education Research** at the annual conference of the North American Association for Environmental Education San Antonio, Texas, USA: 1-7 November.

Marcinkowski, T. (1990b) Interpreting and Applying Results of Research on Responsible Environmental Behaviour. Paper presented at the annual conference of the North American Association for Environmental Education, San Antonio, Texas, USA: 1-7 November.

Ramsay, J.; Hungerford, H.; and Volk, T. (1989) A Technique for Analyzing Environmental Issues. Journal of Environmental Education 21 (1), 26-30.

Robottom, I. (1985) Environmental Education: Time for a change in perspective? Journal of Environmental Education 17 (1), 31-36.

Robottom, I. (1987a) Contestation and Consensus in Environmental Education. Curriculum Perspectives 7 (1), 23-27.

Robottom, I. (1987b) Two Paradigms of Professional Development in Environmental Education. The Environmentalist 7 (4), 291-298.

Robottom, I. (1987c) Towards inquiry-based professional development in environmental education. In Robottom, I. (ed.) Environmental Education: Practice and Possibility. Geelong, Victoria, Australia: Deakin University Press.

Shaw, K. (1976) Paradigms or Contested Concepts. British Journal of Educational Technology 7 (2), 18-24.

Smith, J (1983) Quantitative versus qualitative research: An attempt to clarify the issue. Educational Researcher 12 (3), 6-13.

Stapp, W (1969) The concept of environmental education. Journal of Environmental Education 1 (3), 31-36.

Volk, T; Hungerford, H; and Tomera, A. (1984) A National Survey of Curriculum Needs as Perceived by Professional Environmental Educators. Journal of Environmental Education 16 (1), 10-19.

Willis, G. (1981) A reconceptualist perspective on curriculum evaluation. Journal of Curriculum Theorising 3 (1), 185-192.

ABOUT THE AUTHOR

Ian Robottom is an associate professor in the Faculty of Education at Deakin University, Australia. He has a first class honours degree in science, BEd and MEd in education, and a PhD in environmental education. He has teaching and research interests in environmental education, science education, and educational research. Ian is editor of the Australian Journal of Environmental Education and on the editorial panel of the Journal of Environmental Education.

Ian taught secondary science and senior biology in secondary schools before joining Deakin University. He has recently collaborated in the development of off-campus (distance education) courses in environmental education and science education at graduate (Master of Education) level. These courses represent one of the very few forays into distance education for graduate students in these fields. As part of these distance education courses, Deakin University offers a series of contemporary monographs in environmental education and science education.

Ian is chair of the Science, Health and Environmental Education Teaching and Research group within the School of Mathematics, Science and Environmental Education. The work of the Teaching and Research group recognises the essentially political and unstable nature of the relationships among science, environment, health and education, and adopts a critical perspective in exploring the role of 'expert scientific knowledge' in such issues. The group regards the question of the relative adequacy of alternative approaches to educational and social research in respect of teaching and curriculum issues in science, environment and health as problematic, and itself a proper research topic. Ian is project coordinator of several externally-funded research projects in environmental education and science education and has published extensively in journals and books in these fields in Australia, North America and the United Kingdom.

DESIGNING FOR IMPACT: A PERSPECTIVE ON RESEARCH IN ENVIRONMENTAL EDUCATION

Martha C. Monroe and Stephen Kaplan

Abstract

The use of research in Environmental Education must be helpful to the teacher. It must also provide something tangible to guide the teachers in a positive direction in improving teaching methods and curriculum. This paper addresses possibilities for communicating research results for greater application.

If research in environmental education is good for anything, it must be helpful. It must be helpful for teachers, naturalists, and curriculum developers. It must assist them in answering the salient questions they have about their work and provide them with direction for making improvements. And when the emphasis shifts to the users of research results, then the ultimate issue is one of transfer. Judged in this light, a debate over sample size or research methodologies becomes of secondary importance. More critical might be: What questions do practitioners have? What are the beliefs, the assumptions, the models that guide their everyday work in the classroom? And how can research play a constructive role in all this?

The issue of transfer, of communicating useful research results to practitioners, is an interesting lens through which to view the qualitative/quantitative continuum, for neither extreme appears to contribute to this goal. Although the traditional scientific research methods which have dominated our field allow us to frame studies for some degree of generalization, one must admit that the application of research principles to practice doesn't often happen. Perhaps this is due to the quantitative researcher's own admission of constraints and her reluctance to think broadly about the transfer of her results. Another indication that something is inadequate with the quantitative position is the recent growth of interest in alternative models of research.

The qualitative researcher, however, is even less able to address the issue of transfer. This paradigm adheres to the belief that context is everything and that each case is unique (Lincoln and Guba, 1985). Therefore, each teacher in each classroom must ask his own researchable questions, and seek his own answers. Nothing more than the research procedure can be learned and shared from one experience to another. Busy teachers who want simple answers, unfortunately, don't find this perspective very helpful.

Given that transfer is important and that these two extreme positions of research paradigms have little to contribute to understanding how to transfer usable knowledge to practitioners, it may be helpful to reconsider what we know but all too often ignore about knowledge transfer, particularly that which directly influences research reports.

1.   <u>What is taught is not always what is learned</u>. Even in the best environments, from the most effective teachers, and with the most interested learners, information transfer may not occur.

Resnick (1983) suggests that a critical and often overlooked element for effective learning is understanding the mental model, the assumptions, and the misconceptions that the learner is currently using. What is learned, in other words, is not merely a function of what is given to the learner, but may be strongly affected by what the learner already knows (Rumelhart, 1984). In a sixth grade unit on photosynthesis, Roth (1989) observed that a well-delivered, hands-on, inquiry-oriented science unit failed to overcome and instead confirmed the students' original perception that plants utilize water and soil as food, not raw materials for manufacturing food.

Additionally, the measurement of learning requires that the student activate the cognitive structure into which the new information was coded. Thus the introduction of new material is not the only time when it is helpful to understand the learner's mental model. It is also important to understand their model (in this case, the newly acquired model) when creating the appropriate context for retrieval. Understanding the learner's mental model is thus helpful in engaging the appropriate cognitive elements both at the initial exposure and retrieval.

Therefore, we should not assume that environmental education practitioners are without conceptions of human cognition and behavior. If knowledge transfer is one of the reasons we engage in research, we should work to uncover these existing mental models that contribute to the practice we wish to affect. Our results should be communicated in such a way that the practitioner's misconceptions are adequately addressed and the appropriate mental model is engaged.

2.   <u>Data are not the most effective conveyors of new information</u>. Most documentation of research highlights one experiment or the results of one test in the context of how this particular issue has been treated in the literature.

If we continue to use the practitioner as the recipient and her behavior change as the goal in the communication of research results, it is rather unlikely that the reporting of one set of data will lead to an understanding of the issue sufficient for application. Single points of information are difficult to remember. Repeated exposure to similar, but not identical, messages is a reasonable way to build a cognitive structure around the issue under study (Medin and Smith, 1984). The practitioner's understanding is more likely to grow from several sets of related data, complemented with his own experience. Swamping the practitioner with pages of data is not a recommended approach. Data can be useful, if they are not the focus of the report. The key to the appropriate niche for data is the key to relevant research, but before opening this issue it may be helpful to examine more closely exactly what researchers are trying to achieve.

Goals for Environmental Education Research

If the improvement of the practice of environmental education is the reason we are engaged in EE research, then some very clear goals can be articulated that will form the foundation of a research agenda that respects the above understanding of human cognition.

1.   The results of the research should be useful to practitioners. This implies that the researcher understands the problems practitioners face and their needs. Further, the results should carry some element of credibility so that practitioners have some requisite level of confidence in the recommendation.

2.   The success of the transfer of research results to a learner is dependent on how the information is communicated and the extent to which it is memorable. The learner cannot bear the full responsibility of remembering a poorly designed message.

The implementation of these suggested goals present us with a great variety of relevant, discussable, and researchable questions. Among them are: how does the researcher come to understand what practitioners need?, do researcher's observations influence the event?, what contributes to memorability in a research paper?, and what approach or combination of approaches achieves the most credibility with the intended audience? On these issues, we will no doubt have many opinions. And consequently, these discussions could be very helpful in moving forward the realm of EE research. One version of the possible answers follows.

Toward Relevant Research

Let us assume for the moment that the researcher, working in conjunction with dedicated practitioners, has come upon an issue that has significant application in the EE world. The results of this research could help teachers develop among students a concern for the environment and a willingness to take action. What should the researcher communicate that the practitioners will find useful and memorable?

Provided that teachers want to improve their practice, a clearer understanding of what they are doing and what they could do to improve their student's education could be helpful. One way to build understanding is with theory; theory can empower people to improve their practice (Murphy and Medin, 1985). Most teachers, however, don't have the patience, the interest, or the memory for theory; it is rarely perceived as useful, despite researchers' claims. Now then, can researchers communicate theory?

One suggestion is to provide a <u>portable model</u> of the relevant theory (Kaplan and Kaplan, 1982). A portable model is a mental understanding that is rich enough to give the owner confidence, flexible enough to be applied to new situations, yet simple enough to be easily communicated. It is a coherent yet partial version of the entire theory, with landmarks to provide guidance but not so many details that one could become lost. In short, a portable model is something a teacher would want to own (because of its usefulness) and would be able to own (because of its simplicity). It does not require the investment that expertise does, and it builds upon the knowledge a teacher already has.

The idea of a portable model is in keeping with the constraints and goals mentioned earlier. The model is the framework to which the data apply, and from which new situations can make sense. This makes the model quite helpful to practitioners and easier to remember than a series of numbers, unconnected rules, or nebulous theses. The second goal presented for EE research addresses <u>how</u> information is communicated and here, too, the portable model provides guidance.

Concrete illustrations are a useful way to communicate a portable model. Examples help explain the theory. Data are a type of example; they provide support for the theory presented in the model. We know that direct experience is a strong source of mental examples, but people cannot have enough experiences to adequately be prepared for everything. Consequently, we use other people's experiences through examples, illustrations, cases, and data to build our own mental models (Copeland. 1931; Monroe and Kaplan, 1988). In addition, concrete illustrations help the learner by providing interesting, memorable landmarks throughout the model and direction for activating the relevant receptor of their existing cognitive structure. These goals might also be achieved by using a story-like structure for explaining the cases and examples (Vitz, 1990). The strong tradition and great potential of stories as a medium for communication offer possibilities for further exploration.

So how do these components of the portable model help achieve the goals for EE research? The first goal, usefulness with credibility is aptly provided by appropriately chosen concrete illustrations; the usefulness is possible because the theories are generalizable. The second requires that the portable model enhance both communication and memorability of the theory. The illustrations contribute interestingness through easily remembered examples or landmarks.

The portable model respects the constraints of human cognition, as well. Rather than data and literature, the examples allow the practitioner to glean the most relevant elements for themselves, to ignore one illustration, or lean more heavily on another. Since educators already have experience with the problem, it is important that the model allow the recipient to engage their own ideas. Crafting the message with examples enables the practitioner to construct their own understanding -- their portable model -- as the research message unfolds. This is a very different process from telling learners the answer. It instead allows the learner to actively participate in their own learning.

Qualitative vs Quantitative Research Methods

If a simple, coherent, example-rich and theory-based portable model is <u>what</u> practitioners should receive from EE research efforts, some may still ask <u>how</u> to obtain this model. How should the researcher go about collecting the data and confirming the theory to share with practitioners?

If the portable model is driving the research agenda, it should be obvious that both research paradigms have important contributions to creating portable models. Qualitative research is known for building case collections and exploring the fine detail of particular scenarios. Quantitative efforts are essential in helping practitioners understand the generalizability of the model. In fact, research often benefits from using both qualitative and quantitative research tools, even on the same question. For example, a qualitative study may provide the basis for a more structured and quantitative approach, or an inconsistency uncovered in a quantitative survey may lead to further exploration through qualitative methods.

Conclusion

Our field's current discussion about appropriate research paradigms has opened the door to increased reflection and attention to the goals and outcomes of research in environmental education. Once we are over the obligatory hurdle of the qualitative/quantitative debate, a rich and potentially highly rewarding discussion around a host of issues might take place. We can improve, for example, on how we communicate research results for greater application, how we choose appropriate topics for research, and how we assist practitioners who are interested in doing their own research.

References

Bower, Gordon H. (1982). Plans and Goals in Understanding Episodes, in Flammer A. and W. Kintsch (eds.). <u>Discourse Processing</u>. Amsterdam: North-Holland, pp. 2-15.

Copeland, Melvin T. (1931). The Development of Principles by the Use of Cases in Fraser, Cecil (ed.). <u>The Case Method of Instruction</u>. NY: McGraw-Hill, pp. 26-32.

Kaplan, Stephen and Rachel Kaplan. (1982). Cognition and Environment: Functioning in an Uncertain World. New York: Praeger. Republished by Ann Arbor, MI: Ulrich's Books 1989, pp. 181-83.

Lincoln, Yvonne S. and Egon G. Guba. (1985). Naturalistic Inquiry. Beverly Hills, CA: Sage, pp. 36-43.

Medin, D.L. and E.E. Smith. (1984). Concept and Concept Formation, Annual Review of Psychology, pp. 114-37.

Monroe, Martha C. and Stephen Kaplan. (1988). When Words Speaker Louder than Actions: Environmental Problem Solving in the Classroom, Journal of Environmental Education. 19(3), 38-41.

Murphy, Gregory L. and Douglas L. Medin. (1985). The Role of Theories in Conceptual Coherence, Psychological Review. 92(3), 289-316.

Resnick, Lauren B. (1983). Mathematics and Science Learning: A New Conception, Science. 220(4596), 477-78.

Roth, Kathleen J. (1989). Science Education: It's Not Enough to 'Do' or 'Relate', American Educator. 13(4), 16-22+.

Rumelhart, David E. (1984). Schemata and the Cognitive System, in Wyer, R.S. and T.K. Srull (eds.). Handbook of Social Cognition. Hillsdale, NJ: Erlbaum.

Vitz, Paul C. (1990). The Use of Stories in Moral Development: New Psychological Reasons for an Old Education Method, American Psychologist. 45(6), 709-720.

ABOUT THE AUTHORS

Martha Monroe

Martha C. Monroe is an international environmental educator, training teachers, developing curricula and developing international programs that build skills among environmental education practitioners. She completed her PhD at the University of Michigan combining a cognitive psychology perspective with environmental education goals. She was on the faculty at the University of Wisconsin - Stevens Point from 1986-88 where she taught inservice and preservice teachers. Prior to that, she coordinated community environmental programs at the Dahlem Environmental Education Center in Jackson Michigan. Her programs received recognition in the NSTA Search for Excellence in Science Education in 1983, and she served NAAEE as the President of the Non-formal section from 1988 to 1990. Her extensive work with students and practitioners influences her view of what is important in the field of environmental education research.

Stephen Kaplan

Stephen Kaplan holds a joint appointment in the College of Engineering and the Psychology department at the University of Michigan, where he was also the Director of the Program in Environmental Studies for many years. He has authored three books and hundreds of articles that apply cognitive psychology to principles of environmental design, architecture, policy planning, playground design, wayfinding, restoration, etc.

CRITICAL PHENOMENOLOGY AND ENVIRONMENTAL EDUCATION RESEARCH[1]

Arjen E.J. Wals

Abstract

In this contribution the author argues that applying the empirical-analytic science tradition to educational research in general and environmental education research in particular is at least problematic. He suggests that the epistemology on which positivistic science is built is flawed when applied to the study of human events. Human ideas, experiences, and intentions are not objective things like molecules and atoms. The author suggests that social scientists should shy away from using so called "objective" methods that allow for control, predictability and "generalizability." Instead of boxing, categorizing and labeling people, he maintains that researchers need to re-evaluate the kinds of knowledge and understanding they are after, and the ends they serve. This, he argues, inevitably implies that we need to re-consider our own role as researchers. In seeking answers to resolving the apparent contradictions between the rigorous application of the conventional scientific method and the whole idea of environmental education, the author has arrived at the crossroads of interpretive and critical science traditions in the form of critical phenomenology.

> *"The surrender of our thinking to rationalism and of our artifice to technics have consequences which console us with the feeling that we are progressing, but make us neglect or deny fundamental forces of our inner life which are then turned into forces of destruction. The sclerosis of objectivity is the annihilation of existence." (Philip Mairet, describing the ideas of German existentialist Karl Jaspers in the introduction to Jean-Paul Sartre's "Existentialism and Humanism" (Sartre, 1948).)*

> *[S]tories of environmental education produce and reproduce the kinds of metaphors and myths that support the positivist "scientific detachment" from nature rather than "intractable involvement" in it. There is nothing particularly surprising about this: the cultural successes of modern Western science are founded on the heuristic value of separating matters of "objective" facts from matters of "subjective" value. ...But we can no longer take it for granted that what once was good for modern science is necessarily good for the postmodern planet (Noel Gough, 1991:34).*

Introduction

Several presuppositions lie at the core of this argument for rethinking the foundations of knowledge in order to arrive at a research approach that complements -- as opposed to contradicts -- environmental education as I see it. First, there is the idea that environmental education has the potential to lead to educational reform that ultimately can help reshape

---

[1]This contribution is a modification of Chapter I "Problem Statement and Research Approach" from my dissertation: "Young Adolescents' *Perceptions of Nature and Environmental Education: Implications for Environmental Education.*(Wals, 1991).

relationships between people, and, between people and their surroundings. This assumption that environmental education is seen as a *process* that can lead to *educational change* (as opposed to an instrumental tool that can lead to behavior modification in a pre, expert, determined direction); that educational change (as opposed to educational enhancement) is needed; and, finally, that there is something wrong with *relationships* between people and between people and their environment (as opposed to there is something wrong with peoples' individual and collective behaviors and the systems they control).

The second presupposition is that environmental education should lead to the development of autonomous thinking about issues that affect the quality of life of humans and other species. This idea has several implications that need to be considered carefully as well. Autonomous thinking about environmental issues, or any issue for that matter, suggests that it would be wholly inappropriate to prescribe behavioral outcomes that a learning activity or sequence of activities need to foster. Bob Jickling, for example, writes that he would not want his children to be educated <u>for</u> sustainable development, because it goes against the idea of education: 1) it suggests education then becomes *training* which is the acquisition of skills and abilities which has instrumental connotations and can technically occur through repetition and practice without leading to understanding, 2) the concept of sustainable development is contested,[2] which makes teaching *for* it doubtful at least, and 3) the prescription of a particular outlook conflicts with the development of autonomous thinking. (Jickling, 1991). This is not to say that we should not educate *for* something. Educating for the environment, for instance, is needed to prevent this planet from dying. The issue here is: how do we go about teaching for something and who decides what we are for? In schools, for instance, do we involve teachers, students and community resources in deciding what is good for the community and the local environment or do we decide for them?

A similar concern is expressed by Max van Manen in his discussion of the popular skill of critical thinking which he argues is often regarded as being synonymous with cognitive skills represented by terms such as "good thinking," "thinking straight," "logical reasoning," or with "problem-solving skills." Van Manen, concerned with emancipatory education, suggests that all these abstractions are part of the empirical analytical tradition which lacks a more reflective reference frame:

> *"The theoretical base of empirical-analytical science is too narrow, not taking into account a more complete concept of social science inquiry, and it is inappropriate simply for reasons that it is essentially not critical in a more emancipatory sense.*

---

[2] The concept of sustainable development is contested for several reasons. For one, the word sustainable poses problems. A landfill, for instance, is a sustainable ecosystem, but of very low quality. The word development in the context of Third World development is also problematic for reasons to be described later. Combining the words to "sustainable development," technically leads to an oxymoron. Without ascribing qualities to the concept, the concept becomes hollow. It is precisely the ascribing of qualities that is political and contested. It is therefore more useful for students to learn about sustainable development and the different ways of looking at it so that they can make up their own minds.

Emancipatory awareness leads to the possibility of self-determination with some degree of freedom from blind psychological, political or economic compulsions. ......It involves inquiry into the social origins, consequences, and functions of knowledge" (Van Manen, 1975:17).

The above reasoning suggests that environmental education not be defined in terms of desired behavioral outcomes and that the for part of Lucas' widely cited article "The Role of Science Education in Education for the Environment," should be re-examined (Lucas, 1980). Defining environmental education thus becomes problematic and undesirable if it would require universal goals and objectives that would be superimposed upon schools and communities regardless of the contextual realities that challenge them. Doing so would reduce environmental education to an untouchable, abstract object and would reduce the people affected to the status of things. Jickling even suggests that environmental education then becomes "a treasure hunt for an infinitely illusive abstract object." (Jickling, 1991:5).

The third presupposition is that our planet is facing destruction as a result of *symptomatic* environmental problems such as; overpopulation, deforestation, excessive waste and the degradation of water, air and soil, which ultimately are rooted in the unequal distribution of wealth, the uninhibited strife for economic growth, and inadequate education (CEI, 1991). Again this idea includes several points of view which are still contested, including the ideas that there are limits to growth, and that resources, including human resources such as education, should be distributed in a more equitable manner. Many international statements on environment and development do not seriously challenge the principles of economic growth or even the inequitable distribution of resources (IUCN, 1980; World Commission on Environment and Development, 1987). At the same time the statements generated on the subject of environment and development, tend to perpetuate the myth that there are developing countries (generally countries in the southern hemisphere) and developed countries (generally are located in the northern hemisphere). This myth suggests it is possible for a country *not* to develop. It separates the problems of the North from problems of the South which in itself makes finding solutions more problematic given that they are interrelated. On another level it allows governments in countries from the North, also referred to as "the West," such as the United States, to deny that environmental degradation within their own borders is often the result of the same processes that take place in the so-called developing countries. The conveniently created "North-South" or "developed-developing" dichotomy might just as well be used as metaphors to describe differences between "inner-city" and "suburb" or "working-class" and "upper-class" or "middle-class" on a national, regional and local level.

These three presuppositions; environmental education (EE) as educational reform and the rejection of EE as an instrument to modify behavior in a predetermined direction; education as the process that leads to autonomous thinking; and the environmental crisis as a crisis rooted in inequitable distribution of resources and the uninhibited strife for economic growth, form the main biases I bring to any attempt to research environmental education. Hence, these biases have and should have consequences for my research interests and research approach which I will describe in this paper. The challenge is not so much to find a research method that eliminates or, as is often the case, obscures these personal, but often shared, biases, but to find a method that will make them explicit and put them to use throughout the inquiry.

As somebody concerned with environmental education, I am interested in the way people come to make sense of their own environment through their everyday interactions with(in) the lifeworld[2a] ; the kind of world they create for themselves; the extent to which this world is shared with others, and; finally, what meaning they ascribe to concepts important to environmental education such as nature and environmental problems. To satisfy this interest, I need to obtain some insights into human experiences and in commonalties of understanding that could lead to improved communication and meaningful interactions between theorists and practitioners, teacher and students, and school and community (Van Manen, 1975, 1977). The concepts *human experience, commonalties of understanding, meaningful interaction,* are concepts which emerge from interpretive science traditions and stand in sharp contrast to concepts such as; *behavior modification, scientific generalizations, systems analysis,* which are used in the in North America dominant empirical analytical science tradition. A third tradition, the critical science tradition, not only rejects notions of behavior modification, prediction and control, but also maintains that in order to facilitate communication, meaningful interactions and commonalties of understanding, we need to examine the *power structure* that underlies aspects of social life and communication (Freire, 1986; Habermas, 1974; Van Manen, 1975; Misgeld, 1985).

Bearing in mind the three presuppositions stated earlier, I will argue that given the nature of education, the nature of the environmental crisis, and given the non-prescriptive role environmental education should play in stimulating and shaping educational change, it is prudent to use a research approach that does not distort communication by manipulation and control, but instead will allow those who are affected by education and educational change a) to express their ideas, b) to point out inequalities in resource access and power imbalances, and c) to help determine changes that they themselves find important.

[2a] The word "lifeworld" is derived from the German "Lebenswelt" and is used to described our own individual and socially constructed reality; our orientation towards the world which helps us determine how we define our situation, the way we look at things, what we believe to be true, valuable and real. In short; the kind of world we create for ourselves.

The research approach I will discuss here, critical phenomenology,[2b] draws upon interpretive and critical science traditions in an attempt to understand the participants' view of the world as manifested in their actions in their own lifeworld and their reflections on their position in this world. From an environmental education perspective, research should then focus on gaining a better understanding of peoples' own perceptions, ideas and theories in relation to their environment, environmental issues and nature in order to obtain new insights in adapting (environmental) education to the social and physical context in which the school community is embedded. An additional challenge in research of this kind is to capture the drama and the every day life of the participants, without doing it unjustice in the process (such as controlling and narrowing choices). The results of such research would be to affect not only the people, but also the institutions and the society that (fail to) support them.

Research Dilemmas and Philosophical Considerations

"Causal or mechanical thinking will have to be supplanted by dialectical thinking because..... experiencing creatures do not so much follow laws as norms, the difference being that experiencing creatures contribute to the constitution of the norms they follow. However, if one follows rules to which [s]he has contributed, then the relationship is not linear but dialectical because it is an internally generated relationship that carries with it the possibility of further change and development in either the behavior or the norm itself. With a positivism of laws, however, no deviation of growth is possible; things must simply submit." (Giorgi, 1975; 322).[3]

Human ideas, experiences, and intentions are not objective things like molecules and atoms. Nevertheless, just like some of their colleagues in the Natural Sciences, many educational researchers attempt to use "objective" methods that allow for the control, predictability and "generalizability" needed to uncover the "laws" or "patterns" that guide human behavior and the systems in which that behavior occurs. The scientific method constructed to do this has long been claimed to be a value free tool of inquiry, allowing many social scientists to create a dichotomy between themselves, their methods and their research. This separation is a very dangerous one, for it gives scientists a false authority of truth that stems from the claims that there is an objective way to study an "objectifiable" world and that the only way to study this world is through rigorous application of the scientific method. I will suggest that; a) there is no objective way to study human phenomena, b) it is counter-productive and

---

[2b] I have added the word critical to phenomenology to emphasize the potential of phenomenological studies to say the unsaid; shed a new light on every day events; reveal, for instance, social injustice and/or alienation; and present these findings in an accessible form (e.g. dialogue) to those involved in these events. If used critically, phenomenolgy has the ability to transform and change existing situations. Examples can be found in Jules Henry, 1971; Valerie Polakow, 1982; Robert Everhart, 1983; Denzin, 1984; and Taylor & Dorsey-Gaines, 1988).

[3] Amedeo Giorgi in discussing Merleau-Ponty 's critique of traditional psychology which can also be found in: Merleau-Ponty, M. The structure of behavior. Translated by Alden L. Fisher, Boston: Beacon Press, 1963.

even dangerous to objectify the world, and c) that there is more than one way of knowing.

It is interesting to note that while the physicist's model of "billiard-ball" causality is still being used in much psychological, social and educational research, the model has been abandoned by many physicists themselves. Frank Smith writes:

> "To find exciting and imaginative theories today, throbbing with color and with marvel, one has to turn to astronomy, nuclear physics, or genetic biology. To try to comprehend what is dimly perceived through powerful microscopes and telescopes seems to require the mind of a poet. Why then should that most remarkable universe of all, the human brain, be approached in such a grey and mechanistic matter?" (Smith, 1985; 211).

Smith argues that science generally tends to derive its metaphors from contemporary technology in which the world, society and individuals and their brains are perceived in terms of computers. The <u>brain</u> is seen as a repository of information, <u>thought</u> as information processing, and <u>learning</u> as the mechanism by which new information is acquired (Smith, 1985, see also: Freire, 1986). The alternative, according to Smith and many others (e.g. Giorgi, 1975; Roche, 1973; Beekman, 1984), is

> "that the primary, fundamental, and continual activity of the brain is nothing less than the creation of worlds. <u>Thought</u> in the broadest sense is the construction of worlds, both "real" and imaginary, <u>learning</u> is their elaboration and modification and <u>language</u> --especially written language-- is a particularly efficacious but by no means unique medium by which these worlds can be manifested, manipulated, and sometimes shared" (Emphases mine) (Smith, 1985; 197).

The metaphors we use to describe and interpret our world are important since they structure the way we perceive it. Just as metaphors can expand our horizons and can create new realms of experience, they can narrow our choices, if we limit ourselves to the ones used by positivistic science or, for that matter, to those of any other single way of looking at the world. The use of the so-called "scientific method" in the social sciences illustrates how emphasis on one single way of knowing can limit understanding and the creation of new possibilities. Within the positivistic sciences or the objectivist tradition of research, the researcher's task is still seen as identifying laws which govern human events by utilizing the scientific method in a personally detached manner. Marshall and Barritt suggest that language within the objectivist tradition is used only to report and not to create. "Research [in the objectivist tradition is] not a rhetorical process of argumentation, but rather a scientific one of method. The writing of research [then becomes] ancillary to the actual work of finding out" (Marshall and Barritt, 1990; 605).

In addition to considering the implications of the metaphors we live by, and recognizing that the relative value of metaphors cannot be quantified or assessed "objectively" to be right of wrong, we need to decide whether the goal of research in the human sciences is to measure and control human behavior or to understand it.   Knowledge and human interests are interwoven as reflected in the choice of methods and the ends to which such methods are put (Habermas, 1971). The idea that there is a world out there that eventually can be totally analyzed, predicted, and controlled --the world of positivistic science-- is frightening to me. Aside from the question whether it is even remotely possible, imagine for a moment that we would live in a world in which there would be little uncertainty, in which we could predict the future, a world without doubt and surprises, a world as a three dimensional clock that has been totally analyzed and can be manipulated and controlled in any desirable direction, and ask yourself: "What would life be like under those circumstances? "Who would be the ones in control and who would be the ones under control?" "Who determines in what direction to go?"

Unless we reflect on the ends to be served by science, we risk that prediction and control and the methods that come with it might exclude other ends, such as improved understanding among people, the release of human potential (Susman and Evered, 1978), the forming of a "sustainable" relationship with our surroundings, and to generate new possibilities of experience. Table 1, borrowed from Van Manen (Van Manen, 1975) summarizes the world views, metaphors, aims and practical significance of three types of epistemology. Considering the arguments put forward in this position statement, I find myself most comfortable with the research traditions which lie in what Van Manen refers to as, the critical and interpretive sciences.

TABLE 1

Epistemology of Dominant Inquiry Models in the Social Sciences
(After Van Manen, 1975; 5)

type of system & science	pretheoretical category	unit of analysis	validation procedure	telic mode or aim	meaning of explanation	general theoretical orientation & social theories	practical significance or applicative significance
action system: interpretive science	intentional behavior	experiential meanings of purposes, motives, etc.	constructing inter-subjectively shared understandings	sense-making	establishing "resonance" or "striking a responsive chord by clarifying motives, authentic experiences, common meanings	**action theory**, hermeneutics, language analysis, ethnomethodology, phenomenology, analytical sociology	**humanistic:** acquiring insights into human experiences, facilitating communication, enabling meaningful interactions, seeking a continuity of cultural traditions, providing commonalities of understanding
pseudo-natural system: empirical-analytic science	observable behavior	observable and inferrable behavior	corroborative empirical observation	nomological explanation, prediction and control	causal, functional, or hypothetico deductive arguments, involving natural laws or scientific generalizations	**behavioral theory:** S-R and S-O-R theories of learning, cybernetics, systems theory, dialectical materialism, structural functionalism	**technical:** behavior modification, human engineering, systems analysis applied to cultural, social and institutional systems, e.g. in instructional design and programming
moral/ therapeutic system: critical science	disturbed and distorted communicative /instrumental behavior	values, communications, and instrumental actions	practical discourse	process of enlightenment and emancipation	tracing back to underlying hidden or unreflected aspects of social life	**critical theory:** neo-Marxism, psycho-analysis, critical theory, analytical ethnomethodology	**emancipatory:** humanization, social change, therapy

160

Critical Phenomenology

Having reflected on a research philosophy I will now discuss critical phenomenology as an example of a research approach that is congruent with this philosophy in that it a) does not reduce people to clusters of interacting variables and does not impede communication, reducing human beings to the status of things, b) is more than a data-collecting activity, in that it actively seeks to understand as well as to improve the school and its community, and c) does not focus on finding causality, generating generalizable results and predicting the future with statistical accuracy. Additionally, it is an approach that suggests that (environmental) education research should have a pedagogical end in the sense that the participants somehow benefit from the research. Hence, research is seen as not just an attempt to learn about people, but to come to know with them the reality which challenges them. With those parameters in mind, I believe that research can help in producing knowledge with emancipatory relevance that can promote the autonomy of the individual and the solidarity of the entire community,[4] rather than the production of technically exploitable information.

As a way of knowing, critical phenomenology, as I see it, has elements of both action research (Lewin, 1946; Kemmis, 1980; Carr, 1989) as a methodology and phenomenology[4b] (Spiegelberg, 1960; Husserl, 1970; Giorgi, 1976; Barritt et al, 1985; Wittgenstein, 1985) as a way to come to understand the everyday world of experience through language. Both the tradition of action research and phenomenology use --although not exclusively-- qualitative research methods such as field research, descriptive research, and ethnography in which the researcher takes, the role of observer, interpreter and/or participant. Research here becomes more than a data collecting activity, in that it actively seeks to understand as well as to improve the school and its community through simultaneous action and reflection.

In researching education within these traditions, one continuously tries to make sense of an ongoing process that may go in many directions--making initial observations, developing tentative general conclusions that suggest particular types of further observations, making those observations and thereby revising one's conclusions, and so forth. This "research spiral" is very similar to the spiral of action and reflection learners (students and teachers) ideally follow throughout a school based action research project (Kemmis, 1980; Hustler et al, 1986; Bull, et al, 1988; Wals et al., 1990).

The emphasis in this kind of research shifts from finding or proving causality in order to generate a theory of human behavior, to documenting and describing, using, in addition to diagnostic instruments, one's own

---

[4] Kracklauer, 1974 in: Amedeo Giorgi, *"Phenomenology and the Foundations of Psychology."* Nebraska Symposium on Motivation, 1975.

[4b] Spiegelberg describes phenomenology in the 20th century as the name of a philosophical movement whose primary objective is the direct investigation and description of phenomena as consciously experienced without theories about their causal explanation and as free as possible from unexamined preconceptions and presuppositions. (Spiegelberg, 1975:3).

observations and those of teachers and students; interpreting these with all involved participants; relating the results with the foundations, goals and objectives of (environmental) education; and feeding back the results to the participants, and others interested in the improvement of education. Instead of emphasizing the kinds of changes that occur in the learner as a result of an (environmental) education project, the main focus is on finding out whether a certain educational project or program and the structure of schooling provide for such change.[5]

In my own research, for instance, I looked at the way young adolescents perceive, experience and define "nature," "environment," "environmental issues," and "environmental/social change" and how these perceptions, experiences and "definitions" relate to schooling in general and environmental education in particular (Wals, 1991). Experiencing here is more than the sum of feelings, encounters with the world and people's ideas. Experiencing also involves attaching meaning to various interactions with the world and the naming of these encounters. The process of meaning making (or making sense) and naming of the world does not only involve cognitive conception as such, but also includes lived meanings and concepts manifested in people's actions and non-actions (Freire, 1986: 102).

In critical phenomenology, the researcher does not begin the research with preconceived hypotheses to test but, as discussed earlier, with a general frame of reference to guide him or her. Human science can not exclude the knowledge of the inquirer from an understanding of how knowledge is generated. I too have a consciousness, world view and language that are a product of the history of ideas, social and cultural development and my individual encounters with the world. Much like reading a good novel, what we bring to the text [research] is as important as the text [research] itself (Smith, 1985). Phenomenological traditions acknowledge this by maintaining that the immediate subjective experience is the basis of knowledge. A challenge in phenomenological research is to either minimize the *constraints* of preconceptions, or to acknowledge one's preconceptions so that one allows another's experience to be communicated in a relatively undistorted fashion. Hence, putting a study in any kind of theoretical framework can best be postponed until after the researcher has reflected on his or her own guiding assumptions and metaphors, in order to: a) obtain better insight in what he or she is bringing to the research setting and participants, and b) to obtain an understanding of how that would influence the research experience itself.

One of the things I hoped to achieve with my own research on young adolescents' perceptions of nature and environmental issues was to be able to come to understand the students' world views[5b] in their richness, their

---

[5] After Marjan Margradant van Arcken in a research proposal to the Dutch Foundation of Educational Research (S.V.O.), 1988.

[5b] The notion of world view is often used without reflection. I see a world view as a construct that has historical, cultural, social and personal dimensions. Because it is historical it also is dynamic: it changes over time. A world view is the result of a person's inter-actions with the world in order to make sense of future encounters with the world. It has to do with the meaning people attach to words, the way people interpret their situation, the way people see their future, the way people interact with one-another, the way people transform their world, that is; make

significance, their transformations, and in their historical composition. Without actively participating as an actor -- as opposed to being an observer -- in the investigation, I did not think the study would lead to its pedagogical end, considering that "thematic investigation is justified only to the extent that it returns to the people what truly belongs to them; to the extent that it represents not an attempt to learn about the people, but to come to know <u>with</u> them the reality which challenges them." (Emphasis mine) (Beekman, 1989;18-22).

Active participation here means being an integral part of the classroom events rather than being a distant observer.[6,7] In a phenomenological study this also means that one has to reflect on, make explicit, and <u>temporarily</u> put aside, any preconceived notions or theoretical assumptions in order to be able to look with an open eye at the everyday life-world the students inhabit (the way they respond to certain questions, the way they experience a particular project session; a class, lunch, social interactions, neighborhood, family, etc). Active participation also has the advantage that it allows for the researcher to build some trust between him/herself and the participants. Building trust between the researcher, the students and the teachers is crucial for creating an atmosphere that allows for communication to take place in a relatively undistorted fashion.

During my own research, I not only engaged in participant observation, I also interviewed students and kept a research journal. Students were also asked to keep their own journals to reflect upon their learning experiences. With permission of the teachers and the students these journal entries were used for analysis and interpretation as well. The majority of my research findings resulted from thirty taped in-depth interviews conducted with students from four middle schools. The selection of the students needs to be discussed since it deviates from the conventional random sampling methods used in empirical analytical research traditions. In selecting the students for a phenomenological study it is more important to have good informants who are capable of providing insightful information than it is to have a statistically representative group of people obtained through random sampling. Nevertheless, it is important to have some strategy in mind when selecting students in order to get the most out of relatively short interviews. The strategy I used was based upon Glaser and Strauss' "theoretical sampling design" which is a compromise between opportunistic or pragmatic sampling and probability sampling (Glaser and Strauss, 1967). Agar points out that this is an open sampling design in that you only stop interviewing

---

it their own or the way people are deprived from making it their own, and the kind of self they accept for themselves. I also believe "perception of change" has to do with it.

A world view is thus more than just opinions and attitudes; it is the interpretive structure students have acquired to make sense of their schooling experience as well as their experiences outside of school.

[6] Beekman, A.J. *Onderzoeker met hart en ziel*; Een pleidooi voor de lijfelijke aanwezigheid in het veld van onderzoek. Kollege bij zijn afscheid als hoogleraar in de theoretische pedagogiek en de algemene methodologie van het pedagogisch onderzoek aan de Rijksuniversiteit Utrecht, 1986.

[7] Paulo Freire uses the process of coding and decoding in his conscientization method. Mary Cole in her *Summer in New York* used pictures in the black ghetto. One of her pictures showed a picture of a pile of garbage in the same street where the teacher and a group of teenagers were discussing the picture. One of the participants said at once: "I see a street in Africa or Latin America." "And why not in New York?" asked the teacher. "Because we are in the United States and that can't happen here."

informants when you feel you have reached the "theoretical saturation point." This is the point where patterns seem to repeat themselves and the interviews don't seem to reveal anything new anymore (Agar, 1980).

With this strategy in mind, I first asked the teachers 1) which students he/she considered representative of the class or certain groups within the class,[8] and 2) which students he/she thought were best able to express themselves verbally in a one-on-one interview. Furthermore, I felt that it was important to interview as many boys as girls. All students were seventh-grade students age twelve or thirteen. A final, but crucial criterion, in the selection of students for the interviews was their own willingness to be interviewed. I would not have interviewed students who did not volunteer. Fortunately, none of the students selected declined the interview. If some would have declined that in itself could have pointed at a phenomenon worthwhile investigating.

In phenomenological research there is a conscious effort to share participants' perspectives without using a theoretical model with which to judge these perspectives. The researcher therefore neither tests hypotheses nor uses observation matrices. This does not mean that "theory" does not play a role. Preconceived ideas, sometimes even prejudices, are temporarily put aside and existing theories come back into the picture after the data have been collected and analyzed. This is difficult, since one is often not aware of one's prejudices. In order for my research not to be naive, I had to analyze the pre-given meaning structures embedded in myself as well as in the situation and context of the research. Beekman suggests that this implies reflection on:

"a) the actual situation as perceived by the researcher; making him her aware of the prejudices (s)he has;
b) becoming aware of the usual privileged position one occupies in relation to the subjects in the field one wants to research; I in my comfortable office think about researching the homeless...
c) becoming aware of the possible impact my judgements have on the research process, protocols and outcomes.
d) realizing how much one's own judgments are dependent on the tradition (cultural history), of which one is part." (Beekman, 1989; p. 88).

These reflections would have to be made explicit for them to play their essential role in all phases of the research. During the actual field work, I tried to gather and describe as many impressions and experiences as possible. These impressions included; the way space and time were used,

---

[8] It is important to point out that even within one classroom different groups of students may represent different phenomena. From our experiences at Potham Middle School in Detroit, for instance, we know that students who lived East of Livernois street had a socio-economic background and experiences that were different from students who lived West of that street. Ulf Hannerz who lived in a African-American Public Housing project for an extensive period of time to do phenomenological research (Hannerz, 1969), discovered that even within the same building people representing different phenomena could be found. This makes the reasoned selection of the interviewee's all the more important.

rituals, group interaction, the way new members of the group were dealt with, social networks and so forth. The impressions and experiences were reflected upon and written down in a research journal usually at the end of the day. Since it is impossible to capture and describe everything that happens during the day, the descriptions inevitably were a selection. The selection was based on the research questions I had in mind. These questions helped me focus my attention which subsequently led to sharper observations. Phenomenologists point out, however, that sometimes seemingly irrelevant events that somehow draw the researcher's attention either because they are striking or because of their frequent occurrence, may later turn out to be quite important (Bleeker and Mulderij, 1984). In a phenomenological research approach the researcher does not determine prior to the actual participant observation what data are relevant, but instead, lets the experiences as a participant observer determine the relevance of the data. At the same time (s)he has a definite perspective as stated earlier. This perspective is not a fixed point, but rather a historical vantage point.

The interview transcripts, participant observations, and journal reflections are analyzed and compared with the intention to discover some structure and coherency in the reflections. Usually experiences tend to repeat themselves with some variation, but after several rounds of interpreting, a deep structure of common themes emerged. The writing process itself becomes the making sense of data which allows for temporary themes, categories, or patterns to emerge. This is crucial for it prevents the research from running blindly into a dead-end street. The describing and temporary analysis of the data makes it possible to refocus the research by looking at aspects that initially were thought to be irrelevant.

Once the themes emerged, they had to be brought together in meaningful, coherent and understood sentences (language). Determining these sentence structures always involves interpretation of the rough data, the generation of themes, and the choosing of the best descriptive metaphors. It is important to point out, however, that these interpretations and selections are not made in a vacuum but are bound to the life-world. The life-world determines the validity of the interpretations. The reader of the research report is likely to test the interpretations using his or her own experiences as a frame of reference -- parallel to the reading of a good novel analogy used earlier -- and is therefore able to give well founded critique. "Knowledge obtained through phenomenology is not subjective in the sense of opposite to objective, but is subjective in that it finds its origin in a 'subject' that is at the core of a world which is [partly] shared with other 'subjects'." (Margadant-van Arcken, 1988; 7).

An interpretation is not only tested against the experiences of the reader but also against the rough data themselves. When the researcher has to mold the data in order to make them fit into a category, (s)he knows that (s)he is on the wrong path. A category has to leave interpretation space. In other words, the research data have to fit in "naturally." Phenomenology holds that interpretations that show coherency of meaning become a descriptive theory and that the understood structure of sentences describing that theory make up scientific knowledge. In order to reach some form of inter-subjectivity and consensus with others, it is advisable to have outside researchers read interview transcripts to discuss and modify the direction of the interviews, during the interview stage and, furthermore, to have one or more co-readers (which could include participants in a study) comment on the researcher's interpretations during an early stage in the writing process.

A next step in the research process is to put the descriptive theory in a broader framework in order to find "family" related patterns in the way children perceive and experience nature and their environment; the way these perceptions and experiences affect the way they perceive their own role in resolving environmental issues; the way environmental education in particular and education in general can build upon these perceptions. In this phase the findings are confronted with existing theories and research results. These theories include goals, foundations, assumptions and concepts used in environmental education in general and a school's curriculum which includes teachers, students, subject matter and milieu. The result of these confrontations are a mixture of the confirming, specifying, refining, putting in perspective and rejecting of existing theories.

Without getting into the debate about whether descriptive research concerned with non-randomly selected particulars can be generalized or transferred to other situations, I will say the following. Through a phenomenological study within the realms of educational experience, the research tries to tell several stories that have to do with students, schools, communities. The phenomena or themes that emerge from systematic investigation are described in such a way that readers hopefully can visualize the scene, can understand the meanings ascribed to certain phenomena by the students and other members of the school community, and can follow the interpretations of these phenomena and their relevance to (environmental) education, as seen through the eyes of the researcher. Every student, school or community displays not only itself, but also features it has in common with other students, schools and communities. In the words of Eisner, "every particular is also a sample of a larger class. In this sense, what has been learned about a particular can have relevance for the class to which it belongs. The theme embedded in the particular situation, extends beyond the situation itself." (Eisner, 1991; 103). What one learns about one student or a small group of students' thinking about environmental issues, for instance, can raise one's consciousness of features that might be found among other students. However, research of this kind does not claim that other students will share identical or even similar features but rather that these are features one might look for among other students. Philosophically speaking, one cannot generalize from one situation to another when the situations are identical, only when they are different. As Eisner points out, skills, images, ideas, perceptions and experiences are never identical; some features of the situations always differ. It is therefore better to speak of the transfer of generalizable features to a different context than to speak of generalization of the results to a broader population.

Finally, the results of the study need to be communicated with the teachers of the schools who participated in the study. This needs to be done for otherwise the study will not have a pedagogical and emancipatory end. The feedback phase of the research will usually require going back to the schools and finding a way of sharing the results with the broader educational community. The product as it appears in written form in a journal, report, or dissertation should not be seen as the final product, but as an intermediate stage in gaining better understanding, while acknowledging that it is impossible, perhaps even undesirable, to obtain complete and permanent understanding.

Figure 1 displays these phases on the time-line using my own research as an example. Table 2 summarizes the some steps in critical phenomenology by distinguishing interrelated and overlapping phases. (Wals, 1991).

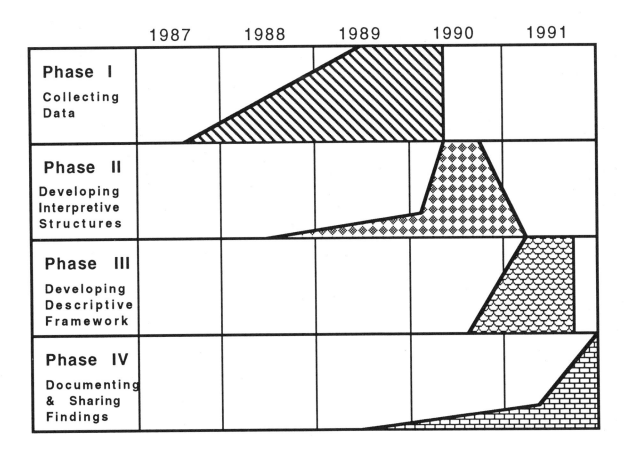

**Figure 1:   Research Phases and Timeline
as in Wals, 1991.**

Phase I: **Collecting Data** through participant observation and the interviewing of students and teachers in the field. Activities: Interviewing, participating, observing, journal writing, reflecting on students' writings and other expressions with students and teachers, getting to know the school, the neighborhood, building a relationship, trust, and mutual understanding	Phase II: **Developing categories/ interpretive structures** that capture the rough data. Activities: Analyzing and interpreting the data, discussions with co-readers, ordering the rough data into "natural" categories/themes. Dialectical relating of the parts to the whole, reconceptualizing when incongruence takes place.
Phase III: **Developing a descriptive framework** by bringing together the categories in order to build a kind of theory, if you will, and confronting this framework with existing theories and research results. Activities: Synthesizing of the categories into coherent understood sentence structures in order to generate theoretical implications grounded in possibilities for action. Reading of similar studies; comparing the findings; confronting the findings with existing theories of learning, environmental education in general and the involved schools' educational program in particular. Formulating conclusions and recommendations.	Phase IV: **Documenting and communicating findings** and results. The actual writing up of the research in a structured and coherent form and sharing the findings and results with the schools who participated in the study, and the broader environmental education community. Activities: The actual writing of an article or report and discussing them with participants and outside researchers throughout the writing process. Feedback of findings and results to the participants of the study. Proposals for adjustments of environmental education projects and the restructuring of the curriculum in collaboration with the school community. Writing of spin-off articles to share insights with the broader education community.

Table 2: Some Phases and Activities in a Critical Phenomenological Study

Summary and Conclusion[9]

In this contribution I have taken a position which suggests that human ideas, experiences, and intentions are not objective things like molecules and atoms and that social scientists therefore should shy away from using so called "objective" methods that allow for control, predictability and "generalizability." I have argued that we need to move away from boxing, categorizing and labeling people, and need to re-evaluate the kinds of knowledge and understanding we are after, and the ends they will serve. This inevitably implies that we need to re-consider our own role as researchers. Rather than detaching ourselves, our biases and pre-judgements from our research using the umbrella of objectivity as a hiding place, we should make our biases and preferred way of knowing explicit and begin to speak a new language in which overt subjectivity, rhetoric, argument and metaphor play a central role.

If knowledge and human interests are interwoven as reflected in the choice of methods and the ends to which such methods are put, then the idea that there is a world out there that eventually can be totally analyzed, predicted, and controlled --the world of positivistic science-- is frightening. Unless we reflect on the ends to be served by science, we risk that prediction and control and the methods that come with it might exclude other ends, such as improved understanding among people, the release of human potential, the forming of a sustainable and quality relationship with our surroundings, and the creation of new possibilities of experience.

Critical phenomenology is an approach that begins to address some of the dilemmas raised in this paper. I have suggested that this approach has elements of *action research* and *phenomenology* which use qualitative research methods such as; field research, descriptive research, and ethnography, in which the researcher takes the role of observer/participant and interpreter. Research becomes more than a data collecting activity, in that it actively seeks to understand as well as to improve the school and its community through simultaneous action and reflection with all parties involved. The emphasis in research is no longer on finding causality, generating generalizable results and predicting the future with statistical accuracy, but instead on documenting and describing human experience and intentions, using, in addition to diagnostic instruments, one's own observations and those of teachers and students; interpreting these with all involved participants; relating the results with the foundations, goals and objectives of EE and discussing ways to adjust the curriculum and classroom practise as a result of newly obtained insights. The main objective is not to find out the kinds of changes that occur in the learner as a result of an EE project, but to find out whether an EE project on the one hand, and the structure of schooling on the other, provided for such change.

---

[9] This conclusion is similar to a statement I wrote on environmental education research that appeared in the research column of the NAAEE's periodical Communicator in the November/December issue of 1990 under the title: "What you can't measure still exists."

A researcher has the moral obligation to work for and with the participants in his/her study in order to justify his/her presence in an educational program. EE research should have a pedagogical end in the sense that the participants somehow benefit from the research. Thus, research should not just be an attempt to learn about people, but to come to know <u>with</u> them the reality which challenges them.

In closure, I would like to suggest that before uncritically accepting the dominant positivistic paradigm, we have to consider alternatives. It is my belief that it is the very same world of positivism that allowed for environmental deterioration to take place at its current pace and scope in the first place. I realize that I have only scratched the surface in critiquing positivistic science and introducing an alternative paradigm for EE research. Hence, I refer the interested reader to the included references for more thorough descriptions of alternative ways of knowing and understanding.

<u>References</u>[10]

Agar, M.H. (1980). <u>The Professional Stranger: An informal introduction to ethnography</u>. Academic Press.

Barritt, L., Beekman, A.J., Bleeker, H., Mulderij, K. (1985). <u>Researching Education Practice</u>. University of North Dakota Press.

Beekman, A.J. A Call for Reflection and Awareness in Research. (1989). In: Levering, B., Vriens, L. (Eds.). <u>De Zaken Zelf: Bijdragen uit de Utrechtse Wijsgerige & Historische Pedagogiek</u>. Utrechts Pedagogisch Cahier, nr. 9. Utrecht.

Berger, P. and Luckman, T. (1967). <u>The Social Construction of Reality: A Treatise in the Sociology of Knowledge</u>. London: The Penguin Press.

Bleeker, H., Mulderij, K.J. (1984). <u>Pedagogiek op je knieën</u>. Boom, Meppel.

Bull, J.; Cromwell, M.; Cwikiel, W.; Di Chiro, G.; Guarino, J.; Rathje, R.; Stapp, W.; Wals, A. E.; and Youngquist, M. (1988). <u>Education in Action: A Community Problem Solving Program for Schools.</u> Dexter, MI: Thomson-Shore.

Caretakers of the Environment/International (CEI). (1991). <u>San Antonio Declaration on Environmental Education and Development</u>. Closing Statement of the Fifth International CEI conference held in Cusco, Peru, August 27-September 1, 1991.

Carr, W. and Kemmis, S. (1986). <u>Becoming Critical: Education, Knowledge and Action Research.</u> London: Falmer Press.

---

[10] Most of the references have been cited in this paper. Those which have not been cited are included for their major contributions to critical and interpretive science traditions, and/or for the impact they have had, and continue to have, on my thinking about research.

Carr, W. (1989). Action Research: ten years on. Journal of Curriculum Studies, 21(1), 5-90.

Denzin, N. K. (1984). Toward a phenomenolgy of domestic, family, violence. American Journal of Sociology, 90, 483 - 513.

Eisner, E.W. (1991). The Enlightened Eye: Qualitative Inquiry and the Enhancement of Educational Practice, Macmillan Publishing, New York, NY.

Everhart, R.B. (1983). Reading, Writing and Resistance. Routledge & Kegan Paul, Boston, MA.

Freire, P. (1986). Pedagogy of the Oppressed, 25th Edition, New York: Continuum.

Geertz, C. (1983). Local Knowledge. New York: Basic Books.

Giorgi, A. (1976). Phenomenology and the Foundations of Psychology. In: Proceedings of the Nebraska Symposium on Motivation. University of Nebraska, Lincoln.

Glaser, B., and Strauss, A. (1967). The Discovery of Grounded Theory. Chicago, Il: Aldine.

Gough, N. (1991). Narrative and Nature: Unsustainable Fictions in Environmental Education. Australian Journal Environmental Education, 7, (2)31-42.

Habermas, J. (1974). Theory and Practice. London: Heinemann.

Habermas, J. (1971) Toward a Rational Society. London: Heinnemann.

Hannerz, U. (1969). Soulside: inquiries into ghetto culture and community. Columbia University Press, New York.

Henry, J. (1971). Pathways to Madness. Vintage Books Edition, New York.

Husserl, E. (1970). The Crisis of European Sciences and Transcendental Phenomenology. Evanston: Northwestern University Press.

Hustler, D., Cassidy, A., Cuff, E.C. (1986). Action Research in Classrooms and Schools. London: Allen and Unwin.

International Union for the Conservation of Nature (IUCN). (1980). World Conservation Strategy: living resource conservation for sustainable development. IUCN in cooperation with UNEP and WWF. Gland, Switzerland.

Jickling, B.J. (1991). Why I Don't Want my Children to be Educated for Sustainable Development. Paper Presented at the 20th Annual Conference of the North American Association for Environmental Education. Saint Paul, Mn. September 27-October 2.

Kemmis, S. (1980). Action Research. International Encyclopedia of Education, Oxford.

Lewin, Kurt. (1946). Action Research and Minority Problems. Journal of Social Issues, 26, 3-23.

Lucas, A.M. (1980). The Role of Science Education in Education for the Environment. Journal of Environmental Education, 12(3), 33-3.

Margradant-van Arcken, M.J.A. (1988). Natuurbeleving bij acht tot twaalfjarige kinderen. Onderzoeksvoorstel ingediend bij de S.V.O.

Marshall, M.J., Barritt, L.S. (1990 winter). Choices Made, Worlds Created: The Rhetoric of AERJ. American Educational Research Journal, 27(4), 589-609.

Misgeld, D. (1985). Education and Cultural Invasion: Critical Social Theory, Education as Instruction, and the "Pedagogy of the Oppressed." In: Forester J. Critical Theory and Public Life, MIT press, Cambridge, MA,.

Polakow, V. (1982). The Erosion of Childhood. University of Chicago, Chicago, IL.

Popkewitz, T.S. (1984). Paradigm and Ideology in Education Research. London: Falmer Press.

Robottom, I. (1985). Evaluation in Environmental Education: Time for a change in perspective? Journal of Environmental Education, 17(1), 31-36.

Robottom, I. (1987). Towards Inquiry-based Professional Development in Environmental Education. In: Robottom, I. (ed.), Environmental Education: Practice and Possibility, Deakin University, Victoria.

Robottom, I. (1987). Towards Inquiry-based Professional Development in Environmental Education. In: Robottom, I. (ed.), Environmental Education: Practice and Possibility. Deakin University, Victoria.

Roche, M. (1973). Phenomenology, Language and the Social Sciences. London: Routledge and Kegan Paul.

Sartre, J.P. (1948). Existentialism and Humanism. Translation and Introduction by Philip Mairet. London: Methuen.

Smith, F. A, (1985). Metaphor for Literacy: Creating Worlds or Shunting Information? In: D.R. Olson, N. Torrance and A. Hildyard (Eds), Literacy, Language, and Meaning; the nature and consequences of reading and writing. Cambridge University Press, Cambridge.

Spiegelberg, H. (1960). The Phenomenological Movement: A Historical Introduction. The Hague: Martinus Nijhoff, 2 vols.

Spiegelberg, H. (1972). Phenomenology in Psychology and Psychiatry: A Historical Introduction. Evanston: Northwestern University Press.

Spiegelberg, H. (1975). Doing Phenomenology: Essays on and in Phenomenology. The Hague: Martinus Nijhoff.

Spreadley, J.P. (1980). Participant Observation. New York: Holt Rinehart and Winston.

Spreadley, J.P. (1979). The Ethnographic Interview. New York: Holt Rinehart and Winston.

Susman, G.I., Evered, R.D. (1978). An Assessment of the Scientific Merits of Action Research. Administrative Science Quarterly, 23.

Taylor, D., Dorsey-Gaines, C. (1988). Growing Up Literate: Learning from Inner-City Families. Portsmouth, NH: Heinemann.

Van Manen, M.J. (1975). An Exploration of Alternative Research Orientations in Social Education. Theory and Research in Social Education. 3(1), 1-28.

Van Manen, M.J. (1977). Linking Ways of Knowing with Ways of Being Practical. Curriculum Inquiry. 6, (3), 205-228.

Wals, A.E.J. (1991). Young Adolescents' Perceptions of Nature and Environmental Issues: Implications for Environmental Education. Dissertation, University of Michigan, School of Natural Resources, Ann Arbor, MI.

Wals, A.E.J., Beringer, A. and Stapp, W.B. (1990). Education in Action a Community Problem Solving Program for Schools. Journal for Environmental Education, 21(4), 13-20.

Wittengenstein, L. (1985). Philosophical Investigations. New York: Macmillan, Third Edition.

World Commission on Environment and Development. (1987). Our Common Future. Oxford University Press, Oxford.

ABOUT THE AUTHOR

Arjen E.J. Wals, Ph.D. in Environmental Education was done at the University of Michigan's School of Natural Resources, Ann Arbor, MI. He is a researcher at the Department of Agricultural Education at Wageningen Agricultural University in the Netherlands. He currently serves as Director/Networking for Caretakers of the Environment/International and is a member of the North American Commission on Environmental Education Research (NACEER). He also is a consultant to the Global Rivers Environmental Education Network (GREEN) which is based at the University of Michigan.

NARRATIVE INQUIRY AND CRITICAL PRAGMATISM: LIBERATING RESEARCH IN ENVIRONMENTAL EDUCATION

Noel Gough

Abstract

Narrative inquiry is a distinctive form of critical and methodic research in education concerned with the ways in which individuals and communities construct their experiences of the world. This essay outlines structural and poststructural approaches to narrative inquiry in environmental education, and offers *critical pragmatism* as an alternative to debating the theoretical vices and virtues of 'alternative research paradigms'. The essay also argues that discourses, practices and structures in environmental education should be defended or rejected by reference to moral rather than theoretic arguments. Two examples of the products of narrative inquiry are offered by way of illustration: (i) a deconstruction of the language of systems theory in an environmental studies course and (ii) suggestions for the construction of an alternative agenda for curriculum research and development in regard to climate change.

Introduction

It may be time for us to move beyond what Gage (1989) has called 'the paradigm wars' in educational research. While much of my own recent work has been focused directly on the analysis and criticism of alternative paradigms in curriculum and teaching (Gough 1987, 1989), I do not now believe that the concept of 'alternative paradigms' is a particularly fruitful focus for debate. In part, this is because the particular paradigms that are being contested are rarely conceptualised, either by their adherents or their critics, in ways that provide adequate substance for attack or defence. For example, in two contemporaneous reviews of educational research paradigms, Gage (1989) and Candy (1989) distinguish three approaches: (i) traditional/scientific (Gage) or positivistic (Candy), (ii) interpretivist (Gage) or interpretive (hermeneutic) (Candy) and (iii) critical. Their respective descriptions of each approach are similar, but it is not without significance that each writer gives the dominant paradigm a different name while choosing the same or similar names for the alternatives. Few educational researchers who work within a traditional/scientific paradigm (and who might be willing to accept that name for their practice) would consent to being stereotyped as positivistic. Indeed, positivism has for some time been something of a "straw-paradigm" (Phillips, 1983) and many attacks on examples of traditional/scientific research may have been misdirected. While there are many examples of such research activity that are deserving of strong criticism, their propensity for being labelled positivistic may be among the least significant of their vices.

Other versions of "the paradigm wars", such as those concerning the debate between <u>quantitative and qualitative research paradigms</u> (Salomon 1991: 10), may have degenerated to the level of trivial pursuits, not only because <u>quantitative</u> and <u>qualitative</u> are attributes of *data* rather than of paradigms as such, but also because the terms of the debate rarely transcend the language of the dominant paradigm. For example, Salomon argues that criteria such as validity, reliability and generalisability should be applied within all research paradigms whereas several self-described qualitative researchers suggest that these criteria are either 'overrated' (Van Maanen 1988) or should 'be given up as a goal of inquiry' (Guba and Lincoln 1989).

Both Gage and Candy suggest that the practical response to alternative research paradigms is to be eclectic — to accept what each of the different approaches offers. However, I share Ernest House's (1991: 2) view that none of the current versions of alternative research paradigms in education 'offers an adequate understanding of where we have been and where we should go' (although my reasons for this belief are somewhat different from his). At this time, it seems to me that 'narrative inquiry' *does* offer such an understanding while also providing a perspective on alternative research paradigms that has the potential to liberate environmental education from the more debilitating effects of 'the paradigm wars'.

A concise rationale for narrative inquiry in education is that

> humans are storytelling organisms who, individually and socially, lead storied lives. The study of narrative, therefore, is the study of the ways humans experience the world. This general notion translates into the view that education [and educational research] is the construction and reconstruction of personal and social stories; teachers and learners are storytellers and characters in their own and other's stories (Connelly and Clandinin 1990: 2).

In other words, educational knowledge is construed discursively — most of what we (collectively and individually) claim to 'know' in or about education comes from telling each other stories of educational experience. These stories are constituted in both the informal (anecdotes, gossip) and formalised discourses of our work (policy documents, textbooks, journal articles, research papers, conference presentations and so on). Narrative inquiry is concerned, in part, with analysis and criticism of these stories, the texts (oral and inscribed) in which they are embedded, and the myths and metaphors they employ.

In this essay I will first locate narrative inquiry within the broad spectrum of educational research activities. I will then describe some characteristic approaches to narrative inquiry with particular reference to the ways in which poststructural criticism may illuminate debates about alternative paradigms for research in environmental education. Finally, I will provide two brief examples of the products of narrative inquiry in environmental education.

Narrative inquiry as a form of critical and methodic research in education

The particular contribution that narrative inquiry can make to environmental education may be appreciated by considering the range of meanings which attach to the term 'research'. In common English 'research' signifies an 'endeavour to discover new or collate old facts etc. by scientific study of a subject, [or] course of critical investigation' (*Oxford English Dictionary*). But, in addition to these two meanings, 'research' is also the means by which a discipline or art develops, tests, and renews itself (Reid 1981: 1). These three meanings are complementary (and overlap) and there is a place for each kind of research activity within environmental education. But while environmental education clearly requires the production of relevant data (about learners, teachers, schools and their interrelationships with environment-related subject matters and so on), it also needs 'critical investigations' and modes of inquiry which contribute to the development and renewal of the discipline itself. Narrative inquiry not only exemplifies both of the latter approaches but also can be used to provide a critical perspective on the discursive authority of empirical studies.

Another way of locating narrative inquiry in a research continuum for environmental education is by considering three ways in which a given activity can be identified as 'research', namely, (i) by its adoption of a characteristic theoretical perspective, (ii) by its pursuit of a characteristic central question or problem, or (iii) by its adoption of a characteristic method.

Much research in education has been conceived and conducted within a theoretic paradigm similar to that which the social and behavioural 'sciences' borrowed from the natural sciences. This kind of research seeks to establish warranted propositional knowledge — often based on quantitative data — about teachers, learners, subject matters, schools, classrooms, curriculum plans and resources (and so on) and various interactions among them. Propositions that have been generated, verified and refined through such research have influenced the design of curricula and the content and methods of teacher education programs. This kind of research is commonplace in environmental education and, indeed, until relatively recently seems to have been the dominant approach to research in the field.

Other approaches to research in education have included inquiries which address questions of what should be taught and learned. Such approaches, which include various techniques of philosophical analysis, epistemological studies and so on, are explicitly directed toward a consideration of normative questions rather than empirical ones. While the literature of environmental education has always included discussions and debates about normative issues, these have not often been recognised as constituting or representing 'research' in environmental education.

177

Several recent approaches to research in education have emphasised the refinement of a method which might apply to any form of curricular or pedagogical work. Methodically defined research includes, for example, action research, reflective deliberation, some forms of curriculum history, 'critical pedagogy', *currere* (autobiographical curriculum inquiry) and narrative inquiry.

Methodically defined research is particularly appropriate to a conception of education as a practical (i.e., moral) art, but the scope of such research currently includes areas within both theoretical and practical disciplines. For example, within the natural sciences, the problems and subject matters of research areas such as radio astronomy or X-ray crystallography are delimited by characteristic techniques or methods and their research goals include the development and improvement of technique and method. In these cases the most valued outcome of research is propositional knowledge and this theoretical end tends to take precedence over the methodical means. In practical arts the main purpose of research may be the reconstruction of method through its engagement with appropriate subject matter. Method itself then becomes both an end and the means of research. Both kinds of methodical research are exemplified by literary critics. In so far as they are concerned with the *advancement* — rather than the routine practice — of their art, their major purpose is the establishment and defence of critical methods. But, whereas some critics see the development of method as a means of arriving at generalised propositions about writers, readers and texts, others focus their attention on the elaboration of the method itself which is to be the means by which the practical art goes about its business — the pursuit of unique understandings in unique works of literature.

Environmental education is different from literary criticism but there are significant parallels. As I have argued elsewhere (Gough 1990b, 1991ac), environmental education involves cultural as well as textual criticism and the development of criteria for such criticism is an appropriate subject for educational inquiry. Methodical research is also appropriate to the work of environmental educators who are concerned with elaborating the practical arts of environmental education — the self-reflective curricular and pedagogical arts which engage environmental educators in the pursuit of unique understandings in the unique circumstances of their practice.

Structural and poststructural approaches to narrative inquiry in environmental education

Narratives of environmental education are *constructions* — stories created by particular writers or speakers that are interpreted by particular readers or listeners (all of whom act within a social context) for purposes which may or may not be similar. The terms 'structural' and 'poststructural' are sometimes used to identify two critical methods for revealing the constructedness of stories.

Structuralists and poststructuralists share the view that the objects, elements and meanings that constitute our understandings of 'reality' are social constructions — they are not assumed to exist independently of human perception and activity. For example, semiotics (a structuralist discipline) is concerned with identifying and describing the codes and systems of signification with which we articulate experience and produce meaning. Poststructural inquiries are concerned, in part, with a refinement and critique of the kinds of stories that semioticians (and other structuralists) construct — stories which purport to describe and explain the structures of other stories (any study of a narrative construction is itself a narrative construction; narrative is thus both phenomenon and method in narrative inquiry). To paraphrase Jonathan Culler (1990: 4), poststructural criticism is concerned with the extent to which analyses of narrative constructions are caught up in the processes and mechanisms they are analysing. Poststructuralists are thus critical of the view that anyone can get 'outside' a cultural discourse or practice to describe its rules and norms. For example:

> any analysis of, say, the political forces in a society cannot situate itself outside of the realm of political forces; it is necessarily caught up in the processes, affected by the forces it is describing, and itself involves a political move or stance. So that one way to study the political forces at work would be to analyze the analyst's own stance and investigate how his or her analytical discourse is worked by the forces it is analyzing. That is the post-structuralist move.

> The analytic posture, then, is not one of scientific detachment but of intractable involvement. The problem that emerges here... is thus the problem of *metalanguage*: that the analytical system or set of categories does not offer a grounded perspective on the phenomena from the outside, but proves rather to be problematically caught up in the processes and functions of the phenomena that it is studying... Any metalanguage turns out to be more language, subject to the forces it claims to be analyzing... (Culler 1990: 4)

Another way of putting it is that structural thought seeks 'rationality, linearity, progress and control by discovering, developing, and inventing metanarratives,... that define rationality, linearity, progress and control' whereas poststructural thought is 'skeptical and incredulous about the possibility of such metanarratives' (Cherryholmes 1988: 11). Thus, for example, positivist science can be regarded as an attempt to write a metanarrative of science — a story or set of rules characterising positive knowledge. The positivist story attempted to make rules for other stories from its categorical distinctions between analytic and synthetic, linguistic and empirical, observation and theory, and so on. Poststructural thought questions whether *any* stories can (or should) be legitimated by reference to (or by being grounded in) other stories which are regarded as 'foundations' or 'first principles'. The poststructural position is that a metanarrative is just another narrative, a social agreement constructed by the participants in a particular 'conversation' — or, as Cherryholmes (1988: 12) puts it, metanarratives are as 'incomplete, time-bound, interest-relative, ideologically informed, and shaped by power' as any other narratives. This skepticism towards the authority of foundational discourses and 'grand theory' is culturally pervasive and equivalents to poststructural literary criticism can be found in postanalytic philosophy and in the postmodern movements of most arts, humanities and sciences.

For example, the positivist metanarrative has for the most part been abandoned by postmodern scientists — though not yet by many science educators. Indeed, the poststructural skepticism towards *all* metanarratives, including the positivist story, is very largely a product of developments in the physical sciences that began in the late nineteenth century. Postmodern science embraces the relatedness of the observer and the observed, the personal participation of the knower in all acts of understanding, the inseparability of organism and environment, and the ambiguities and paradoxes of a non-realistic, indeterminate, chaotic, quantum universe.

It does not seem unreasonable to suggest that environmental educators should adopt the incredulity towards metanarratives that characterises postmodern science. As Jean-Francois Lyotard (1984: xxiv) puts it: '[postmodern society] falls less within the province of a Newtonian anthropology (such as structuralism or systems theory) than a pragmatics of language particles'. Or, in the words of a poster I once saw in an English (language) classroom, 'the universe is not made of atoms — it is made of stories'.

Critical pragmatism and environmental ethics

It should be apparent by now that the term 'metanarrative' is in large part interchangeable with 'paradigm'. It should also be apparent that a poststructural perspective on 'the paradigm wars' in educational research does not privilege one paradigm over another but, rather, affirms the need for a critical pragmatism to be applied to all narratives. If we accept the possibility that there are no 'foundational' narratives to anchor our discourses and practices, then we must be prepared to consider carefully and critically the choices we make in constructing what we say and do, the standards and conventions which structure those choices, and their practical (i.e., moral) effects.

Critical pragmatism may be one way of liberating research in environmental education from the colonising discourses of the dominant culture, including the paradigms (attempted metanarratives) which presently dominate educational research. It does not, however, absolve us from the moral responsibility for negotiating social agreements about criteria for the conduct of environmental education, including criteria for the conduct of research in environmental education. In the present circumstances, it seems to me that it may be morally defensible to privilege two kinds of discourses in environmental education, not on the grounds of their 'foundational' status but on a critical consideration of their practical effects. One of these is the kind of 'oppositional consciousness' that has been explicated by a number of feminist postmodernists which privileges discourses constructed in opposition to those forged by the dominant culture. For example, Sandra Harding (1986: 193) sees a feminist postmodernist standpoint emerging from political struggles in opposition to "the longing for the 'one true story' that has been the psychic motor for Western science". Another discourse which environmental educators may wish to agree to privilege is that which seeks a postmodern reconceptualisation of environmental ethics. Such a discourse is also likely to be oppositional in the first instance, although some ecophilosophers are making commendable and constructive efforts to refine postmodern environmental ethics around such concepts as 'bioregional narrative' (Cheney 1989) and 'transpersonal ecology' (Fox 1990).

Oppositional discourses include those which deconstruct the dominant discursive formulations of environmental education — the narratives with which we construct our 'storied lives' as environmental educators. As Lawrence Durrell (1963) puts it:

> We live... lives based on selected fictions. Our view of reality is conditioned by our position in space and time — not by our personalities as we like to think. Thus every interpretation of reality is based on a unique position. Two paces east or west and the whole picture is changed.

The community of environmental educators owes its very existence to a particular interpretation of reality and poststructural criticism provides us with a method of evaluating the 'selected fictions' on which that view of reality is based — of examining the ways in which our perceptions of environmental problems and issues, and the narratives and texts we construct around them, are 'conditioned by our position in space and time'. A deconstruction of these narratives and texts (see Gough 1990ab, 1991ac) reveals that some of them can be regarded as *unsustainable fictions*. I am using 'fiction' here in the original sense of *fictio*, that is, something fashioned by a human agent. All narratives and texts are 'fictions' in this sense. When we label a story as 'non-fiction' we are not usually intending to deny that it was fashioned by a human but, rather, are asserting something about its 'truth' or warrant or its correspondence with our taken-for-granted understandings of 'reality'. But, as noted above, the postmodern sense of 'truth' and 'reality' is that they are the 'agreed stories' of participants in particular discourses. Poststructural criticism leads me to suggest that such stories are only one narrative thread among the many that constitute the fabric of our 'storied lives' and critical pragmatism leads me to conclude that some of these stories, regardless of their agreed 'truth' or warrant, are less defensible and less sustainable than others.

Many of the formalised narratives of environmental education (such as conservation strategies, curriculum policies, textbooks and the like) are, in a superficial sense, components of an oppositional discourse, since they often have been constructed in response to perceived structural dysfunctions of modern societies (such as the forms of economic production and development which have resulted in land degradation and air pollution). But they are only superficially oppositional because they also are embodiments of the dysfunctions they oppose. The dominant narratives of environmental education continue to produce and reproduce the kinds of metaphors and myths that support a 'scientific detachment' from nature rather than 'intractable involvement' in it. There is nothing particularly surprising about this: the cultural 'successes' of modern science are founded on the heuristic value of separating matters of 'objective' fact from matters of 'subjective' value. In poststructural terms, the narratives of environmental education are legitimated by reference to the metanarrative of modern science. But we can no longer take it for granted that what was once good for modern science is necessarily good for the postmodern planet.

Many narratives of environmental education embody a conception of the earth as an object of instrumental value. For example, the metaphorical language of texts dealing with such subject matters as environmental management and resources conservation constructs an image of the earth as a silo of resources, an archive of our heritage, a laboratory in which to make discoveries, a gymnasium in which to exercise, a recreational amenity, and so on. Much environmental education is concerned with protecting the earth's instrumental value through promoting the recycling of resources, reversing arable land degradation and so on, often by reference to the instrumentalist slogan of 'conservation for sustainable [economic] development'. Such slogans are part of the 'conventional wisdom' of environmental education which poststructual analysis and criticism seeks to deconstruct.

For example, *Our Common Future* (World Commission on Environment and Development 1987) has attained almost biblical status among many environmental educators but it is riddled with modernist assumptions emphasising order, accountability, systematisation, rationalisation, expertise, specialisation, linear development and control. *Our Common Future* takes ideological positions (such as commitments to efficiency, control, manipulation, materialism, instrumentalism and utilitarianism) while tacitly denying ideology in its surface rhetoric of 'scientific detachment'. It offers advice about correcting practice that reinforces present practice (such as the application of systems theory to environmental research and management). It largely ignores the effects of power in shaping the discourses of environmental practice. Rather than blindly accepting and 'implementing' the recommendations of texts like *Our Common Future*, poststructural narrative inquiry would lead us to (i) structurally analyse the meanings of its words and discourses, (ii) locate its meanings from historical, political, economic, cultural and linguistic perspectives and (iii) illuminate, explore, analyse and criticise the categories of discourse, modes of expression, metaphors, argumentative styles, rules of evidence and literary allusions that, as a text, it values and celebrates.

We must also consider critically the environmental effects of modernist discourses. The global environmental problems which now seem to threaten the sustainability of life on earth can be seen as consequences of the cultivation in modern industrialised societies of stories in which the earth (or 'nature') is construed, and thus exploited, as an object of instrumental value. Criticism of these stories by educators (and not just environmental educators) is essential because they also include myths about how a person becomes 'cultivated' and the power arrangements through which some people assume cultural leadership and become, as it were, 'cultivators'.

> The cultivator, as artist or critic, like the scientist, has so often regarded nature as low, as threat, as transcended origin and therefore in need of conquest and domination. The cultivated subject is seen to be the mind grown above nature and in command of it, totally separate from the baseness of body.

> This discourse has self-evidently failed. Humanity has damaged its own ecosystem, its collective and interdependent body, through the alienation of self from a nature that is external, other. An ecology of survival extols neither a rationalist command of nature nor a romantic return to it — nature never went away — but a major reassessment of social and economic actions according to their effects on wellbeing within the biological and social ecology. If humanity is to survive, we must recognise that there is no 'outside' from which to speak or act; we must gain a new normative matrix for the conception and production of the world. Survival is the one universal value that transcends the proclamation of difference (Fry and Willis 1989: 230-1).

Modern science has provided many solutions to technical problems of survival — we have abundant technical knowledge ('know-how') of the ways in which humans can sustain a functional and adaptive relationship with the earth. But the stories which tell us *how* to survive rarely address questions of *why* the earth and its inhabitants should survive — they lack the conceptual systems and signifiers from which we might be able to construct meanings, purposes and values for survival. This may be because we have allowed our linguistic tools to limit our creative and critical imaginations. Abraham Maslow is attributed with the aphorism which suggests that 'if the only tool you have is a hammer, you tend to treat everything as if it were a nail.' Narrative inquiry, poststructural criticism and critical pragmatism help us to expose the limitations of our linguistic 'hammers' and to seek new or renewed conceptions of the tools with which we construct meaning and the purposes to which they might be put.

Examples of narrative inquiry in environmental education

The following examples are drawn from my own work as a teacher educator and curriculum scholar. Neither of these investigations is 'complete' (nor are they completely separable from one another), but each represents a characteristic dimension of the continuing process of refining the concepts and methods of narrative inquiry while at the same time using them to reflect critically on the discourses and practices of environmental education in which I participate. Each of the following examples is itself a narrative, a work-in-progress story that my inquiries have led me to construct as a contribution to the deconstruction of unsustainable fictions in environmental education and/or the reconstruction of more sustainable stories of human interrelationships with the earth. Each story was constructed for a specific purpose and a specific audience.

A deconstruction of the language of systems theory with particular reference to environmental studies in the Victorian Certificate of Education

This product of narrative inquiry is a response to the ways in which systems theory is treated in course materials developed for teachers and students in Victoria, Australia. The inquiry examined both the discursive formulation of systems theory in general and its representation in specific course materials. It was first published in a teachers' journal (Gough 1991b) and its intended audience comprises teachers of the subject Environmental Studies in the Victorian Certificate of Education (VCE) and officers of the Victorian Curriculum and Assessment Board (VCAB) which supervises post-compulsory secondary education in the state of Victoria. It exemplifies poststructural criticism (in its deconstruction of the grammar and metaphors of systems theory and in its investigation of the effects of history and power on the shaping of a discourse) and critical pragmatism (in its concern for the moral *effects* of privileging the discourse of systems theory in Environmental Studies).

In both the study design (VCAB 1991) and the CDSM (course development support material, VCAB 1990) for VCE Environmental Studies, systems models are presented as useful and effective tools or techniques for organising, analysing and presenting information in environmental investigations. A systems model can be useful and effective for some purposes — but so can chainsaws, computers, in-vitro fertilization and electronic share trading. Assumptions about the usefulness and effectiveness of tools and techniques often are made with three kinds of questions being unasked and unanswered. These are questions about:

- the *moral purposes* (as distinct from technical purposes) of using the tool or technique
- the actual or possible *harmful effects* (which may be unintended) of using the tool or technique and
- the *limitations* of the tool or technique for achieving the ends it is designed to achieve.

If we explore these sorts of questions with respect to systems models then the answers that emerge suggest that we should not be too enthusiastic about using them to illuminate environmental problems or issues. A systems model is *one* way of simplifying, ordering and organising environmental data but there may be some severe limitations to its value and usefulness and some seriously undesirable consequences of using it. I will illustrate the limitations and harmful effects of applying systems theory by reference to the 'Himalayan ecology' example of a systems model presented in the 1990 CDSM. This example constructs a particular view of the nature and origins of environmental problems in the Himalaya which may be misleading to teachers and students.

Systems theory has arisen from good intentions: as the CDSM (VCAB 1990: 5) puts it, 'the holistic approach of Environmental Studies develops the view that life on Earth must be investigated in terms of the linkages between the atmosphere, ocean, soils and biota'. Systems models clearly are intended to draw attention to (i) *interrelationships* between elements of environments and (ii) *holistic* tendencies in nature. But systems theory in practice works against these good intentions by adopting atomistic schemes of classification and categorisation to name, describe and characterise environmental qualities. This is because systems models fail to break free from the restrictions imposed by (i) the English language itself and (ii) the language and traditions of the natural sciences in modern Western industrial societies.

The grammar of environmental interpretation

The restrictions that the English language places on understanding the relational and holistic qualities of environments can be appreciated by comparing it with the ways in which other languages construct environmental understandings. For example, Watson (1989) describes an incident in which two Australian girls were asked to describe what they saw in a photograph. One girl was a native speaker of English and said: 'canoes are lying on a beach'. The other girl, a native speaker of Yolngu (northeast Arnhemland), said: *'rangi-ngura nyeka lipalipa'* (literally, 'beach-on staying canoe').

In the English sentence, 'canoes' is the subject and 'are lying on a beach' is the predicate. Subjects in English are often *objects* that are characterised as being separate in space. In the Yolngu sentence, the subject is *rangi-ngura* — a spatial relation ('beach-on-ness') between elements of the world. Each language emphasizes different aspects of the world. In English, we focus on separate things in nature and make them the subjects of sentences. References to interrelationships are usually confined to the predicate. In Yolngu, the subject of a sentence both names the thing and points to its relatedness. That is, Yolngu speakers start with the view that the world is a related whole and construct sentences which focus on particular relationships.

The conventions of Indo-European languages dispose us to isolate subject (which usually is a bounded and spatially separate object) from predicate, actor from action, or things from relations among things:

> By these more or less distinct terms we ascribe a semifictitious isolation to parts of experience. English terms, like 'sky, hill, swamp', persuade us to regard some elusive aspect of nature's endless variety as a distinct thing, almost like a table or chair. Thus, English and similar tongues lead us to think of the universe as a collection of rather distinct objects and events corresponding to words... The real question is: What do different languages do, not with these artificially isolated objects but with the flowing face of nature in its motion, color, and changing form; with clouds, beaches, and yonder flight of birds? For, as goes our segmentation of the face of nature, so goes our physics of the Cosmos. (Whorf 1956: 240-1)

Systems models may have the effects that this passage outlines: they encourage us to see environments as collections of distinct objects and phenomena. In a systems model the qualities that are identified as 'inputs', 'processes' and 'outputs' are *objectified* — that is, they are treated like objects and given names which isolate them from other qualities. The difficulty is that we do not seem to be aware of the artifice: we talk and write as though names, symbols and numbers represent and signify the world 'as it is'.

Thus, the *grammar* of the English language encourages us to view environments atomistically rather than holistically, and systems models reinforce that tendency. But grammar is not the only aspect of language that shapes our understandings of reality, nature and human nature. *Metaphor* is also very important in signifying the meanings we give to the objects and events we observe and describe.

Metaphors and nature

Prior to the modern era, humans acknowledged their interdependence with the earth through metaphors of kinship. It is a recurring theme in Australian Aborigines' stories that 'earth just like mother and father and brother of you' (Neidjie 1990). Similarly, native American aesthetics and spirituality are centred on honoring propriety in one's relationships, not only with human kin but with 'the supernaturals, spirit people, animal people of all varieties, the thunders, snows, rains, rivers, lakes, hills, mountains, fire, water, rock, and plants [which] are perceived to be members of one's community' (Allen 1990: 10-11). In Western societies this sense of kinship gradually contracted to the patriarchal concept of 'Mother Nature' — an all-giving, ever-providing presence in the background (Plumwood 1990). In the Christian Middle Ages, nature was constructed metaphorically as a text in which to read God's purposes. As Shakespeare put it (*As You Like It*, II, 1: 12), there were 'books in the running brooks, sermons in stones' and meditation on nature was recognised as an act of devotion. The interpretation of 'nature's text' by the great landscape painters and pastoral poets of the eighteenth and nineteenth centuries enshrined places like the English Lakes District as sacred sites in British culture. The popularity of these painters and poets did not only arise from their technical talents but also from a social agreement about the meanings of art and landscape in a time when there still seemed to be a seamless and educative relationship between nature and people. But in the language of modern science nature has no powers to instruct because nature is no longer constructed metaphorically as kin, mother or text but, rather, as a machine.

The metaphorical language used by the founders of modern science was such as to 'denude the mystique of mother earth in order to open up her orifices to exploitation by commerce' (Curry Jansen 1990: 237). Francis Bacon called nature a 'bride', a 'mistress', and a 'common harlot' — people whom men treat very differently from a 'mother' (Merchant 1980). 'Entering a mother's womb and robbing it of its hidden treasures of gold, silver, iron, and coal is a very different act than seducing or even ravaging a sexual consort or "object". The two acts carry different cultural connotations and value orientations, and are accompanied by different social rituals and interdictions' (Curry Jansen 1990: 239). Other men of The Royal Society rendered nature lifeless: nature was 'a great pregnant automaton' to Robert Boyle and a 'world machine' to Isaac Newton. This renaming of nature supplanted a humanistic natural philosophy with the mechanistic worldview of detached scientific reasoning and ultimately paved the way for the development of capitalism. As Curry Jansen (1990: 9) says, 'how we name nature affects the way we treat it (or her): how we organize our adaptive efforts, how we use resources, how we intervene in and transform natural processes, and how we relate to other species, races, and genders'.

Names are not inherent in nature. They are an imposition of human minds. Naming an object or an event is not just a matter of labelling distinctions that 'really' exist. A name constructs the illusion that what has been named is genuinely distinguishable from all else. In creating these distinctions, we can easily lose sight of the seamlessness of that which is signified by words and abstractions. To think of 'forests', 'scrub' and 'grasslands' as bounded and spatially separate objects leads many well-intentioned people to the naïve belief that a rainforest can be conserved by putting a fence around some trees.

<u>Distortions imposed by systems models</u>

European languages are very hospitable to an atomistic perspective on nature and to the physics and mathematics of Newton, Descartes and their intellectual heirs, who portrayed the universe as a collection of 'artificially isolated objects' and dualisms. The image of the world that modern science constructs from these objects and dualisms is a machine of structures and systems, with sharp lines drawn around detachable parts with distinct names. Systems models do much the same thing: they codify environments in terms of dualisms such as biotic versus abiotic, inputs versus outputs, and positive feedback versus negative feedback. This is the language of machines and cybernetics. Systems models perpetuate Newton's 'world machine' by reinforcing the view that environmental systems are metaphorically equivalent to mechanical or cybernetic systems.

There are two dangers here. First, a systems model systematically distorts 'the face of nature' by leading us to think of environments as collections of distinct objects or object-like phenomena. Second, systems models distort the idea of human rationality. The systems model is the *only* 'tool of [environmental] analysis' that is legitimated by the VCE study design. There is a strong implicit message that systems models are not only the preferred way of organising and analysing data but also that systems theory is the preferred way of thinking rationally about environments. Rationality itself is thus identified with the kinds of logic that we build into mechanical or cybernetic systems. The contradiction inherent in so doing is neatly summarised by Harold Brown (1979: 148): 'The attempt by logical empiricists to identify rationality with algorithmic computability is somewhat strange, since it deems rational only those human acts which could, in principle, be carried out without the presence of a human being'.

Himalayan ecology in the VCE

To exemplify systems models, the CDSM (VCAB 1990: 4-7) outlines 'changes in the Himalayan ecology [which] may be described in terms of systems theory':

> A complex series of interactions between man [sic] and nature in the Himalayan region has many experts... speculating about the probable course of events in the area. The literature on the Himalayan 'eco-crisis' is replete with descriptions of rapidly expanding hill populations exploiting increasingly marginal land in an attempt to produce more food. As agriculture is extended so the forest cover is destroyed. Erosion and landslips decrease the productivity of soil, pasture and forest. There are all manner of self-reinforcing feedback loops in the system and traditional attempts by the farmer to better his [sic] lot or produce more food and fuel often lead to a worsening of the global situation in the hills and in the plains below. The lowlands are subjected to the silt and water runoff from the denuded land above, as well as all attendant effects of migration by hill people. Because of growing populations in the hills and plains, more and more people are displaced or otherwise affected by food and fuel shortages, changes in ground and surface water flows, and mass movements of land, water and people in the area. (Thompson et al 1986; quoted in VCAB 1990: 4)

This passage is followed by a diagram which purports to show 'how the systems view of the Himalayan montane environment may be summarised visually by the use of a systems model'. The diagram depicts 'solar energy, water, land, biota, culture' as discrete 'inputs' and 'biogeochemical cycles +

firewood gathering and agriculture' are depicted as 'processes'. As 'outputs' the diagram depicts (under the general rubric of 'degraded environment'): 'erosion, siltation, reduced food supply, soil loss, forest depletion' (VCAB 1990b: 5).

There are several ways in which this example of a systems model fails to encourage an holistic view of the Himalayan 'eco-crisis'. First, there is no attempt to explain how the hill populations came to be 'rapidly expanding' or how their problems of resource consumption are related to issues of resource consumption globally. The systems model presented in the CDSM artificially isolates the Himalayan 'eco-crisis' from the global political economy in which the Himalayan villagers' difficulties are situated. Second, the ecosystem elements identified in the model oversimplify many of the system's qualities. For example, in what sense is it meaningful to identify 'culture' as an 'input' to this system? What, in fact, does 'culture' *mean* here? Is 'culture' categorically comparable with 'solar energy' and 'water'? Doesn't 'culture' also permeate the environmental qualities identified as 'processes' and 'outputs'? Reducing the complexity and ambiguity of the concept of 'culture' to an entity that can be classified as an ecosystem 'input' is about as far from an 'holistic approach' to environmental understanding as anyone can get!

Representing Himalayan ecology as something that is metaphorically equivalent to a mechanical or cybernetic system suggests that it is like a machine that has broken down but that it can be fixed by a bit of tinkering with the parts. Thus, the model distracts our attention from both the causes of the Himalayan 'eco-crisis' and possible solutions to it because these are artificially excluded from the model's framework. Like many environmental problems in developing countries, the Himalayan 'eco-crisis' does not originate from overpopulation in that country but from overdevelopment and overconsumption in the West. In the Himalaya, the supply of wood and other fuel in many areas has been lost as a consequence of private and commercial 'adventure tourism', including Western trekkers and climbers whose resource demands are met at direct cost to the local people. Family and agrarian life in the Himalaya has been disrupted severely by tourists importing Western diseases and other forms of oppression and exploitation. Locals are employed as guides and porters at pitiful — but 'competitive' — wages for the dangerous work they undertake (see Tuting and Dixit 1986, Lea 1988). Possible solutions also lie outside the model's framework. There is nothing in the model's construction that signals the actions that could be taken in economically developed countries to satisfy the Himalayan people's needs to reforest, rehabilitate degraded soils, stabilise populations and develop economically.

There are many other criticisms that could be made of the Himalayan ecology example in the CDSM. But the main point is that *no* ecosystem functions independently of the global political economy. If systems models can move us closer to such a realisation, then well and good, but the atomistic, reductionist, mechanistic and scientistic language, concepts and procedures that are historically structured into systems theory would seem to work against, rather than for, a holistic approach to environmental studies.

Curriculum development and climate change

This product of narrative inquiry is more conjectural than the previous example, although it is based, in part, on empirical and critical studies. This narrative was constructed in response to the criteria which the Australian federal government's Greenhouse Information Program apply in selecting educational research and development projects for funding. These criteria reflect a 'traditional/scientific' approach to educational research. The audience for this story was a national conference of environmental educators on the theme 'Environmental Education and Climate Change'.

Much research on human adaptation to change focuses on people's responses to external circumstances. Both the circumstances and the responses are treated as 'objective' data and investigated by empirical-analytic ('scientific') methods. Thus, for example, social change tends to be explained by hypothesising and testing relationships between new technologies, demographic data, economic indices and other social and behavioural variables. In the case of climate change, emphasis is given to observed trends in the atmospheric composition of greenhouse gases and the ozone layer, on causal explanations for these trends, and on predictions about their environmental and social effects. As a possible consequence, much education about climate change seems to be based on the assumption that understanding environmental circumstances 'objectively' is of great importance in encouraging people to respond appropriately to greenhouse and ozone issues.

But human responses to change usually involve more subtle and subjective cultural influences, including values, interests and language. For example, changes in the composition and structure of families may have less to do with demographic variables than with new expectations and values (such as those which have arisen from the feminist critique of patriarchy in Western industrialised societies). Similarly, to understand the influences of anticipated climate change on the ways in which people think, behave and live their lives, we may need to look beyond phenomena like the greenhouse effect and people's immediate and superficial responses to its anticipated consequences. We may also need to examine the cultural perceptions, meanings and values that constitute people's subjective understandings of climate change and mediate their responses to it. Education for a critical understanding of climate change must therefore attend to these cultural perceptions, meanings and values.

Another important reason for attending to the cultural dimensions of climate change is to counterbalance (and, indeed, to subvert) the more common science-based approaches to environmental education. Scientific approaches tend to obscure the ways in which dominant cultural discourses and practices have contributed to these same problems. In effect, by reproducing modern industrialised societies' high status forms of knowledge (like science, technology and economics) in environmental education curricula, we exacerbate the very problems we are attempting to resolve. Thus, my purpose here is to outline some alternative approaches to curriculum research and development that may help us towards an improved understanding of the cultural determinants and manifestations of climate change and the educational problems which attend it.

Language and climate change

Many of the existing curriculum resources which deal with climate change are designed to generate awareness and understanding of the *environmental* aspects of greenhouse and ozone issues and their direct social consequences. But to understand the *personal* and *cultural* dimensions of these issues we need to analyse and critically evaluate the *language* of climate change, especially among young people. Such studies include analyses of the myths, metaphors, analogies and other language constructions that pervade the narratives and texts of popular media, curriculum and public information materials, classroom texts and discourses, and other cultural forms that engage young people (such as science fiction, children's television programs and so on). Particular attention should be given to evidence of changes in meaning over time and the extent to which transformations of meanings reflect cultural adaptations to climate change. It may also be useful to compare the meanings of climate change that are constructed in the dominant discourses of Australian and other western societies with those found in Aboriginal and other community languages. Such comparisons could illuminate distinctively Anglo-European attitudes and dispositions related to climate change.

Curriculum research and development in climate change should be designed to encourage teachers and learners to reflect critically and self-consciously on the language of climate change and the cultural meanings and values that this language reveals. Both teachers and learners need to be constructively critical of their own language usage and to be critical and creative interpreters of popular media and other curriculum materials and cultural resources. Teachers and learners should also be encouraged to undertake their own inquiries into such issues so that they may themselves become active cultural critics rather than passive consumers of cultural criticism.

The potential seriousness of the greenhouse effect may be better understood by learners interacting with cultural forms which speak directly to human emotions rather than those which use 'scientific' styles of inscription, narrative and reasoning. Recently, greenhouse-related issues have begun to infuse popular songs, novels, poetry, theatre and other visual and performing arts. But with few exceptions they are being used only in very restricted ways in greenhouse education programs. For example, it would not be unusual for an Australian teacher to use, say, a song by Midnight Oil (a popular music group), to motivate learning about the greenhouse effect or to 'reinforce' information about climate change. But it would be a rare teacher of science or environmental studies who engaged learners in critical explorations of the song as a cultural text in its right and who sought to elucidate the significance of the cultural meanings of the greenhouse effect for the production and appreciation of the song as a popular media text.

To put this distinction crudely, the more common pedagogical approach to the relationship between the greenhouse effect and a popular text that embodies greenhouse-related meanings is to ask: what can this text help learners to understand about the greenhouse effect? Less common, but possibly more rewarding, approaches include asking such questions as: how do the cultural meanings of the greenhouse effect inform this text? how does an improved understanding of the greenhouse effect help us to appreciate it? what further creative possibilities for the use of greenhouse-related meanings as a cultural resource are suggested by responses to the previous questions?

Cultural myths of climate change and their intertextual significance

Human experiences of climate and weather are socially constructed. The use of common climate-related words, phrases and figures of speech in everyday discourses contributes to the construction of persistent cultural myths, such as shared understandings about the meanings of 'bad' weather or a 'fine' day (these expressions are more obviously laden with cultural values than are descriptive meteorological terms like 'hot' or 'windy'). One very persistent myth is that changes in climate and weather occur independently of human action — hence the oft-repeated jest that 'everybody *talks* about the weather, but nobody *does* anything about it'. The publicity given to the greenhouse effect and other issues of climate change may be altering the nature and status of this myth.

For example, among the first six episodes of the children's cartoon video series, *Teenage Mutant Ninja Turtles* (monitored as part of an empirical classroom study; see Beavis and Gough 1991), two had plots in which the villains deliberately modified climatic conditions. In one of the stories, a 'weather satellite' produced violent storms (incidentally, this was achieved by setting the satellite's control to 'total chaos', an expression which itself suggests changes in cultural understandings of climate issues, since the concept of chaos has been popularised relatively recently and previously was not used widely in connection with weather). In another episode, energy was drawn from the sun into solar cells so as to induce rapid and severe global cooling. Dialogue in both episodes used variations on the conversational cliché quoted above. For example, after the 'weather satellite' had been destroyed by one of the turtles, another said to him, 'Hey, Leonardo! Everybody else *talks* about the weather, but you really *did* something about it!'

Such examples suggest a need for curriculum inquiry which explores how children relate their readings of popular media to their readings of curriculum materials and other information about climate change. The purpose of such research is to explore ways in which the language of climate change is entering the *intertextual* lives of learners. That is, how do young people's readings of curricular and media 'texts' dealing with greenhouse-related issues influence their readings of other texts (and vice versa)? Such inquiries would support the design of curriculum materials and teaching strategies that draw learners' self-critical attention to intertextual constructions that arise from their interpretations of greenhouse information and popular media.

The myths and meanings that are embedded in everyday language are persistent and resistant to change. We need to be able to identify and criticise culturally dysfunctional myths and meanings, such as elements of our language that signify climate and weather as 'acts of God' rather than as social constructions or phenomena susceptible to human agency. We might then be able to develop curriculum materials and strategies which encourage teachers and learners to reflect critically on such meanings and dispose them towards participating constructively in the 'cultural inventions' that may ameliorate their negative effects. We also need to be able to identify language elements in which constructive meanings are immanent. For example, a variety of popular discourses incorporate climate-related metaphors and analogies: administrators speak of 'organisational climate', angry people 'storm' out of rooms and popular songs have titles like 'Raining in my Heart'. The extent to which, say, greenhouse-related meanings are being used metaphorically in popular discourses may be an index of the 'cultural penetration' of greenhouse awareness. Discourse analysis of popular media can be conducted by quite young learners and has the potential to contribute culturally significant data concerning community awareness and understanding of climate change issues.

Conclusion

The above examples of narrative inquiry in environmental education illustrate, respectively, (i) the deconstruction and critique of a dominant discourse-practice in environmental education and (ii) the construction of an alternative agenda for curriculum research and development in environmental education. Many other examples could be quoted, such as the use by teacher education students of their own autobiographical writings as a focus for deconstructing and creatively reconstructing the personal and cultural stories of their interrelationships with the earth.

Environmental problems, regardless of whether they are seemingly localised (like the Himalayan 'eco-crisis') or globally pervasive (like climate change) are produced, reproduced and intensified by the ways in which people in modern industrialised societies experience and interact with the world — by the ways in which *we* live our 'storied lives'. To conceive of research in environmental education in terms of narrative inquiry is, therefore, to seek solutions to our problems where our problems lie.

References

Allen, P.G. (Ed.). (1989). Spider Woman's Granddaughters: Traditional Tales and Contemporary Writing by Native American Women. London: The Women's Press.

Beavis, C. and Gough, N. (1991). 'Worldviews and popular culture: What do they mean for how we teach?' In Cormack, P. (Ed.). Literacy: Making it Explicit, Making it Possible. Selected Papers from the 16th Australian Reading Conference. Carlton South: Australian Reading Association: 122-32.

Brown, H.I. (1979). Perception, Theory and Commitment: the New Philosophy of Science. Chicago: University of Chicago Press.

Candy, P. (1989). 'Alternative paradigms in educational research.' The Australian Educational Researcher, 16[3], 1-11.

Cheney, J. (1989). 'Postmodern environmental ethics: Ethics as bioregional narrative.' Environmental Ethics, 11(2), 117-34.

Cherryholmes, C. (1988). Power and Criticism: Poststructural Investigations in Education. New York: Teachers College Press.

Connelly , F.M. and Clandinin, D.J. (1990). 'Stories of experience and narrative inquiry.' Educational Researcher, 19(5), 2-14.

Culler, J. (1990). 'Fostering post-structuralist thinking.' Paper presented at the Annual Meeting of the American Educational Research Association, Boston USA, 16-20 April.

Curry Jansen, S. (1990). 'Is science a man? New feminist epistemologies and reconstructions of knowledge.' Theory and Society, 19. 235-46

Durrell, L. (1963). Balthazar. London: Faber and Faber.

Fox, W. (1990). Toward a Transpersonal Ecology: Developing New Foundations for Environmentalism. Boston: Shambhala.

Fry, T. and Willis, A. (1989). 'Criticism against the current.' Meanjin, 48(2), 223-40.

Gage, N. (1989). 'The paradigm wars and their aftermath: A "historical" sketch of research on teaching since 1989.' Educational Researcher, 18(7), 4-10.

Gough, N. (1987). 'Learning with environments: Towards an ecological paradigm for education.' In Robottom, I. (Ed.). Environmental Education: Practice and Possibility. Geelong: Deakin University Press: 49-67.

Gough, N. (1989). 'From epistemology to ecopolitics: Renewing a paradigm for curriculum.' Journal of Curriculum Studies, 21(3), 225-41.

Gough, N. (1990a). 'Renewing our mythic links with nature: Some arts of becoming ecopolitical in curriculum work.' Curriculum Perspectives, 10(2), 66-9.

Gough, N. (1990b). 'Healing the earth within us: Environmental education as cultural criticism.' Journal of Experiential Education, 13(3), 12-17.

Gough, N. (1991a). 'Narrative and nature: Unsustainable fictions in environmental education.' Australian Journal of Environmental Education, 7, 31-42.

Gough, N. (1991b). 'An abominable snow job: Systems models and the Himalayan "eco-crisis" in VCE [Victorian Certificate of Education] environmental studies.' Eingana October: 24-26.

Gough, N. (1991c). 'Coyote, crocodile, chaos and curriculum: Premodern lessons for postmodern learning.' Paper presented at the Annual conference of the North American Association for Environmental Education, St. Paul, Minnesota USA, 27 September-2 October.

Gough, N. (1991d). 'Curriculum development and climate change: The contribution of narrative inquiry.' Paper prepared for Environmental Education and Climate Change: A National Conference, Brisbane 28-29 September.

Guba, E.G. and Lincoln, Y.S. (1989). Personal Communication. Beverly Hills: CA: Sage.

Harding, S. (1986). The Science Question in Feminism. Ithaca: Cornell University Press.

House. E.   (1991). 'Realism in research' Educational Researcher. 20 (6), 4-9.

Lea, J. (1988). Tourism and Development in the Third World. London: Routledge.

Lyotard, J-F. (1984). The Postmodern Condition: A Report on Knowledge. Minneapolis: University of Minnesota Press.

Merchant, C. 1980. The Death of Nature: Women, Ecology and the Scientific Revolution. New York: Harper and Row.

Neidjie, B. (1990). Story About Feeling. Broome: Magabala Books.

Phillips, D. 1983. 'After the wake: Postpositivistic educational thought.' Educational Researcher. 13(5), 4-12.

Plumwood, V. (1990). 'Gaia and greenhouse: How helpful is the use of feminine imagery for nature?' In Dyer, K. and Young, J. (Eds.). Changing Directions: The Proceedings of the Ecopolitics IV Conference. Adelaide: Graduate Centre for Environmental Studies, University of Adelaide.

Reid, W. A. (1981). 'The practical, the theoretic, and the conduct of curriculum research'. Paper presented at the Annual Meeting of the American Educational Research Association, Los Angeles USA.

Salomon, G. (1991). 'Transcending the qualitative-quantitative debate: The analytic and systemic approaches to educational research. Educational Researcher, 20(6), 10-18.

Tuting, L. and Dixit, K. (Eds.). (1986). Bikas-binas? Development-destruction? The change of life and environment of the Himalaya. Munich: Geobuch.

Van Maanen, J. (1988). Tales of the Field: On Writing Ethnography. Chicago: University of Chicago Press.

Victorian Curriculum and Assessment Board. (1991). Environmental Studies Study Design. Melbourne: Victorian Curriculum and Assessment Board.

Victorian Curriculum and Assessment Board. (1990). Environmental Studies Course Development Support Material. Melbourne: Victorian Curriculum and Assessment Board.

Watson, H. et al. (1989). Singing the Land, Signing the Land. Geelong: Deakin University.

Whorf, B.L. (1956). Language, Thought, and Reality. New York: Wiley

World Commission on Environment and Development. (1987). Our Common Future. Oxford: Oxford University Press.

ABOUT THE AUTHOR

Noel Gough is a senior lecturer in the Department of Curriculum and Teaching at Victoria College, 662 Blackburn Road, Clayton Victoria 3168, Australia, where he teaches and conducts research in curriculum studies, environmental education and futures study. He is the editor (Australasia) of the Journal of Curriculum Studies and a member of the editorial board of the Australian Journal of Environmental Education. He has been a member of the Executive Committees of the Australian Teacher Education Association and the Australian Association for Environmental Education. He is currently the convenor of the Futures Study Network of the Australian Curriculum Studies Association and director of the Narrative Inquiry in Teacher Education project at Victoria College.

THE NEW GENERATION OF ENVIRONMENTAL EDUCATION FOCUS ON DEMOCRACY AS PART OF AN ALTERNATIVE PARADIGM

Søren   Breiting

Abstract

Environmental concepts are now in a different generation. This new generation uses democracy as a factor in this alternative paradigm. This paper compares characteristics of former versions of environmental education with a new generation of environmental education.

Introduction

We know from our work in Denmark that students working with a heavy emphasis on nature investigations often will have difficulties in attaining the complexity of environmental issues. Often they will focus on an imaginary conflict between nature and people at the cost of focusing on the central social conflicts between interests of people involved in the solution of environmental issues.

Let me present a comparison between "the new generation of environmental education" and some former versions of environmental education. This overview summarizes in an international perspective the development of environmental education, changing the focus of study from nature-study to investigating environmental issues as community issues. This development shall be in full agreement with the Brundtland-report on Development and Environment.   In reality it is not just a quantitative change in the understanding of environmental education but a qualitative step towards a new paradigm much more in accordance with the aim of environmental education.   As I see it, there are, during these past years, examples of environmental education from the new generation which have not yet gotten rid of all the characteristics of former versions of environmental education.

Former Versions of E.E.	The New Generation of E.E.
Goal:	Goal:
Behaviour modification	Action qualification
Characteristic aspects:	Characteristic aspects:
We (environmentalists + educators) know the solution to E.E. issues	All people should be involved in decisions about the best solutions

Former Versions of E.E.	The New Generation of E.E.
Leadership	Democratic participation
Preserving sites for conservation	Creating sites for conservation
We must stop/delay the development The past as the measure of our activities today	There are many possible directions for development Thoughts of "Utopia"
Looking for harmony with nature (the concept "Nature in balance")	Looking for harmony with our descendants
Intrinsic values in nature	Our values concerning the best way of using the World including nature
Environmental ethics	Ethics concerning proper behaviour against other people now and in the future
Argument for preservation: We feel sorry for the animals	Argument: We feel sorry for the future generations of human beings, who might miss the animals
Alter Nature as little as possible	Don't make irreversible changes in nature
The human communities and Nature.	Human-nature relationships as inseparable
Natural science as the main subject matter in E.E.	The social sciences and humanities as the main subject matter in E.E.
Focusing on nature ecology (The household of Nature)	Focusing on human ecology (Mans' householding with the resources of the World)
Nature experience is central in E.E.	Community experience is central in E.E.
The concept of (human) health is not prominent in E.E.	The concept of health is very prominent in E.E.
Balancing the quality of human life and the quality of the environment	Balancing the needs of present generations to the needs of the future generations
Human needs as a factual concept	Human needs as a normative concept

Former Versions of E.E.	The New Generation of E.E.
Sustainable use as a nature defined limit	Sustainable use as a man created measurement of what <u>we</u> judge as proper use in the light of use in the future
Focusing on different values	Focusing on conflicting interests/social conflicts
No emphasis on equality between people	Much emphasis on equality between people

I hope that it is possible through this short exposition to get an overview of what is regarded as the new generation of environmental education.

One of the central topics for discussion about the new generation of environmental education is the distinction between nature ecology and human ecology. I know the term "human ecology" is a loaded term which covers a lot of different areas. Therefore it is important to point out that here it is regarded in the meaning "Our human household with nature". Therefore it isn't a biological research area but an interdisciplinary one where a lot of research areas can be useful, but never adequate by themselves. What is most important is that we can't go to any scientific discipline and get the answers to our question: "What is the right way to manage our household with nature/natural resources?" We have to decide for ourselves, taking into consideration the needs and wishes of future human generations and people in other parts of the World now, taking into consideration the needs of other people in our own community today.

But because human ecology deals with our householding with nature we can get one basic answer: "Don't make any irreversible changes in nature!" And that should be a guiding star for all human activity at all times.

Now I turn to the use of the phrase: "harmony with nature". Formulations about harmony with nature can be exemplified by the editorial of The IUCN-Bulletin from March, 1991. Here it is argued that ".....to achieve an enduring harmony between humanity and nature...." and stated that "....people and natural resources may be on a collision course...."

Couldn't we argue more logically by saying "...to achieve an enduring harmony between people living today and the future generations"? and state that "today's use of natural resources is on a collision course with the next generations' demands of natural resources?". You may say "Oh, that's different formulations only!" Maybe, but I don't think so. That is why I talk about a new paradigm for research in environmental education and "The new generation of environmental education."

References

Andersen, Annemarie Møller, Søren Breiting & Kirsten Nielsen. (1990). The Nature Excursion - A Promoter or a Problem in Environmental Education in: Report from "International Symposium on Field work in the Sciences, Westerbork - The Netherlands, April 22.-27. 1990. Jacques van Trommel (ed.), Institute for Curriculum Development (SLO), Enschede.

Breiting, Søren. (Juni 8. - 10., 1988). Sustainable development and the ideological foundation of Environmental Education. P. 40-43 in Sustainable development - learning for tomorrow's World. Report from International Conference on Environmental Education, Bø, Telemark. Telemark Distriktshøgskole. Bø, Norway.

Christensen, Christian U. (1988). Environmental Education in Denmark. p. 4-40 in Environmental Education. International Contributions. (Eds. Christian U.Christensen and Kirsten Nielsen. Proceedings from the Research center for Environmental and Health Education no. 5. The Royal Danish School of Educational Studies, Copenhagen.

Jensen, Bjarne Bruun. (1988). Naturen har værdi! (Nature has a Value!), p. 10-29 in: J.Christensen (ed.): Natur og moral. Arbejdspapirer fra Nordisk Sommeruniversitet (NSU) nr. 27, Aalborg. (In Danish).

Thompson, Janna. (1990). A Refutation of Environmental Ethics. Environmental Ethics, 12,147-160.

World Commision on Environment and Development. (1987). (The Brundtland-report) Our Common Future, Oxford University Press.

SHEDDING SOME LIGHT: EXAMPLES OF ENVIRONMENTAL EDUCATION RESEARCH

GOALS AND CONFLICTS IN UNIVERSITY-BASED ENVIRONMENTAL EDUCATION CENTERS: A CASE STUDY

Jackie Palmer

Abstract

In 1986, a survey was sent to the directors of fourteen university-based environmental education centers that cooperatively form a network organized and supported by the Tennessee Valley Authority. Center directors were asked to respond to eleven open-ended questions. Results of the survey were compiled and disseminated by TVA in 1989 as "Ten Steps to a Successful Center." The Ten Steps have since been adopted by the National Network for Environmental Education that is now gaining membership in the U.S. This study takes the Ten Steps and applies them to one of the TVA network centers, the Center for Environmental/Energy Education at Memphis State University in Memphis, Tennessee. Using a blend of quantitative, qualitative and historical research methods, it analyzes the Memphis State center and demonstrates how the use of alternative research paradigms can reveal information not possible through the sole use of traditional qualitative methods (i.e., the open-ended survey). The study reveals that while the Ten Steps offer good general suggestions to follow, they lack comprehensiveness as a model. In particular, they fail to account for conflict. A list of lessons learned from the experiences of the Memphis State center adds new dimensions to the Ten Steps and provides a more accurate portrayal of what is involved in establishing a successful environmental education center within a university.

Introduction

With rising concern over environmental problems in the early 1970s, representatives from the Tennessee Valley Authority (TVA) conducted a geographic and demographic analysis of the Tennessee Valley and found that a network of seventeen environmental education (EE) centers would allow all citizens within the Tennessee Valley to be located within fifty miles of a source of environmental information (Ambry, 1985). Using recommendations made by state, national and global organizations, TVA designed a strategy for working with universities in the Tennessee Valley.[1] Between 1977 and 1989, TVA established fourteen university-based and two non-university-based centers.

Each of the TVA centers has four primary functions: 1) teacher training, 2) program development, 3) regional service, and 4) research (Hodges & Judy, 1989). Teacher training may supplement regular university training or may involve on-site in-service programs or special teacher workshops. Program development is most often regionally oriented, although network

---

[1] The National Environmental Policy Act of 1969, the Environmental Education Act of 1970, UNESCO Conferences in Stockholm (1972) and Belgrade (1975), the Intergovernmental Environmental Education Conference at Tbilisi in 1977 and recommendations published by the Kentucky State Department of Education pertaining to environmental education.

centers have cooperated on several joint curriculum development projects. Often practitioners, teachers, and students participate in the development of a program, which is then delivered to other network centers (and thus to local educators) throughout the region. Hence, the overall network promotes local development and regional use of educational programs and materials. Regional services include hosting public meetings; providing speakers or presenters for conferences, classrooms, or community meetings; consultation services; curriculum and technical assistance; newsletter networking; and other outreach programs. Research projects may be done in-house or contracted from outside agencies. Examples include validation of educational materials, field testing of new products, and testing for impact and knowledge resulting from programs.

In 1986, the EE center at Murray State University in Kentucky contracted with TVA to obtain information from center directors for developing a Guide for Center Development (Cleminson, 1986). The survey included eleven open-ended questions through which TVA center directors were asked to evaluate their centers. The results were compiled, and in March of 1989, TVA presented Ten Steps for a Successful Center in a report entitled "Fundamentals of Environmental Education" (Hodges & Judy, 1989). These steps have since been adopted by the National Environmental Education Network, which hopes to achieve the same cooperative spirit exhibited by the TVA network. The steps are intended to guide interested persons in establishing new university-based EE centers that would qualify for membership in the national network. However, they also provide a framework for analyzing the success of a mature center—Memphis State University's (MSU's) Center for Environmental/Energy Education (CEEE).

Research Purpose

This study explores an urban university-based EE center linked with a coordinated regional and national network. It documents key elements in the center's formation and examines the extent to which TVA's Ten Steps for a Successful Center reflect the development and the trials of a particular center.

Methodology

A blend of quantitative, qualitative and historical research methods were applied in this study. Quantitative methods were used to gain a precise accounting of

1) specified values that could be used to determine budgetary and activity trends over time and

2) characteristics and preferences of people impacted by the CEEE.

Historical methods were used to establish chronological time frames and to confirm information elicited via qualitative means. Systematic reviews were conducted of all center correspondence files, newsletters, MSU/TVA contractual agreements, and Quarterly/Biannual reports to TVA.

Qualitative methods were used to explore operation and evolution of the CEEE. From September of 1988 through August of 1990, the researcher was a participant observer in the role of Associate Director of the Memphis State CEEE. As Fetterman (1989) noted, "Participant observation combines participation in the lives of the people under study with maintenance of a professional distance that allows adequate observation and recording of data... [and] helps the researcher internalize the basic beliefs, fears, hopes, and expectations of the people under study" (p. 45). Participant observation involves more than just data collection and leans towards action research as described by Wals (1990). Action research "actively seek[s] to understand as well as to improve the... community [under study] through simultaneous action and reflection with all parties involved" (p. 12). As suggested by Wals, the emphasis is placed on "documenting and describing human experience and intentions...; interpreting these with all involved participants; relating the results with the foundations, goals and objectives of EE; and discussing ways to adjust the curriculum and classroom practice as a result of newly obtained insights" (p. 12). EE research, then, attempts to reveal whether or not the project and the structure of the experience provided for qualitative change.

Data Collection

Field notes and personal journals were kept by the participant observer during her affiliation with the CEEE through April, 1991. Field notes included detailed observations of space and presentations; videotaping; notes from meetings of environmental groups, teacher workshops and personal consultations; and transcriptions of taped proceedings and interviews. Personal journal entries were kept in computer data files. Twenty formal and ten informal interviews were conducted. Protocols of formal interviews were prepared. Questionnaires were mailed to subjects not able to be reached by telephone. In addition, all in-state recipients of the CEEE newsletter (numbering about 750) received surveys to determine characteristics of people impacted by the CEEE. Seventy-five surveys were returned and analyzed.

Data Analysis

Data analysis was primarily ethnographic in nature and involved systematic searches for patterns, discrepant events, and rival explanations. Triangulation, the "testing [of] one source of information against another to strip away alternative explanations and prove a hypothesis" was used to eliminate personal bias, "to test the quality of the information (and the person sharing it), to understand more completely the part an actor plays in the social drama, and ultimately to put the whole situation into perspective" (Fetterman, 1989, p. 89)

Contents of all CEEE files were examined, ordered chronologically, and then categorized. All interviews, field notes, journals and observations were entered into separate computer files. Categories of interest were determined. New computer files were constructed pertaining to each identified category.

Transcriptions of interviews, field notes, observations and journal entries were then coded according to the above categories. Coded information was transferred from each of the original files to the category files. Relevant information from correspondence files (including over one hundred letters and memoranda), financial records, quarterly reports, and other CEEE records was similarly catalogued, coded and entered into each category file. In this manner, triangulation of data was achieved. In many cases, information was corroborated from more than three sources. Category files were then analyzed using pattern matching, time series analysis (tracing the changes in the operation and function of the center over time), constant comparisons (comparing constantly while integrating categories and sub-categories in order to delimit theories) and further codification (see Yin, 1984).

Setting

The Center for Environmental/Energy Education (CEEE) is housed in the College of Education at Memphis State University (MSU), a comprehensive state-funded university geographically situated in the largest metropolitan area in Tennessee. The CEEE was established in 1979 in one of seven academic departments—the Department of Curriculum and Instruction—as a joint effort of the University and TVA. The MSU CEEE is now in its twelfth year of operation.

Ten Steps for a Successful Center: The CEEE Experience

The ten steps toward a successful EE center developed for TVA were, of course, not available when the MSU CEEE was established. In fact, they were determined, in part, from a retrospective accounting by all TVA center directors of their experiences at trying to establish and maintain successful EE centers. They represent, then, a composite picture of what is needed to achieve a successful center. As such, they can be viewed as criteria for determining the success (or lack thereof) of an EE center. In turn, the ability of an individual center to achieve the goals represented in the steps sheds light on the realism and practicability of those goals. This two-edged critical approach will be used to examine the experience of the CEEE at Memphis State University.

Step 1. A strong base of support should be established as early as possible and built upon as the center develops.

Based on the principle that a diversity of inputs, stakeholders, and funding sources usually produces a program that does not depend on a single entity, this guideline promotes cooperative efforts involving both the University and the community—a consortium of stakeholders.

University Support: Initially, the MSU CEEE had both financial and administrative support from the College of Education; however, initial efforts to include representatives from the College of Arts and Sciences in the planning and operation of the CEEE were unsuccessful. While scientists and non-education professors did attend a planning conference in 1978, they quickly realized that the CEEE would probably not enhance their opportunities for research (and thus for tenure and promotion) (Cleminson Interview, 8/3/90).

Broad-based support within the University was thus victimized by the trend of ranking research in content areas higher than community service, teaching, and pedagogically oriented research—a controversial, but widespread trend (see, for instance, Koshland, 1991; Shore, 1990; and Sykes, 1988). The CEEE, as it was originally planned, listed research as one of its primary functions, and no doubt, that was one reason it originally garnered strong administrative support (with TVA funding being another). However, there has been almost no bona fide research generated by the CEEE. Its primary function to date has been a dual one of teaching and community service.

Administrative support of the CEEE has also depended on the amount of money brought in by the center. The following graph depicts the financial history of the CEEE since its inception in 1979. The Column 2 line represents external funds contributed by Memphis State. The Column 3 line represents those contributed by sources other than Memphis State (primarily TVA). It is important to note, however, that the figures below are derived only from official MSU/TVA contracts. They do not, therefore, include either release time for the professor in charge of the center or space (and associated costs) for a resource library, yet both have been provided by MSU since the center began.

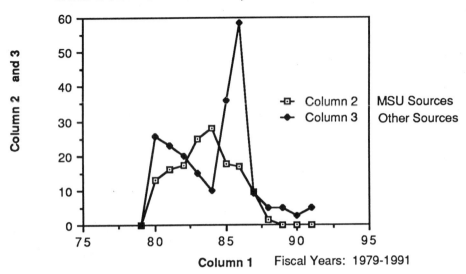

Figure 1. A Comparison of CEEE Contractual Funds Provided by Memphis State University and by External Sources

It is apparent from the graph that during the original five-year contract (1979 through 1984), funding support went as scheduled. According to a 1989 TVA report, "In the contractual agreements, TVA funds are matched by the University. TVA funds are generally committed on a reducing basis over a five year period. As TVA funds are reduced, university contributions are increased, allowing an average budget to be maintained" (Hodges & Judy, 1989, p. 17). Indeed, TVA did not withdraw its support at the end of the initial five-year period, but has continued to provide sufficient funds to keep the center functioning, though, in recent years, on a greatly reduced level. The University, on the other hand, increased its contributions over the five-year period, as agreed. Contrary to TVA's expectations, the University has not continued its financial support of the center. Once the original contractual agreement ended, the University withdrew most of its financial support. An evaluator predicted this in his 1985 report of the TVA network: "There are some problems within the network. As initial funding is expended, there is a possibility that certain universities may not be in a position to carry out their responsibilities, even though their original contracts with TVA required a pledge to support the EEE [environmental, energy education] centers beyond the five-year TVA supported startup period" (Ambry, 1985, p. iii).

In a network survey conducted in 1986, a center director discussed problems inherent in the contractual arrangements: "It is assumed in the contract that the University will provide continuous support for the center, with their effort increasing over a five-year period... however, many of the university's contributions are in services and personnel support, not dollars. Dollars determine what we are able to do" (Kirkland, 1986, p. 1).

According to the MSU Vice-President for Academic Affairs, centers are generally created from external funds "to meet a need, and once that need has been met, they can be dismantled rather quickly... [if] funding is no longer available" (Feisal Interview, 8/17/90, pp. 6-7). He further explained that in-depth evaluations should be conducted on centers every five years in order to determine whether or not they are still effectively meeting current needs. However, in those cases where centers continue to bring in outside funds, such evaluations are rarely conducted. "If there are outside funds for it, then somebody perceives there's a need" (p. 7).

Community Support: While it is clear that the CEEE has affected a significant number of teachers and students each year, there has been very little feedback from program participants. The CEEE secretary related her frustrations of sending out a survey in the summer of 1984: "I got despondent... because... out of 550, we received three responses" (Donnenwerth Interview, 11/7/89, p. 10). A subsequent survey (1989) received a better return rate (10%), but few agencies, businesses, or even schools have ever volunteered even verbal support of the CEEE, much less organizational or financial support.

A community leader revealed his enthusiasm for educational consultations and curriculum assistance received through the Center's efforts: "If it croaks out, that's the biggest waste of anything that's in Memphis" (Golden Interview, 10/31/90, p. 24). Yet this supporter was in no position to offer financial support; like most groups with an environmental focus, his was struggling for funds to survive. An effort was made in the Fall of 1989 to extend the services of the CEEE into the community by forming a Metropolitan Environmental Awareness Network (MEAN) ("CEEE," 1990). Such efforts to elicit community support of the CEEE have been successful only in that environmental groups have begun working together more, cooperating in such ventures as Earth Day activities and public meetings. Many groups have gained respectability among city and county government officials by their association with the CEEE. Yet, the cornerstone of a center's continued existence in a university setting, was absent. If a center is to garner community support that will help ensure its continued survival, it must establish and maintain ties with businesses, industries, or other sources that could afford to make regular, substantial monetary donations.

While there is no doubt that a strong basis of support from within the University will strengthen a center, it must not be forgotten that such support depends heavily on a center's ability to bring in a continuous supply of external funds. The very nature of centers (created to meet a societal need and dismantled once the need has been met) prevents them from becoming permanent institutions in the University setting. However, a strong research focus (resulting in *both* refereed publications and grant monies) could extend its lifetime indefinitely. The Memphis State CEEE has not had such a focus. Attempts to conduct center activities on a shoestring budget have met with constant frustrations. The CEEE director described his current role as "a maintenance effort" (Cleminson Interview,

8/3/90, p. 5). Moreover, time spent in conducting formal research and in mounting campaigns for external funding could only decrease the time and energy spent on community eduction and service. Thus, directors of university-based centers face a formidable double bind.

Step 2. <u>Assess the environmental education needs of the region</u>.

Before the CEEE was established, a TVA representative wrote, "It is important that someone within the University scope the need for... a center" (Paulk, 1978, p. 1). There is no indication, however, that a formal needs assessment was conducted before the center was opened. During the initial TVA planning conference, informal discussions were used to corroborate the feeling that, indeed, there was a need for the center.

A first attempt at eliciting feedback from Memphis area residents regarding EE needs did not come until 1984, and, even then, was unsuccessful (only seven surveys were returned). A second survey, distributed to about 750 people on the newsletter mailing list in the Fall of 1989, produced a better response (75 returns) that revealed a relatively strong, latter-day base on interest in the center.

The following pie chart illustrates the occupations of respondents, who were predominantly male (52.3%), educators (45%), between the ages of 36 and 50 (48.6%), holding a Masters Degree (63.5%).

Data from "OIKOS Reader Professions"

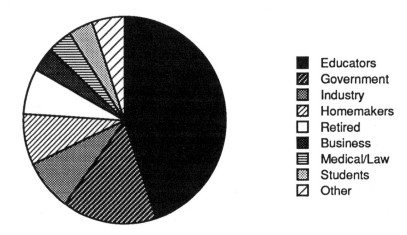

Figure 2. *OIKOS* Reader Professions

CEEE services that were found most useful included the newsletter (82.4%) and public meetings sponsored or co-sponsored by the CEEE (44.6%). 18.9% of respondents said they had used the resource library and 24.3% had referred it to others. 17.6% of respondents had attended teacher workshops and/or had received information from the CEEE by telephone.

The CEEE services respondents most wanted to see continued were the newsletter (78.5%), public meetings (66.2%), the distribution of free educational materials (66.2%), providing guest speakers (61.5%), the resource library (55.4%), local networking efforts (the MEAN) (52.3%), teacher in-service programs (48.5%), and teacher workshops (46.2%).

Despite the lack of funding from external sources, then, the CEEE demonstrated a base of grassroots support and a strong interest in continuing the center. The typical equation of university administrators—external funding equals worth of mission—should perhaps be reconsidered in light of such data. Unlike corporate and government sponsors of research projects, environmental awareness groups and local schools—the primary clients of EE centers—cannot afford to buy the services of the University.

Step 3.   Identify program strengths that already exist within the host institution.

Sites for EE centers were originally selected by TVA according to geographic and demographic distribution, but the placement of centers within universities has depended on interest expressed by individual professors and/or the existence of strong programs within the host institution. All but three of TVA's university-based EE centers are based in Colleges of Education;   the rest are in biology departments (Rhyne Interview, 8/16/90). When the CEEE was first established in 1979, the College of Education's Department of Curriculum and Instruction had a strong science education component—two full-time and several part-time faculty members (Cleminson Interview, 10/19/89).   Yet, no other departments on campus were involved in environmental programs at the time. In addition, cooperative efforts between departments and/or colleges were almost non-existent.

More recently, courses and programs have arisen with an environmental focus that could potentially strengthen the CEEE. For example, several departments have begun offering environmental courses (biology, chemistry, psychology, social studies) and non-university groups housed on campus (e.g., Clean Tennessee) began researching the possibilities of initiating a campus-wide paper recycling program. In 1989, a group of MSU faculty members and students formed an Environmental Research and Issues Forum, an interdisciplinary group concerned with sharing ideas and projects pertaining to environmental research. The group has provided a supportive environment for discussing on-going research efforts and eventually aims to secure collaborative funding for interdisciplinary research projects. In 1990, a student environmental action group was formed.

These programs complement the efforts of the CEEE, but have (at best) a tangential relationship to its activities. They may even compete for internal support. While it may be useful to identify program strengths within the institution, there are no guidelines offered as to what to do with the strengths once they have been identified. How does a center link into or draw upon the identified strengths? How can a potentially competitive relationship be modified to a cooperative one that could benefit the center? It would seem, therefore, that a center's program strengths depend more on the relationships that are constructed between the University, the sponsoring agency, and the EE center than on existing program strengths within the institution itself.

Step 4.   Form a program advisory board.

An eight-member CEEE Advisory Board was formed in 1980 to: "1) serve as an advisory body for the center to assure that proposed programs and the resource library are meeting the needs of the West Tennessee area, 2) assist in identifying available resources that can be utilized by the center, and 3) serve as a vehicle for communication between the educational institutions, service organizations/groups and business/industry participating in the center" ("CEEE's," 1981, p. 2). Included in the membership of the Board were MSU science and education professors, the Assistant Superintendents of both the city and county schools, a county environmental agency director, a local utility company president, and two area school teachers (one elementary, one junior high).

The CEEE Advisory Board had two meetings and was subsequently dismantled. According to the center director, "it soon became obvious that... the only attention they really gave us was when we called a meeting" (Cleminson Interview, 8/3/90, p. 23). Further, " ...advisory boards have a way of being helpful initially. Everyone says you should have one. But in order to maintain them and to secure attendance... it's a pull job" (p. 22). "It's time-consuming to operate" (p. 24). The director felt that since he was familiar with the EE field and was ultimately responsible for the success of the center, it was his job to make decisions regarding center activities: "My finger was on the pulse of what needed to be done" (p. 23). He seldom felt he needed assistance in making such decisions, although he has continued to consult people regarding specific projects, on an individual basis. He asks, "If... you can deal with it on an individual basis, why call everyone together?" (p. 24). Thus, in one sense, an Advisory Board represents just one more chore that keeps center personnel from carrying out its mission.

For the past few years, the CEEE has been operating strictly at a maintenance level. Without funds for program development or expansion, few important decisions need be made. When the need does arise, the director telephones a few friends, bounces a few ideas off them, and makes decisions based on the interchanges. While more efficient than trying to maintain an active Advisory Board, the system does not allow for building grassroots support. Only one person has really had a stake in the CEEE and its survival. Without an active Advisory Board, the center director has had to bear the responsibility of its successes and failures alone.

Step 5.   Seek to fund and maintain the center/cooperative through a broad set of sources.

According to a 1989 TVA report, "Each center markets its unique program delivery and program development capability. Funds are gathered from foundations, grants, and contracts with other organizations" (Hodges & Judy, 1989, p. 17). A director of another TVA EE network center stated, "The only means we have for survival is multiple funding" (Kirkland, 1986, p. 1). The CEEE director added, "Murray State had funding from thirteen or fifteen rural counties who all came together to provide environmental education programs. But, that placed the director every year in a brokering position... the director's job... depends upon his being able to convince several counties that they should provide some funds for his center " (Cleminson Interview, 8/3/90, pp. 11-12).

Since its inception, the CEEE has received about $143,900 from MSU, $204,600 from TVA, and $10,300 from additional sources (foundations, other universities and a private donation). There are, however, potential problems with multiple external funding. As the CEEE director explained, "with outside funding, your priorities are based on your funded purpose, and your funded purpose may not go hand-in-hand with those that were originally identified for the centers. So, your goals and your mission change based on what they're giving you the money to do" (Cleminson Interview, 10/19/89, p. 14).

The TVA Program Manager realizes both the importance of and impediments to securing outside funding. "The point... is that we continue to work together to try to secure enough money to keep the centers operating... But most of the funding, be it grants or NSF [National Science Foundation] funding, are provided on a three-year basis. It takes a lot of time... grant-finding... writing... some people don't have the time to do it" (Judy Interview, 4/11/90, p. 16). One of the TVA Program Manager's roles is to assist centers in identifying other funding sources; he has encouraged network centers to seek cooperative funding and supports their recent decision to form a consortium independent of TVA. The consortium would "provide the vehicle by which... centers can go after funding where association with TVA might be detrimental to their program" (Judy Interview, 4/11/90, p. 13).

The CEEE director is less sanguine about the multiple funding concept, feeling that most center directors have neither the time nor the staff support to seek out such funds. He asserts that TVA has a continued responsibility to support the network centers financially, a goal he suggests could be accomplished by abandoning TVA's long-range goals of establishing centers to reach every TVA citizen and of channeling all financial support into just a few centers. "I think they should... identify maybe six or eight universities to have centers at, not twelve or eighteen. There simply is not enough to go around" (Cleminson Interview, 10/19/89, p. 10). The director further elaborated, "The general feeling... is..., amongst the directors, ...if the money goes away, the centers are going to go away" (p. 10). And, "When it goes, the program goes. A center exists from grant to grant and must change the focus of its programs as the grants change" (Cleminson Interview, 12/12/89, p. 2).

At first glance, it would seem that continuing support from TVA would 1) provide continuity to the program and 2) alleviate personnel efforts (time, money, and energy) at grant-hunting. However, a periodic change of focus might be just what an aging center needs to survive.
What it really boils down to, then, is that yes, multiple funding sources are highly desirable and would increase the stability of a center. However, insufficient time and staff support are obstacles to obtaining alternate funds. With sufficient funds, a center could hire a graduate assistant to assist in generating successful proposals that would bring in more funds—a self-perpetuating cycle.

Step 6. <u>Create a resource center.</u>

The CEEE's resource library opened in May of 1981, a year and a half after the CEEE was established. Located in a dual classroom area, it included a wide range of resources for educators: "K-12 curriculum materials, TVA resources on energy and EE, reading materials on a variety of energy sources, numerous periodicals, references, and catalogues, information on a variety of workshops and conferences" ("CEEE," 1981, p. 11). The former assistant coordinator described the resource room: "In the back corner, I painted this big mural of a forest scene, with... the forest animals and the forest plants. It was... a three-dimensional display. We brought in this huge dead tree and leaves and we built up this little platform and put in all the leaves and... [some] taxidermed animals and some mushrooms... and some of the kids over at the Campus School did some paper mache birds for us... so we had birds hanging from the ceiling... we had our big tables in there for workshops, ... our video equipment... It was a really attractive room. You wanted to go in and... look around" (Norvell Interview, 8/8/90, p. 12). By the summer of 1984, the TVA Quarterly Report listed ninety-four resource room requests for the three-month period ending in June.

But, in 1985, the resource library was moved out of its spacious quarters into a small office adjacent to the director's. The secretary elaborated, "The administration wanted to use that room for something else... it is now what they wanted it to be"—a MacIntosh computer lab (Donnenwerth Interview, 11/7/89, p. 12). According to a professor in the department, "it was just priority use of space" (Giannangelo Interview, 8/13/90, p. 2). However, the center director felt this was the first overt indication of the University withdrawing support from the CEEE. He explained, "The reality... is that money drives space, and if you're the new kid on the block with a lot of money and funding, you get the most attention... Environmental education, like apple pie and motherhood are all good things, but when it comes down to the reality at any institution... the dollars will drive the amount of attention" (Cleminson Interview, 10/19/89, p. 15).

The CEEE still provides a resource library, although it doubles as a graduate assistant office. The room is small, cramped and windowless. Insufficient clerical assistance has resulted in a backlog of materials to be filed. New materials are rarely purchased. Much of the environmental resource information is outdated. Finding specific items is nearly impossible. Like everything else, then, the space to provide this valuable service is linked to funding and status within the University hierarchy.

Step 7. <u>Offer workshops and seminars on topics, issues, and curriculum trends that meet the needs of the target audiences and address the current trends in environmental education.</u>

TVA keeps records of kinds of programs and number of people impacted by its centers. According to a 1990 report, centers within the TVA network conducted 263 workshops reaching 7,627 teachers during the 1989-90 fiscal year. They developed and field tested 76 new programs and provided outreach to 173 counties or 86% of the TVA service area. Further, TVA reported to have impacted "approximately two-thirds of the students in the Tennessee Valley region at a current annual cost of 24¢ per student impact to TVA" ("Performance," 1989, p. 4).

While the numbers reported by TVA may seem impressive, the data may be skewed. Committed to the cause of EE, the CEEE director has included an environmental component into virtually all of his professional activities. For example, science methods courses normally taught by the director were legitimately reported to TVA as EE classes, workshops, or seminars, simply because of the inclusion of an environmental component. Even his involvement in a nationwide science teacher recruiting effort (Project 30) became a part of his reported CEEE activities. When questioned about the possible discrepancies, the TVA Program Manager expressed indifference, replying, "The fact is that the workshops are being held... there have been classes held... that may not have been held had there not been a center" (Judy Interview, 4/11/90, p. 7).

This factor cannot be disputed. For instance, during her association with the CEEE, the researcher—an unpaid volunteer—conducted numerous presentations for school and community groups that would not otherwise have been done. According to an MSU English professor, the center is "...an established place. People know about it. People call you on the telephone to ask for things. It's an established center" (Golden/Killingsworth Interview, 10/31/90, p. 20). Past experience has shown that the more presentations made by CEEE personnel, the more requests are received. Even without funds, as long as CEEE personnel agreed to conduct environmental classes, workshops, seminars, and off-campus in-service and classroom presentations, the center would continue to be a source for environmental information and education.

Step 8. <u>Maintain a strong communication network.</u>

There are several levels of networking that go on in the TVA university-based centers—on-going communications within the University; communicating with local educators, environmental groups and community leaders; and networking with regional, state, national, and global organizations.

At the University level, a center must communicate effectively with students, administrators, and other educators on campus. The CEEE has had no difficulty in communicating with students, and in fact, during the first few years, the center director regularly spoke to classes in other departments within the College of Education in an attempt to drum up interest in EE. Administrative communication has been more difficult, partly due to different management styles and partly due to lack of time and support staff. While the CEEE regularly sent copies of TVA Quarterly Reports to the department chair and the dean's office, there was never any feedback unless the director made a point of personally discussing the reports with them (Cleminson Interview, 4/24/91). Such meetings often required time taken from other center responsibilities, so were rarely conducted. Other professors on campus have been, for the most part, totally unaware of the center's existence. For instance, the department chairman shared the same building as the CEEE for ten years before he became chairman and learned of its existence (Rakes Interview, 8/15/90). The College of Arts & Sciences' Director of Research and Graduate Studies (on-campus for the past twenty years) only learned of the CEEE during well-publicized Earth Day events of 1990 (Haddock Interview, 8/9/90). Further, his attempts to invite the director to participate in the MSU Environmental Research and Issues Forum were futile. Other than occasional collaboration with College of Education professors, a biology professor, and department chairmen from four science departments (Project 30), the CEEE director has remained isolated from other professionals on campus, a factor that has not helped to stimulate interest in the CEEE.

The second level of communication—that between a center and those people in its service area—has been successfully accomplished by the MSU CEEE in four ways: publication of the center newsletter, regular public meetings, teacher workshops and the formation of the MEAN.

The third level of networking involves organizations outside of the greater Memphis area. TVA has deliberately and conscientiously built up a network of professional environmental educators throughout the Tennessee Valley. Its strength, according to the TVA Program Manager, lies in diversity and cooperation. "The diversity allows them to develop [a wide range of materials]... The cooperation really allows them to share some of their ideas before they start inventing and re-inventing the wheel" (Judy Interview, 4/11/90, p. 10). An evaluator hired by TVA to study the network in 1984 made the following remarks about the TVA network: "What is amazing is that it is working and working well—both for TVA and the universities involved. The synergism created by weaving together this kind of syndicate lends credence to the old adage that the whole is greater than its collective parts" (Ambry, 1985, p. ii). Further, "the network brought together by TVA has created other tentacles and interlocking inner-networks between and among cooperating institutions and other agencies and organizations throughout the Valley" (p. 14).

Directors Meetings are a key feature of the TVA network. At each biannual (formerly quarterly) meeting, participants spend a concentrated two or three days together, interacting both formally and informally. All center directors have the opportunity to submit items for the agenda and TVA officials plan additional programs they feel would be beneficial to network members. In addition to presentations, Directors Meetings provide opportunities for publicity photos, formal exchange of information between professionals engaged in similar endeavors, and informal interchanges between center personnel and TVA representatives. Programs range from introductions of newly-developed curricular materials, to presentations from groups or individuals seeking assistance from the network, to previews of EE videos and computer laserdisc software programs.

In 1985, the CEEE purchased can Apple IIE computer and modem with TVA funds, ostensibly to participate in a regional microcomputer network with other center directors. But the CEEE was never linked into the system. More recently, center directors have been encouraged by TVA to join EcoNET, the national computer network with an environmental focus. Although TVA centers were offered a discount for their subscription to EcoNET, the CEEE has never participated. However, it has frequently received copies of EcoNET printouts and other relevant EE information from the TVA Program Office.

In addition to networking with regional TVA centers, the MSU CEEE has established connections with national (e.g., Earth Day Committees in both Washington, D.C. and California, Greenpeace U.S.A., the Wilderness Society, and the Green Committees for Correspondence) and global organizations (the North American EE Association, Canada's *Environment Views*, and UNESCO/UNIPUB's *Connect*). The communication effort has thus been uneven. The best connections have been with local interest groups and with other TVA centers. Intramural communication at the University has been weak because of the effects of conflicting values and territorial disputes.

Step 9. <u>Identify course structures or sequences that can be accessed and/or developed to provide the University with an academic identity in environmental education.</u>

A university-based EE center should strive to make itself an integral part of the institution, through whatever legitimate means it can muster. There are several approaches that can be taken. The CEEE director explained his approach: "I have chosen to take the resources and the activities that we have and make them more a part of ongoing courses than for us to run off and design new programs" (Cleminson Interview, 10/19/89, p. 7). By incorporating an EE component into existing courses he teaches, he has attempted to encourage and inspire students to pursue individual projects in EE. As he explained it, "It's pretty hard to draw the line between faculty member and center director and I've never tried to separate the two" (Cleminson Interview, 12/12/89, p. 2).

Achieving and maintaining high visibility on campus can also lead to establishing a firmer identity. That is, if people know of the center, they are more likely to identify with it. As one ex-dean observed, one of the biggest problems he perceived with the CEEE was "trying to build appreciation for the importance of it" (Saunders Interview, 8/16/90, p. 2). The CEEE director seconded this opinion. When asked what he considered to be the largest obstacle the CEEE has encountered in its presence on the MSU campus, he responded, "university, departmental and College recognition" (Cleminson Interview, 8/3/90, p. 24).

Visibility has been a recurring problem with the CEEE since its inception. As one department chairman observed, "if you're not visible, I don't think you have the impact... You're only as good as what you did last year... if I see that the center is producing or providing information that personally is relevant to me... then I'll pay attention to it" (Rakes Interview, 8/15/90, pp. 7-8). He further observed, "It's very tough to have good visibility unless you've got a major research focus or something that generates the dollars to get that word out" (Rakes Interview, 8/15/90, p. 7). Note that this discussion of visibility assumes a "closed" university environment. Research is not often "visible" to the public, just as public service is not "visible" to university administrators. You "see" what you value most.

Step 10. <u>Seek opportunities for student involvement in the operation of the programs.</u>

MSU has had no official environmental studies or EE programs in spite of the presence of the CEEE on campus (only isolated EE courses, workshops, or seminars). There are officially no EE students—a Catch 22 situation. As the center director explained it, university administrators "say that you have to have many, many students before... you have the degree. On the other hand, [if] you don't have the degree, you're not going to get the students" (Cleminson Interview, 8/3/90, p. 4). Even so, the CEEE has utilized the services of work-study students for some of its bulk mailings and filing. According to a March, 1989 TVA report, "student staff have proven to be hard working, dedicated, and financially feasible for most centers" (Hodges & Judy, 1989, p. 21).

There are two primary advantages to involving students in the operation of center programs. First, students traditionally are a cheap source of labor in institutions of higher education. Work study students can perform the numerous daily tasks associated with operating a center (filing, etc.) at a relatively small cost. Undergraduate and graduate students can be hired to assist in making presentations and in researching and writing proposals. Second, students who are actively involved in EE provide free advertising for the center. The advertisement may be in the form of verbal information exchange or as bona fide research reports. Either way, it could help elicit administrative support, since it demonstrates that a center is providing a service students consider worthwhile.

CEEE activities have traditionally been conducted either by the director, salaried coordinators, graduate assistants or volunteers. Graduate students have been both salaried and unsalaried, depending on funds available. In some instances, students have paid tuition fees to take a course that involved working for the CEEE. For example, one MSU graduate student enrolled in an Independent Study course to research and write a proposal for the CEEE. Although not funded, the research effort resulted in a two-year volunteer association with the center that included "free" presentation of EE programs to school and community groups.

Discussion

What lessons have been learned from this dialectical analysis that pits the "Ten Steps" model for successful centers against the actual case history of a single center?

1. The **base of support** recommended in Step 1 refers to both monetary and administrative support. With monetary support, administrative support is more likely to be forthcoming. If at all possible, monetary support needs to be tied to research efforts that can result in refereed publications (so that center directors can continue to be competitive in the tenure review process) and that will provide for the continuous generation of additional funds. Callous though it may seem, community support and/or support from other departments within the University are important only as they serve to further draw in funds and/or enhance administrative recognition of the center.

2. Remembering that centers are created to meet a societal need, regular **needs assessments** can provide insights into characteristics and preferences of the targeted population, and into how well a center meets the needs as determined by those in its service area. Centers can then modify the focus of their programs and activities so that they continue to meet local EE needs. Further, the information can serve as ammunition if administrators question the continued existence of a center.

3. For the most part, **program strengths** depend on the people behind them. If this viewpoint is taken, then Step 3 suggests identifying and recruiting people to support the center who are already interested and/or involved in environmental activities. If, however, program strengths refer to environmental programs (or activities with an environmental focus) that might exist within the host institution, perhaps the step refers to finding ways to tap into other resources available on campus. In this respect, jointly

sponsored events might serve to draw more attention to the center (and thus increase visibility) and collaborative funding efforts might prove financially beneficial.

4. **Advisory Boards**, while perhaps difficult to organize and gather for regular meetings, can provide several indispensable services to a center. First, they provide direction and advice. They can help keep a center on task, to insure that it continues to meet the needs of the target population. Second, they can potentially help access additional resources and perhaps even external funding from local sources (e.g., school districts, local businesses, etc.). But last, and more important, they can help stave off personnel burnout.

5. A center cannot exist within a university setting without external funding. **Multiple funding sources,** then, are an absolute imperative for EE centers. While it would be nice to receive unlimited funds from a single source indefinitely, it is also unrealistic. A large portion of the energy expended in operating a center must therefore be allotted to fund raising. However, funding sources often drive the direction a center will take. Few funding sources will allow a center to freely use money as it chooses. Hence, either a center's goals must be modified or funded research efforts must be pursued and chosen on the basis of how well they fit in with the center's overall mission.

6. A **resource library** lends credibility and stability to an EE center. It is an actual room where students and community members can obtain specific information on environmental issues of concern. Curricular materials and audio visuals pertaining to EE are loaned to educators (community and academic), although much of it is simply given away, rather than loaned. Yet without proper organization and management, materials in a resource library are inaccessible. Provisions need to be made for continuous funds to hire personnel to organize, catalog, file, check out and update resource materials.

7. By **offering workshops and seminars in EE**, a center fulfills one of its stated goals (in-service and pre-service of teachers) and continues to advertise its existence (and thus to increase its visibility within the University). When presented to schools (students and/or teachers), academic support is strengthened. When extended to the community, local grassroots support is achieved. An important role of the center director, then (second only to fund raising), is to actively plan and present programs addressing current trends in environmental education.

8. **Networking** has proven to be extremely successful in the EE arena. It can enhance the prestige of a fledgling center (by association with a respected organization) and it can extend the resources available beyond the local level. It encourages information exchange and collaboration at the departmental, college and university levels, and provides a means for establishing continuous communications at the state, national and global

levels. But, networking costs money. Optimally, initial funds need to be secured for computer hardware and software (for accessing EcoNET), as well as for subscriptions to relevant journals and environmental publications. Additional funds are needed to cover long distance telephone charges and, if a newsletter is published, publication and dissemination costs.

9. It may be impossible for a center to become an integral part of the University without actually evolving into another form (e.g., a program of studies within a department), yet an EE center can make itself relatively secure by generating both substantial research dollars and publications in professional journals. They could ensure that the center maintains high visibility within the academic environment. Whether by formal courses, public meetings, educational programs, formal publications, or research dollars, the goal is to somehow **get the University to identify with the center** and with EE.

10. **Student involvement** can potentially strengthen a center in two ways. First, visible demonstrations of student interest in EE could provide administrative rationale for continuing a center. Second, student workers could provide an inexpensive source of labor for day-to-day operation of a center.

The ten steps are good general suggestions but they lack comprehensiveness as a model. In particular, they fail to account for *conflict*. The central conflict that directors of university-based centers must inevitably face is the division of values between the information-generating function of academic research and the information-consuming needs of public education.

References

Ambry, E. J. (1985). TVA interpretive case study—environmental/energy education program. Knoxville, TN: Tennessee Valley Authority.

CEEE open house. (1981), OIKOS, Spring, 11.

CEEE survey. (1990). OIKOS, Spring, 2-3.

CEEE's advisory committee. (1981). OIKOS, Spring, 2.

Cleminson, R.W. (1986, August 7). Memorandum to Carla Kirkland, Murray State University, Murray, KY.

Fetterman, D. M. (1989). Ethnography step by step. Newbury Park: Sage.

Hodges, L.M. and Judy, J.M. (1989). Fundamentals of environmental education. Knoxville, TN: Tennessee Valley Authority.

Kirkland, C.N. (1986). Center/cooperative development questionnaire. (A portion of the center/cooperative development manual) [Unpublished]. Murray, KY: Murray State University.

Koshland, D.E. (1991). Teaching and research. Science, January 18, 249.

Paul, J.R. (1978, April 17). Letter to Dr. Roger Bennett, Director, Department of Curriculum and Instruction, Memphis State University College of Education.

Performance — TVA network 1989. (1989). Knoxville, TN: Tennessee Valley Authority.

Shore, B. M., et al. (1990). Research as a model for university teaching. Higher Education, 21-35.

Sykes, C. J. (1988). ProfScam: Professors and the demise of higher education. New York: St. Martin's.

Wals, A. (1990). What you can't measure still exists. Environmental Communicator. November/December, 12.

Yin, R.K. (1984). Case study research: Design and methods. Beverly Hills: Sage Publications.

ABOUT THE AUTHOR

Jackie Palmer grew up in the Midwest (KS, TX, OK and MO). She earned her B.S. degree in biology from the University of Missouri in Kansas City (UMKC) in 1976. Her pre-college teaching experiences began in Belize, Central America where she taught in the Peace Corps, and continued in Missouri and New Mexico. Ms. Palmer pursued graduate studies at UMKC, the University of New Mexico (UNM) in Albuquerque, Highlands University in Las Vegas, NM and the New Mexico Institute of Mining and Technology (NMIMT) in Socorro. She participated in Honors Workshops at UNM(astronomy), the University of Colorado at Boulder(radiation biology), Los Alamos National Scientific Labs(chemistry) and NASA(space science). She earned a Masters degree in Science Teaching from NMIMT in 1985. In 1987, she designed and taught a course in Basic Science for Non-Majors at South Plains Junior College in Lubbock, Texas.

While pursuing a doctoral degree at Memphis State University (MSU) in Tennessee, Ms. Palmer was a teaching assistant in the Departments of Biology and Curriculum and Instruction. She worked in the Dean's Office as Coordinator of MSU's Project 30 and served as associate director of MSU's Center for Environmental/Energy Education. During the 1990-091 academic year, she worked as a research associate for the Texas Alliance for Science, Technology and Mathematics Education, (a business/education consortium housed in the Texas A&M University College of Education). Ms. Palmer's dissertation was "The Center/Network Concept of Environmental Education: A Qualitative Study of the Memphis State University Center for Environmental/Energy Education".

Ms. Palmer is the author of two articles ("Three Decades of Recombinant DNA," The Science Teacher, December, 1985 and "Sensing in the Womb," The American Biology Teacher, October, 1987) and is co-author of a book Ecospeak—The Rhetoric of Environmental Politics (with M.J. Killingsworth, Southern Illinois University Press, 1992).

ENVIRONMENTAL EDUCATION IN THE WAR YEARS: A CASE STUDY

Giovanna Di Chiro

Abstract

An account of environmental education curriculum development, in a tertiary context, using the methodology of action research is presented. An argument is made for the need for an alternative research paradigm for environmental education that would incorporate feminist theoretical and methodological approaches. Traditional research paradigms, characterized by objectivist, "applied science" perspectives fail to meet environmental education's goals of critical problem-solving and social action on environmental issues. Using a case study model, the article discusses the action research process undertaken by the co-instructors of an upper-division Women's Studies course concerned with issues of feminism, science and technology. A key focus of the study is the development of strategies for empowerment and political efficacy in the University classroom in the context of the Persian Gulf war.

Introduction

In a number of critical ways, research in environmental education suffers from a sort of "paradigmatic paralysis." A brief perusal through the US, European and Australian professional journals in environmental education provides evidence of this assertion. The vast majority of scholarly articles and curriculum designs are characterized by what Robottom has called the "technocratic rationality" of the "applied science" approach to research and development in the social sciences (Robottom, 1986; 1987; 1989). The ideology of scientism that underpins this tendency in the field has effectively "paralyzed" or at least successfully controlled the possible directions that research in environmental education could take. As Robottom (1987) has argued,

> ...the presently dominant perspectives of educational change and research are responsible for structuring 'the innovation' [of environmental education] in such a way that its operational form is incapable of meeting its socially and environmentally critical charter. A managerial-hierarchical form of organization, informed by an empiricist, objectivist epistemology, and adopting an RDDA or similarly depoliticized, technocratic view of educational change, far from being...a neutral administrative process, is itself political. Its politics are the politics of the preservation of the status quo, or reproduction, in this case, of non-critical education about the environment. (99)

Although numerous educational theorists[1] have constructed well developed critiques of both the objectivist epistemologies presupposing value-neutrality in educational change and the managerialist claims that problems in the success of educational innovations arise from teacher failures in implementing the curriculum or student deficiencies and resistances to learning, the scientism of the applied science paradigm persists in the pages of professional journals of environmental education.[2]

In the context of environmental education, the history of the "technocratization of environmental education" and the arguments supporting it have been thoroughly elaborated by Robottom (1986; 1987; 1989) and will not be reproduced here. Moreover, there have been efforts to challenge some of the traditional environmental education research paradigms using some theoretical approaches arising from outside of the field--for example the use of action research approaches in environmental education evaluation, curriculum development and professional development (Di Chiro & Stapp, 1986; Markowitz & Robottom, 1987; Wals et al., 1990) and as I have argued elsewhere, the use of feminist analyses and methodologies in environmental education research (Di Chiro, 1987a; 1987b).[3]

It will suffice to say that alternative paradigms to environmental education research are available in the literature and as evidenced by the 1990 NAEE Conference Symposium, "Alternative Paradigms in Environmental Education Research" there are increasing moves to disrupt the hegemony of the dominant paradigm and to open up and critically examine the question of what constitutes research in environmental education. Whether this is evidence of a burgeoning Kuhnian revolution, it is difficult to say. What is certain, however, is the radical incommensurability between environmental education's dominant paradigm of research and educational change and its stated goals of social and political empowerment and socio-environmental justice.

In the following sections of this essay I present a discussion of a case study in environmental education, written through a feminist lens, that I hope will contribute to the continuing development of alternative approaches in environmental education curriculum development and also to the continuing

---

[1] For example, Wilfred Carr, Stephen Kemmis, Michael Apple, Stanley Aronowitz, Paulo Freire, Henry Giroux, Patti Lather

[2] For example, a recent article in the Journal of Environmental Education (Monroe & Kaplan, 1988) on evaluation of the effectiveness of EE curricula in the schools concludes with the remarkable statement, "this research only restates what educators have known for a long time: students don't know more than we teach them, and teachers are more successful with strategies that are esier to implement," (40) which not only assumes that students are nothing but empty receptacles to be filled up with objective knowledge conveyed through the relatively simple-minded teacher, but also that an educator (or and EE researcher) can objectively measure and accurately control the knowledge that they are teaching or funneling to the pupils empty mind.

[3] Despite the influx of feminist perspectives and critiques in both educational research and in the literature on social justice and the environment, a recent computer search of the descriptors "feminism" and "EE" in ERIC yielded only two articles. One of them was mine and the other was a piece written by the Australian ecofeminist and social theorist Ariel Kay Salleh (1989)

debates about the constitutive values and goals of environmental education as a socially, politically and culturally critical educational innovation.

Environmental Education in the War Years[4]

The University classroom in a country waging a fighting war, whether inside or outside its national boundaries, is a highly charged educational environment and raises a complex array of pedagogical issues relevant to environmental educators in post-secondary education. At the time the US initiated the war (or more accurately, the massacre) in the Persian Gulf, I was co-teaching a Women's Studies course titled "Feminism, Science and Technology"[5] at the University of California, Santa Cruz. We recognized the criticality of this historical event, not only as a US atrocity and a tragedy on an international scale, but also as a critical pedagogical moment suffused with an immediacy that provided the opportunity to make our curriculum materials socially critical and politically relevant in interesting ways. We began the process of restructuring our syllabus and re-designing our classroom activities and assignments to integrate and center an analysis of the war. Part of this evaluative, or action research[6] process was aimed at creating the conditions in the University classroom so that students could begin to make critical connections between the issues of feminism, science and technology and the immediate, daily, relentless bombing that was being perpetrated on the people of Iraq. Part of the process of changing the curriculum midstream was also to consider pedagogies appropriate to the University context that would engender action programs and a sense of empowerment in our students. Given that our students were adults, much of the negotiation process was undertaken collectively in the classroom although most of our planning and reflection work was conducted in daily meetings with just the two instructors.

Our student's emotional and intellectual presence and participation in the course was variously affected by a number of factors: their commitments to anti-war work, their concerns about how the war was personally affecting family members or friends, their fears of the draft either for themselves or friends and relatives, and the often confusing bombardment of jingoistic rhetoric and demonizing images of Iraqis that permeated the media coverage of the war. One of the challenges that emerged for us almost immediately was confronting the profound sense of helplessness that arose as our students (mainly women) grappled with powerful feminist critiques

---

[4] A version of this paper is forthcoming with co-author Marita Sturken (1991)

[5] This course was concerned with the intersections of gender, scientific theory and practice, and technological culture. It focussed on the feminist critiques of western science and scientific rationality as they are expressed in socio-cultural productions such as race, gender and class oppression, war technologies concerned with women's reproduction and fertility. The course also centered on women's active engagement and interventions, as educators, health activists, environmentalists, scientists, and scholars in the process of reconstructing science and technology.

[6] The use of action research in environmental education has been thoroughly described and documented by Robottom (1987; 1989), Di Chiro (1987b), Kemmis & McTaggart

exposing the ideological underpinnings of the war, including western, masculinist scientific rationality justifying this most recent version of US neo-colonialsm.   How could we utilize, in our curriculum, theoretical criticism providing historical explanations of the current state of affairs, and avoid students' common response of feelings of powerlessness and political ineffectiveness? Megan Boler (1991) writes about what she calls the "post-modern" emotional phenomenon of powerlessness:

> The conglomerate of forces that constructs the experience of powerlessness marks a particular historical moment in the social construction of emotion. The success of this social order depends on the censorship of particular emotions--namely, anger, rage, and empowerment...this historical moment's experience of powerlessness [is] a new phenomenon that requires attention in our classrooms if we wish to construct some sort of effective "citizens." (4-5)

Boler poses the following questions that arose for her during a course she was teaching during the Persian Gulf war: "what forms of educational 'business as usual' enable a fruitful analysis relevant to war(s)? If the interconnection of pedagogy and curriculum with agency and resistance seems farfetched to us, why? Is complicity in numbness, denial, and silence a perpetuation and enabling of this war? What is our obligation to educate, counter, elicit, explore intersections of the realities of war, its emotional impact, and the interconnected relationships of emotion-violence-war-powerlessness-emotion?" (6) These were some of the questions that we considered in trying to come to grips with the emotional field of powerlessness that was paralyzing our classroom.

As environmental educators in the context of active war, we needed to seriously reflect on the pervasive issue of powerlessness in order to adequately address our charge of creating the educational conditions for the development of empowerment and the sense of political efficacy in our students. It became apparent that it was essential to our research in environmental education to study the functioning of "postmodern" powerlessness at this historical moment to understand how it "affects, feeds on and drains our sense of agency and power as active creators of self and world-representations." (6) The problem of our students' struggles with the intensifying sense of powerlessness was exacerbated by the mainstream media's underreporting and misrepresentation of anti-war demonstrations that were being organized and staged across the country, on University campuses as well as in large and small communities. It appeared to our students that the media conspired against the success of political organization by minimizing its effect, thereby rendering irrelevant or futile their participation in events protesting the war. Students tended to look on their participation in anti-war efforts only in terms of the potential of these events to generate powerful media images of an effective and widespread antiwar movement, without adequately considering the critical aspects of community-building and political coalition that are primary objectives of direct action politics.

In the context of our Women's Studies curriculum, we were concerned with generating counter-discourses to the tendency among students to think of wars as the territory and domain of men and male desire, together with the related tendency to reinscribe the traditional narratives of the participation of women in warfare as being merely in the role of either "moral mother"[7] pacifist or victim. Given that most of our students were women, this way of thinking limited their sense of efficacy in countering the gendered ideology that supports and sustains militarism. Consequently, we noticed a disturbing development becoming evident in our class discussions--that is, a strategy for dealing with the disempowerment of war, voiced by many students, that consisted of "working at being at peace with myself" and "coming to terms with the violence within," a strategy that seemed to involve working on personal relationships and meditating in the privacy of one's home. This approach, although valuable in certain contexts, tends to privatize what are actually social, cultural and historical problems and often results in feelings of isolation and self-blame and effectively depoliticizes, in this case, the educational environment.

It was problematic for us, as teachers, because this profound sense of isolation and disempowerment resulting from the US war against the people of Iraq, drastically affected the teaching and learning environment. Our action research approach to critically analyzing our pedagogy and implementing curriculum change, took us in a number of different directions. In the remaining paragraphs of this essay, I will discuss a few of the strategies we undertook that are consistent with environmental education's socially critical and problem-solving approach to the study of environmental problems--in this case the environmental problem of war.

The initial curriculum change that we implemented was to use the course materials to mount a feminist analysis of the war in terms of both a feminist critique of the culture of "technoscience"[8] that produces war and an analysis of the role of gender in the war system and its military technologies of destruction. Through our readings dealing with critical analyses of the rise of modern science during the 17th and 18th centuries, (Merchant, 1980; Gould, 1981; Keller, 1985; Harding, 1986) we developed a critique of the ways that the new mechanistic philosophy relied upon the association of woman and nature in order to construct Francis Bacon's heterosexual fantasy

---

[7] This term, "moral motherhood", coined by Micaela di Leonardo (1985), refers to an iconic image, invoked by some feminist and non-feminist pacifist discourses, presenting the vision of women as morally superior (nurturant, compassionate, peace-loving) and men as innately warmongering. She argues that it can be used against women's own interests by pushing women back into full responsibility for home and children and men into an overly deterministic role as the warriors of society. By defining men as innately violent it leaves no room for them to join feminist antimilitarism and places no demands on them to take responsibility for their own children of the world

[8] A term used by Bruno Latour (1987) to signify the false dichotomy that traditionally separates the two social practices and institutions of science technology. He uses instead "technoscience" in order to conceptually show that the two are integrally related, that is, science can not be seen as the pure, objective and disinterested precursor to technological development which is in turn seen as the result of the politically influenced use and abuse of "pure" scientific knowledge. "Technoscience exposes the social construction of the binary oppostions of pure vs. applied, science vs. technology

of the "chaste and lawful marriage between Mind and Nature." Bacon's science of the 17th century was in part a reaction to the historical contingencies of early modern Europe that created the conditions for social and political turmoil and disorder--widespread famine in the peasant populations resulting from both the rise of the Market decimating traditional subsistence economies and unprecedented climatic changes wreaking havoc on annual food production, millenarian movements, peasant revolts, the civil war in England, civil wars between emerging nation-states, the protestant challenge to the Catholic church, the Counter-Reformation, religious intolerance and wars, witch-hunting terrorizing the lives of specifically poor women, and chronic disease and virulent epidemics claiming the lives of hundreds of thousands of people.

The new "natural philosophy," was intended, in part, to respond to and to solve the problems of social and political chaos through the construction of a technology--the experimental method--for wresting nature's secrets from "her." Female Nature was the fickle, uncontrollable, lustful and violent threat to the masculine/capitalist order that was perceived to be in danger during this turbulent time. "Chaos", and particularly a feminized chaos, was inscribed onto the bodies of women of all colors, men of color, homosexuals and people of the lower social and economic classes. Masculine, euro-centric science and its technologies, therefore, were suffused with the racist, sexist and colonialist impulses of the time. Modern science evolved, in part, as a problem-solving mechanism to create order out of this perceived feminized "chaos."

How does this critique of the rise of early modern science relate to the situation in the Persian Gulf? The spectre of the encroaching "Third World" and people's of color demanding full humanity and national sovereignty was not part of George Bush's vision for his "new world order." Once again the rhetoric of the need for order in a time of perceived chaos (an adjective often used to describe the Middle East and Arabic cultures) is invoked as rationale for the development and deployment of new technologies of war and destruction. In our discussions we were able to make visible the stunning orientalism in the West's claims of order, scientific rationality and civilization in opposition to the chaotic, primitive, darkness of the Iraqi culture. Students made the connections that the US's technoscientific rationality was easily able to provide the moral and scientific justification to destroy a "Third World" country, its people and its natural resources.

In her essay "From Secrets of Life to Secrets of Death," feminist science critic Evelyn Fox Keller (1990) discusses how "life has traditionally been seen as the secret of women, a secret from men." (178) Keller suggests that the secrets of men can be seen most clearly in the well-guarded secrets of nuclear war technology--the secrets of men signifying the secrets of death. We attempted to facilitate discussion around the heavily gendered language of war and nuclear weaponry that also operates as a critique of the notion that women as "life givers" are closer to nature. Another theoretical piece we used offered an excellent analysis of military language and its domesticating function in making war and the development of war technologies seem "clean and safe." In her article "Clean Bombs and Clean Language," Carol Cohn (1990) argues that the language of nuclear weaponry is a language filled with gendered images such as "virgin targets", "penetrating weapons", and men creating (birthing) bombs that are referred to as "good boys" if they work and as girls if they are "duds." The sanitized and abstract military language appearing in the media, such as "surgical strikes", "collateral damage" and "Patriot missile", also served to create conceptual and moral distance from the realities of what happens in war. Cohn suggests that to master this militarized language of high-tech warfare is to feel that one is mastering technology, and that the use of such language constructs a consciousness that forecloses on the possibility of thinking either in terms of the pain and mutilation of human bodies that will result from the deployment of these technologies, in terms of the perspective of the potential victims, or in terms of peaceful, non-militaristic alternatives to dealing with conflict.

Although a feminist analysis of the gendered language of war proved to be a powerful tool for students to see the flagrant sexism in the construction and deployment of military technology, it also could operate to frustrate and discourage many students as the negative and infantilizing depiction of women is so extreme and the exclusion of women in military narratives appears so complete and unassailable. We researched articles[9] to include in the syllabus that would subvert the dominant and biologically deterministic estrogen/testosterone arguments that make assertions of the innate pacifism of women and men's inherent, mythical drive to make war due to their need to encounter the life and death experience that women naturally have in the childbirth process (Broyles, 1984).

This essentialist argument preempts the possibility of adequately deconstructing the culture of militarism in any other terms than that it is male and bad. Cynthia Enloe's (1988) work helps us to understand how women have historically and variously been implicated in the war system--as military wives, prostitutes, soldiers, defense industry workers, resistance fighters and anti-war activists. In the situation in the Persian Gulf, the spectre of the "woman warrior" filled media representations of the war, especially in sensationalist accounts of moms going to fight. Fruitful classroom discussions developed around issues of how women were depicted in this war--as US mother-warriors, as victimized and oppressed Arabic women--and the extent to which feminists and anti-war activists should support the efforts of women in the military to attain "equality." This more complex analysis of the gendered construction of the ideology of militarism, and the breaking down of the naturalized relationships of men and women to war, provided a wider perspective for students to think about options for political intervention and strategies for acting on this all-encompassing and overwhelming environmental problem.

---

[9] For example, di Leonardo (1985), Enloe (1988), and Ruddick (1990)

The development of change strategies and action programs that emerged from our class' critical reflections were directed at the different kinds of work undertaken in the contexts of both the classroom and in the community at large. The action research work to change pedagogical strategies in the classroom was conducted collaboratively between ourselves and the students. The actions intended to be implemented in the community were planned in small groups that students organized themselves. Students were more or less successful in making theoretical connections between the two types of critical "environmental educational" activities--reflection and theorizing in the University classroom and implementation of action plans in the community environment. The dialectical tension and interweaving of critical theories about environmental problems and social action for environmental change were always subjects for discussion and analysis.

What were some of the action strategies that developed out of this course taught in the context of the US war on Iraq? The classroom environment was radically altered to be one consisting almost exclusively of collaborative work. Students worked in small research groups to prepare presentations focussing on selected issues of feminism, science and technology and on the ways feminist theory contributed to a greater understanding of the particular issue and its relatedness to the US's socio-environmental policy of international aggression and war. Many students chose to write papers collaboratively arguing that this alleviated the sense of alienation and isolation that the war environment heightened. They also conducted out-of-class "writing workshops" editing and evaluating each other's work. In the context of the larger group, we practiced regular "check-ins" to open up the space for people to voluntarily voice frustrations or positive changes that they were experiencing in doing their work.

We incorporated a significant amount of media critique in the classroom since the Persian Gulf war also reflected a "war" waged against freedom of the press in the US. This pedagogical strategy included collectively deconstructing, through the use of feminist analytical tools, images in the dominant media (for example the confused image of a woman soldier stationed in Saudi Arabia with a photo of her one year old daughter pinned to her helmet, or the remarkable image portrayed as the most popular Desert Storm "pin-up" girl--a white, blond undercover officer from Utah wearing tight wrangler jeans wielding a large shotgun) and also using feminist media and film theory to analyze films and videos representing images of war and cultural militarism. Additionally, we held screenings of a variety of independently produced videos by women that exposed and challenged the sanitized and apparently "seamless" and objective portrayal of news by the mainstream networks.[10]

---

[10] For example, independently produced films and vidoes such as Sherry Milner's, "Scenes from the Micro-War" and "out of the Mouths of Babes" distributed by Video Data Bank, School of the Art Institute of Chicago, 280 South Columbus, Chicago, IL 60603; or the excellent media-critique videos produced by Paper Tiger Television, a non-profit, public access show located at, 339 Lafayette Street, New York, NY 10012

Given that media plays a significant role in constructing powerful and enduring images and representations of ourselves, "others"[11] and our environments, students strategized ways to reclaim their own self-representations and to construct alternatives to the dominant images through targeting a variety of media. Some of their strategies included; producing radio programs discussing the environmental consequences of the war and the issues of women and war, writing letters to the editors of University and city newspapers decrying war technology research being conducted on the campus or arguing for the need for broad-based community involvement in lobbying local representatives to oppose the war, and engaging in "guerilla xeroxing" tactics, that is, designing creative fliers incorporating both images and information for distribution throughout the campus and in the community. Using the tools of feminist critiques of technoscience, students produced interesting and complex analyses of the Persian Gulf war as a most serious environmental problem, thereby empowering themselves by re-appropriating the representational apparatus of the media. The media studies aspect of the course emerged as one of the most successful pedagogical approaches to dealing with the overwhelming problem of disempowerment that early-on severely hindered the teaching and learning environment of our classroom.

As the quarter progressed, the paralysis of the emotion of powerlessness began to subside as students worked together in collaborative groups, using feminist critiques, to understand the connections between scientism, militarism, sexism, racism, and global environmental destruction. Students felt better able to produce counter discourses to the dominant images and conceptions that proclaim the inevitability of war and the related and equally debilitating perception of the ineffectiveness of acting for social change. Finally, one of the most encouraging outcomes of the course was the formation of an ongoing study and action group comprised of Women's Studies, Environmental Studies and Science students, with the purpose of developing proposals to evaluate the curricula of their respective departments and to incorporate the feminist analyses and action strategies that were generated from the Feminism, Science and Technology course.

References

Boler, M. (1991). License to feel: Teaching in the context of war. Journal of Urban and Cultural Studies. (in press)

Broyles, W. (1984). Why men love war. Esquire. November, 55-65.

Cohn, C. (1990). Clean bombs and clean language. In, Elshtain, J. B. & Tobias, S. Women, Militarism and War. Savage, MD: Rowman and Littlefield, 33-55.

---

[11] For example, the widespread image of the demonic, uncivilized Iraqi or the veiled, victimized and, therefore, powerless Arabic woman.

Di Chiro, G. (1987a). Applying a feminist critique to environmental education. Australian Journal of Environmental Education, 3(1), 10-17.

Di Chiro, G. (1987b). Environmental education and the question of gender: A feminist critique. In, Robottom, I. M. (Ed). Environmental Education: Practice and Possibility. Geelong, Australia: Deakin University Press, 23-48.

Di Chiro, G. & Stapp, W. B. (1986). Education in action: an action research approach to environmental problem solving. In Perkins, J.H. et al. (Eds.). Monographs in Environmental Education and Environmental Studies. (3rd ed.) Troy, Ohio: The North American Association for Environmental Education.

Di Chiro, G. & Sturken, M. (1991). Countering the disempowerment of war. Journal of Urban and Cultural Studies. (in press at time of submission)

di Leonardo, M. (1985). Morals, mothers, and militarism: Antimilitarism and feminist theory. Feminist Studies. 11(3), 599-617.

Enloe, C. (1988). Does Khaki Become You?: The Militarization of Women's Lives. London: Pandora.

Gould, S. J. (1981). The Mismeasure of Man. New York: W.W. Norton.

Harding, S. (1986). The Science Question in Feminism. Ithaca: Cornell University Press.

Keller, E. F. (1990). From secrets of life to secrets of death. In, Jacobus, M. et al. Body Politics: Women and the Discourses of Science. New York: Routledge, 177-191.

Keller, E. F. (1985). Reflections on Gender and Science. New Haven: Yale University Press.

Kemmis, S. & McTaggart, R. (Eds.). (1988). The Action Research Planner. Geelong, Australia: Deakin University Press.

Latour, B. (1987). Science in Action: How to Follow Scientists and Engineers Through Society. Milton Keynes, England: Open University Press.

Markowitz, N. & Robottom, I. (1987). Evolution in an environmental education course for teachers. Journal of Environmental Education. 18(9), 9-14.

Merchant, C. (1980). The Death of Nature: Women, Ecology and the Scientific Revolution. New York: Harper & Row.

Monroe, M. C. & Kaplan, S. (1988). When words speak louder than actions: environmental problem solving in the classroom. Journal of Environmental Education. 19(3), 38-41.

Robottom, I. M. (1986). How should we view the innovation issues of E.E.? Environmental Education and Information, 5(2), 107-118.

Robottom, I. M. (1989). Social critique or social control: some problems for evaluation in environmental education. Journal of Research in Science Teaching. 26(5), 435-443.

Robottom, I. M. (1987). Towards inquiry-based professional development in environmental education. In, Robottom, I. M. (Ed.). Environmental Education: Practice and Possibility. Geelong, Australia: Deakin University Press.

Ruddick, S. (1990). The rationality of care. In, Elshtain, J. B. & Tobias, S. Women, Militarism and War. Savage, MD: Rowman and Littlefield. 229-254.

Salleh, A. K. (1989). Environmental consciousness and action: An Australian perspective. Journal of Environmental Education. 20(2), 26-31.

Wals, A. E. & Beringer A. & Stapp, W. B. (1990). Education in action: a community problem-solving program for schools. Journal of Environmental Education. 21(4), 13-19.

About the Author

Giovanna Di Chiro is an instructor in Women's Studies at the University of California, Santa Cruz, working on a doctorate in History of Consciousness concentrating on feminist critiques of science and technology. Her research in this area has focussed on feminist analyses of environmentalism, educational transformation and cultural studies of science.

A PSYCHOLOGICAL AND ETHICAL APPROACH TO ENVIRONMENTAL EDUCATION

MARIA DEL PILAR JIMENEZ SILVA

Abstract

This article presents an analysis of environmental education from an epistemological, theoretical and methodological point of view. It conceptualizes the notion of environmental education and its objectives from a pluridisciplinary perspective. It points out the importance of considering environmental dimensions as a structural base for any education which presents an integrated formation of individuals and at the same time it gives certain elements to define the role individuals and society as a whole must assume in their responsibility towards the environment. The proposal has a plural and multidisciplinary focus: the sociological, ideological, psychological, ethical, cultural dimensions, among others, are considered in this perspective. In particular, the psychological and ethical dimensions are developed.

Considering apprenticeship is a dialectic process, in which individuals are confronted to their mutual references in a process of analysis - synthesis - analysis - a methodology for the organization of curriculum and the development of the process in proposed: group apprenticeship - action research.

Towards a Conception of Environmental Education.

One of the most important aspects to be taken into consideration for the prevention of environmental damage and the preservation of the natural environment, is the formation of social subjects in an integrated approach towards environment (1); that is the formation of a critical and active attitude towards reality.

In this sense, education, as one of the fundamental socializing spaces, plays a central role in this formative process. An education whose objective is to accomplish an environmental attitude in its pupils presupposes certain epistemological, theoretical and methodological principles that will guarantee the learning process towards the incarnation of collective interests in each individual, for a conception of environment as a whole questions any education centered in individualistic interests, in the parcialization of knowledge and[1] unequal competence. On the contrary, an

---

[1]When we speak of environment we understand the social and natural environment in their relationship and mutual determination. When it deals with independent problems we specify natural or social environment.

environmental approach demands for a collective conscience as well as collective actions, considering that the consequences of environmental damage go beyond the "good will" of individuals and compels us/them to search for social alternatives.

In this context, education must be understood as an integrating process, in which reality is approached as a totality and individuals are formed as a whole, in order to be in condition to perform a critical and transforming role in their environment. From this conception, the concept of education assumes that of an environmental education, understanding by it the process in which the emphasis lays on the notions of: social production relations, man-nature relation; man - nature mutual determinations.

The ideal of this education is based on the possibility for individuals, groups, institutions and collectives to acquire conscience of an adequate use of social and natural resources. The conscience that in the appropriation of capital assets, not only individual needs must be observed, but also basic collective needs must be considered.

To achieve this, it is essential to change those social values that contribute to environmental damage. It is necessary to overcome the accumulative economy, the consumers and waste ideology in order to adopt an economy based upon spiritual goods. As Phillip Saint Marc says: "an economy of material goods is based upon possession (...) in having and the economy of spiritual goods is based upon the state (...) in being". This explains the differences in social values of consumption and production.[2]

According to Saint Marc, the option is not between destroying nature or stopping the development of society, as it is usually stated in the accumulative and private property society, but between destroying nature or changing social forms of production and consumption in view of generating the conscience of the need to eradicate social and nature exploitation in order to establish equal relationships in the understanding of respect for differences.

The main problem in any educative process consists in establishing the optimum way to provide the pupils the necessary elements to achieve the proposed goals; in our case, the conscience to take part and make decisions on environmental problems.

By its own nature, an environmental education can not be just another content in the curriculum planning; on the contrary, it must be its structural axis. That is, it must be the organizer and articulating element of the educational process. It must constitute an integrated view of reality, a

---

[2] Cfr. Saint Marc, Ph. La Socialización de la naturaleza. Madried: Gaudiana, 1971.

totalizing optic that supports the whole process. The objective is to enforce an orientation in which the environmental dimension plays the central role and in which the pupil will be conscious that the environment is determined by multiple factors that are constantly in interaction. Therefore the effectiveness of decisions depend as well on interactive actions and not on individual issues.

According to the preceding statements, we can think that an environmental education should propose to:[3]

- analyze the different epistemological and ideological conceptions that have supported the social relations, the man-nature relations, in the different historical moments of society, in order for the pupil to understand the role man has played in these different periods .ó

- provide the necessary theoretical and methodological elements that will allow the pupils to think and construct the transformation of the relations man has established (with other men and with nature), based upon dominion and exploitation, towards relations based upon cooperation and solidarity.

- question the conceptions of science and knowledge based upon absolutes and promote models that facilitate creativeness, construction and searching.

- question models that establish the separation man-nature, the diverse social sciences - natural sciences; models that lead to reductionist and fragmentary conceptions of reality.

- promote a conscious recognition of the differences in rhythms and times between man and nature, in order to establish behavior and interrelation rules according to these differences.

- promote a conscious respect towards cultural and social heterogeneity so that the individuals may intermix with the different geographical, cultural and political regions.

- approach the environmental dimension from a multi and interdisciplinary basis, recognizing the complexity of the object of study.

- recognize that the environmental problem is a world-wide affair that involves the different social subjects (individuals, groups, social

---

[3]Cfr. Jimnez S. Ma. del Pilar, "Propuesta guía para una Educación Ambiental en el Nivel de Educación Media B sica" en Documentos y Materiales de Trabajo del II Seminario-Taller de Educación Ambiental Formal. Mexico: SEDUE, SEP, FFES. 1990.

classes, institutions) in different levels of participation and responsibility.

- integrate a sensibilization process: the acquisition of knowledge and abilities to solve problems, the clarification of values towards the environment.

- develop a critical sense and the necessary attitudes to confront problems and to propose solutions according to specific particularities.

The educational process

Every educational-formative process independently from its content, supposes the interaction of different factors that determine and define the conditions of the process. By education-formation we understand not only the learning of particular contents, but also, and specially, the learning of conceptions, values, and attitudes. This process is determined by different dimensions that interact and define the individual behaviour such as: the psychological, sociological, economical, ideological, political, and cultural.

In our present manuscript we will mention the psychological and ethic dimensions and their importance for environmental education. With this, we do not imply less importance to other dimensions that must be considered if our intent is an integrated educational process; we are only making an arbitrary methodological outline for this particular work.

The Psychological Dimension

Every educational work requires the delimitation of the characteristics of the individual with which it pretends to work, in order to design and organize the contents according to the subject's needs and specific ways of approaching reality. In particular, it is important to delimit the psychological characteristics of the individual to establish the necessary setting to allow the interaction and identity of the subject with the proposed task.

In this context, we will apply the psychoanalytic theory for certain concepts helpful in our task. Within the "psych" discourses, we consider this theory as the most comprising in the comprehension of the complex human-psychology. *The arguments of this theoretical choice exceeds the objectives of the present work, therefore we will just explicit our point of departure.*

An important concept to be considered for our purpose is that of "ego Ideal".[4] This intrapsychological entity, formed in early childhood, is the

---

[4]We understand by ego ideal the psychological entity result of the convergence of narcissism (idealization of ego) and the identifications with the parents, their substitutes and the collective ideals. As a

objectivation of ethic and moral values sustained by the parents which imprint the normative character and the aspirations and hopes in the individual.[5] Aspirations and hopes that are transmitted in different ways and that go beyond the subject's conscience. The individual takes over these parental commands (as a child) and translates them into his own language; this act marks a distance in regard to the parent's message. These aspirations and hopes become part of the ego ideal and constitute one of the gravitational points in the individual's future behaviour.

During his life, the individual will search for references, holdings, identifications that confirm once and again that he has a position in the interactional drama.

From this perspective, we think work can be done in profit of an informative and formative action towards an environmental education. This would deal with objectivizing all through the educational process an attitude facing the environmental problem. The subject is brought to the center of the problem. That is, to find contents and situations that lead the pupils to their particularities (individual and social) in such way to achieve significant apprenticeships. Considering that only significant learning can create bases for conscience and responsibility towards environment. In this sense, the environmental dimension, as a totality, must act as the structural axis of the curriculum, as a meaning articulator of the different contents.

How can we attain this process? How can we remit learning to the pupils particularities? This problem brings up the type of methodology used in the process. What elements are necessary in order to achieve this task? We require a didactic centered in participation and cooperation, in such way that individuals are exposed to their multiple references and from there, in the interaction process, construct common references. By this, we mean a didactic in which the subjects of the process may bring forward their values and ideals, share their needs and hopes, their facilities and difficulties, and in this manner find references that might fulfil their ego ideal and bring sense to their actions.

For the fulfillment of these apprenticeships we propose a methodology centered in group work: a didactic of "group apprenticeship"[6]. In the

---

differentiated entity, the ego ideal constitutes a model to which the individual intends to adjust. Cfr. Laplanche,J. y J.B.Pontalis. Vocabulario de Psicon lisis. Barcelona: Labor, 1979. p.187.

[5]It is important to point out that the ego ideal can be conformed by ideas, symbols, etc.; it is not conditioned to be represented by persons.

[6] By "group apprenticeship" we understand the socialization of the information (contents, values, ideologies, etc), the change of supplementary roles into complementary roles, and the conjunct elaboration of the proposed task. This process allows to enlarge and enrich the reference scheme of each member of the group and of the group as a whole.

group the individual finds and re-finds the possibility to be continent for himself and for others; to construct a horizontal net of identifications and to share the vertical axis - in the Freudian sense[7] - which offers him the opportunity to pass from object of interest to subject of interest, that is form alienated subject to subject of enunciation.

This group methodology, resting on the characteristics of its members, goes through various activities: from the learning of different contents to field practices. This means a curriculum design in which the organization of it's activities is conditioned by the bringing of the group into scene.

It is understood that to implement any educational change, in particular our proposal, teacher training is required. Is it possible to change if this condition is not fulfilled? We think not. To arrive at solutions without creating the necessary institutional conditions is unthinkable. Besides the particular discipline of each teacher, it is necessary to experience a training in group work, in which teachers (in their individual and institutional level) may analyze their own needs, interests and determinations, in order to be able to organize and promote a group apprenticeship among the pupils.

The Ethical Dimension

The articulation with the ethical dimension also makes reference to the ego ideal. This psychological entity represents, besides the things mentioned above, an ethical conception and the social discourse to which the individual gives recognition. From here we can ask: "Which is the relation between a particular ethic, of a certain social discourse, and an ethic in general? Which is the relation of these ethics with the environmental education?"

To answer these questions, we can refer to the interesting ideas postulated by L. Wittgenstein in Cambridge in 1930, in his conference on Ethic[8] . This author states certain ideas that to our judgement are central for an ethical conception and that can be a great support for an environmental education.

The first of these ideas is that the object of Ethic cannot be approached in a scientific manner "... since it surges from the desire of saying something about the final meaning of life, about the absolutely valuable, it can not be a

---

[7]For S. Freud the mass structure (we can understand group) is composed by a net of vertical identifications that each member establishes with the lider (in our case the task) and at he same time by a net of horizontal identifications established among the members, from their vertical identifications; (in our case the members of the group would have as vertical identification the environmental dimension).Cfr. "Psicología de las Masas y An lisis del Yo" en Obras Completas, Vol. 18 p.63-127. Bs. As.: Amorrortu, 1976.

[8]Wittgenstein, L. Conferencia sobre Etica. Bs.As.: Paidos, 1989.

science". We understand that the "valuable" or the "good" are always enunciations of specific facts; that is, they are inevitable "judgements of value". To pretend to speak of universal propositions in relation to what is "valuable", to what is "wrong", to what is "good" implies the intention of subduing what is beyond facts. In Wittgenstein's opinion, this escapes from the scientific approach. This is the important point for our purpose.

This "beyond" facts is something inaccessible for Man. If for Man - according to Wittgenstein - the limit of the world is the language, Ethic is the intent to go beyond these limits. Man's pretension is to understand these "absolutes" that are not facts. His pretension is to go beyond language, to surpass the limits of his own existence: the intent of finding that "ultimate meaning" whose counterpoise is death. About this fact we can make many statements, "say things", but it will always preserve a dimension which belongs to Ethic, for language is silenced there where death is more than a simple biological fact. This is the articulation point with environment. The world-wide situation has converted death in a familiar presence.

The above statements allow us to establish the following:

(a)   death has to do with Ethic meaning "beyond language";

(b)   the way to counter-approach this "unutterable" is determined by relative judgements and therefore historical;

(c)   To "counter-approach" or not is also a matter of ethic (not only) and it reveals the position of the social discourse in a specific historical moment.

In this way, the menace of death is a matter of ethic and so is the way to counter-approach it. For this reason this subject must be included every time a teacher uses environmental education. It is a "reality" that cannot and must not be concealed. It is an error to try to hide it because only in it's recognition is the possibility of becoming conscious of the need of a conjuncted civil action.

Another important reason to "speak" about death is that it has a tight link with a psychological mechanism which, unconsciously, makes us believe that death will never come. Consciously we know that it is inevitable, but we always refer it to others. If the social discourse "denies" it, a sort of complicity is sustained that paradoxically has negative results because it keeps the individuals from taking consequent actions.

We can say that in every individual there is an "ethic aspiration" as he intends an answer to the interrogations of death. Along history, man has found "the" or "diverse arguments" that answer these interrogations. In fact, we can sustain that the ego ideal contents, which recall the ethical values of the parents, express in their psychological equivalence the importance of these social forms for the psychological dynamics. The value the individual gives to those discourses represents the alternatives for the answer to his interrogations. In this sense is the importance of constructing an environmental education that besides offering real and precise information around the problem offers a conscience which enables the individual to counter-approach the limits of language from an environmental position-conception.

Conclusions

Based upon the preceding statements we can say that to accomplish an environmental education which enables the individual for a praxis we require:

- an epistemological, theoretical and methodological approach to reality which allows us to understand its complexity, its multidetermination and its dialectic transformation process.

- the formation of a socializing conscience regarding social relations and man - nature relations.

- to form a critical conscience towards development, the use of science and technology and towards social and economic models that proclaim the exploitation and irrational use of nature.

In this sense and as point of departure to establish bases for this education-formation, it is necessary to think in an inter and multidisciplinary focus of curriculum and its organization in which the pupil and his relation with environment is brought to the center of the process. A conception of education as praxis must be introduced, in order to understand the learning-teaching process as a unity, as a continuous experience where the teacher's role and the pupils role become complementary.

It is necessary to elaborate a didactic in which the pupil finds himself involved as subject of the action; in which knowledge is approached in a dialectic manner in order to comprehend the real dimension of the environmental problem. We think this is possible through a process of action research. This methodology allows the individual to achieve an instrumental appropriation of reality and enables a process of learning and learning to think. We understand this didactic as the strategy to know and mobilize the cognitive, the affectionate and the action structures. That is, this didactic is an articulation destined not only to communicate knowledge but also to develop skills and modify attitudes. To establish this conception of learning involves the search for the theoretical and practical integration as a dialectical unity of the cognizant act.

References

Bachelard, Gaston. (1982). <u>La Formación del espíritu científico</u>. Mexico: Siglo XXI.

Enzenberger, Hans Magnus. (1971). <u>Para una Crítica de la Ecología Política</u>. Barcelona: Anagrama.

Chamizo, Octavio. Implicaciones Psicológicas de la relación Hombre-Naturaleza en <u>Ecología y Educación</u> (Apuntes teórico-metodológicos para su an lisis). Mexico: CESU/UNAM. indito.

Chamizo, O. y Ma del Pilar Jimnez S. (1984). La Pedagogía y los Grupos en el An lisis Institucional en <u>Revista Mexicana de Sociología</u>. Aúo XLVI. Num 1.

Devereux, George. De (1985). la Ansiedad al Mtodo en <u>las Ciencias del Comportamiento</u>. Mexico: Siglo XXI.

Freud, Sigmund. (1976). Psicología de las Masas y an lisis del Yo en <u>Obras Completas</u> Vol. 18. Bs. As.: Amorrortu.

Jimnez S. Ma del Pilar. (1990). Propuesta Guía para una Educación Ambiental en el Nivel de Educación Media Básica en <u>Documentos y Materiales de Trabajo del II Seminario-Taller de Educación Ambiental Formal</u>. Mexico: SEDUE, SEP, FFES.

Leff, Enrique (1986). Ambiente y Articulación de Ciencias" en <u>Los Problemas del Conocimiento y la Perspectiva Ambiental del Desarrollo</u>. Enrique Leff coord. Mexico: Siglo XXI.

Montes, Jos Maria y E. Leff. (1986). óPerspectiva Ambiental del Desarrollo del Conocimientoó en <u>Los Problemas del Conocimiento y la Perspectiva Ambiental del Desarrollo</u>. E. Leff coord. Mexico: Siglo XXI.

Marcuse, Herbert. (1973). <u>Contrarevolución y Revuelta</u>. Mexico: Joaquín Mortíz, 1973.

Pichon-Rivi re, Enrique. (1978). <u>Del Psicoan lisis a la Psicología Social</u>. Bs. As.: Nueva Visión.

Saint Marc, Philippe. (1971). <u>La Socialización de la Naturaleza</u>. Madrid: Gaudiana de Publicaciones.

ABOUT THE AUTHOR

Maria Del Pilar Jimenez Silva was born in Columbia. She completed her B.S. in Sociology at the Universidad de Santo Tomas de Aquino, Bogota, Columbia.   She has an M.S. in Education Sciences from the Universidad Nacional Autonoma de Mexico (NNAM) with psychoanalytical theory and clinical work at the Circulo Pscoanalitico Mexicano, Mexico D.F. Maria is a Ph.D. candidate in Sociology at the Facultad de Ciencias Politicas y Sociales (UNAM).

Maria is presently an Investigador Asociado (associate researcher) with Centro de Estudios Sobre la Universidad (CESU), Coordinacion de Humanidades (UNAM). Her research is in psychoanalysis and education, environmental education, and teacher training (psychology of education and group work). She also conducts private clinical work in individual psycho-analysis and group work.

A MODEL PROGRAM FOR RESEARCH AND DEVELOPMENT INTERACTION

Victor J. Mayer
and
Rosanne W. Fortner

Abstract

The Ohio Sea Grant Education program (Mayer & Fortner, 1987b) can provide a model of an integrated materials development, dissemination, and teacher enhancement program in environmental education. This program was established with funding from the National Oceanic and Atmospheric Administration, Office of Sea Grant, in 1977 and continues through this 1992 writing under it original leadership. A key to its success has been a comprehensive program of formative and summative evaluation covering each of its components. Evaluation efforts are ongoing and employ several research designs. The total effort is offered here as one model of research that has been useful to Environmental Education practitioners.

PROGRAM COMPONENTS AND THEIR FORMATIVE EVALUATION PROCEDURES

Materials Development

The initial efforts of the Ohio Sea Grant Education program focused on materials development. The Oceanic Education Activities for Great Lakes Schools (OEAGLS) started as a three-year project to develop supplementary curricular activities on Great Lakes topics for middle school science classes in the region. It used a unique combination of scientists, teachers and curriculum developers to assemble modules on some 22 different topics such as the ecology of Great Lakes organisms, erosion causes and lake shore protection, and recreation activities in the region.

Once an activity was drafted, content experts and teachers were asked to review it qualitatively prior to testing. A teacher was then identified and asked to use the activity in all of his or her classes. Each activity was systematically evaluated among the middle school audience for which it was intended. Multiple choice items were developed and given to the classes as a pretest and as a post test to assess whether the objectives of the activity were met. The results were analyzed to identify any areas of low achievement. If such areas were found, the related objectives were examined and the sections of the activity relating to those objectives were analyzed for problems.

Students in the pilot classes also responded to three attitude items designed to determine the interest level, difficulty and clarity of the activity.

If problems were indicated, the activity was examined for ways in which it could be made more appealing or clearer to the students. In addition to evaluation through test data. the teacher was asked to critique the activity and its various components using a standard form provided by the project. Information was collected on ease of use of the materials, level of involvement of the class, and amount of additional planning time required for use of the activity.

Perhaps the most useful component of the evaluation process was the visits to the pilot classes by one of the two principal investigators. They were able to observe student reactions to the activity, interview selected students and discuss the activity personally with the teacher. Observational data aided in revision of the draft materials.

All of the information from the evaluation process was then used to rewrite the activity. If very extensive rewriting was necessary, the activity was retested in another classroom. The final stage in evaluation was the submission of the activity to a content expert who provided a final review of the accuracy of the subject matter. After adjustments made necessary by the content review were completed, the activity was then ready for distribution to teachers. The details of formative evaluation of the materials have been reported as a case study by Rhodes (1983).

Initial Dissemination Efforts

When the OEAGLS project was first proposed it was clear that there had to be a dissemination program designed to get the materials and philosophy to Ohio teachers, since the modular format of the materials and the infusion philosophy incorporated into the program precluded publication by a commercial publisher.

An initial means of dissemination was the publication of a newsletter containing a variety of features, including the announcement and description of completed activities. Entitled Middle Sea, it reached a peak quarterly distribution of about 2000 subscribers, primarily Ohio teachers and teacher educators. Early in the development project Middle Sea was a primary means of making teachers aware of OEAGLS availability, and each issue resulted in a flurry of orders for activities. Upon completion of the project, a catalog was published that included descriptions of all activities. The catalog was mailed in response to general requests for information and results in sales of individual modules.

Interest in the OEAGLS activities was also generated along Lake Erie through the work of the three Ohio Sea Grant advisory agents, who disseminated the materials through their workshops. The principal investigators also accepted opportunities to make presentations at teachers' meetings anywhere in the state. OEAGLS were invariably used in the workshop presentations. Programs were given at school district inservice days, regional meetings of the Ohio Education Association, and annual meetings of state science and social studies organizations. In addition, presentations have been made at national and regional meetings of the National Science Teachers Association, North American Association of Environmental Education and other organizations. During the last two years of the development project, these measures resulted in the distribution of several thousand copies of the OEAGLS materials.

Informal formative evaluation efforts were employed during this stage of dissemination, including open response forms completed at the end of workshops, review of issues of <u>Middle Sea</u> by staff of both the education program and Ohio Sea Grant leadership, and tabulation of sales and requests for infomation following publication of newsletter issues.

Awareness Program

The formal dissemination program was conceived as a three year cycle, following the completion of the materials development phase, to promote awareness of the materials throughout the State of Ohio. It was designed to systematically introduce the materials to every section of the state through a series of awareness workshops and to develop a cadre of well trained teachers centered in the major metropolitan areas of the state through a series of implementation workshops.

The awareness component was intended to develop broad awareness among teachers and administrators across the State of Ohio regarding the objectives of marine and aquatic education and a knowledge of the materials available for use in teaching toward those objectives, especially the OEAGLS materials.

The implementation component was intended for in depth training of teachers to provide them with information and resources to implement marine and aquatic education in their classrooms.

Exceptional teacher leaders and administrators, supervisors and faculty in institutions of higher education were identified as a statewide advisory group. They assisted in developing guidelines for the conduct of the awareness program and continued to serve as an advisory group throughout the project.

Workshop Format

Perhaps the major task during the first year was to develop a format for the awareness workshops. They included at least 10 clock hours of instruction, and each participant wrote a paper on some aspect of classroom follow-up activities. The format developed during this first year was piloted in two workshops, one held in Columbus and the other on Lake Erie at Ottawa National Wildlife Refuge. They were evaluated through open response questionnaires and discussions of staff with participants. During the second year this program was modified to take into account the evaluation information.

In designing the final format for awareness workshops, a major portion of the time was devoted to active teacher involvement with OEAGLS activities. An introductory session with all workshop participants provided background on how OEAGLS were developed and involved teachers in the playing of a board game about factors influencing the yellow perch population of Lake Erie. This activity introduced teachers to the style and intent of the OEAGLS materials. Three sets of concurrent sessions conducted the following day presented up to nine additional modules.

An introductory lecture provided a view of the breadth and scope of marine and aquatic education and examples of its interdisciplinary nature. Two additional lectures were presented on important content topics. One dealt with the geology and natural resources of the Lake Erie region and another on the characteristics of the lake water. The lectures were carefully refined to include the most important material extensively illustrated in the form of slides and overhead visuals.

The workshops also provided teachers with opportunities to become familiar with a wide variety of curricular resources. Two sessions were held to accomplish this: one during the first evening in which participants could informally participate in a variety of activities set up as individual learning stations and one the following day where teachers had the opportunity of perusing the best teaching and resource materials from other marine and aquatic programs around the country.

Formative Evaluation

An important factor in the success of the awareness workshops was the continued attention of the project staff to workshop evaluations. Two types were used for each program. First, a three item evaluation was completed by participants following each major presentation and each concurrent session. The form requested the name of the presentation and asked teachers to respond to three items; the relative interest of the presentation to them; the relative increase in their knowledge level as a result of the session; and the degree to which the presented materials would be used by the teacher. Space was also left for comments. When all forms were collected for any one session, the presenter of that session was able to gain immediate feedback on its effects. The project staff was also able to perceive immediate needs of the total group and make adjustments in approach or scheduling to meet those needs.

An analysis of data collected from these questionnaires was performed. Although there was variation between workshops on the degree of interest participants found, the mean response always ranged between interesting and very interesting. The participants' perceptions of the knowledge levels gained from the workshops also were high throughout the workshops with the mean response ranging from increased somewhat (2) to increased greatly (1). Teachers also indicated that they would use the materials with the mean response focussing on the "yes" (1) end of the scale.

There does not seem to be a change in quality of the workshops with time. It was anticipated that there should be some type of improvement with experience. The lack of such a trend in the data can be explained in several ways. First there was not a great deal of room for improvement on participant responses. Even the first workshops were very highly rated. Therefore any upward trend in the data would be difficult to obtain. There also may be a "fatigue" factor; that is the first several workshops were a new experience and so the presenters put extra effort and enthusiasm into them. Therefore, even though there may have been rough spots, this enthusiasm carried the participants over them. Later, and there does seem to be some type of sag in the data on the 5th through 8th workshop, this enthusiasm may have waned a bit with experience and the now polished nature of the workshops influencing the data from workshop 9 onward. Regardless, these data do show that the workshops were well received by the participants. It was a very successful program, and the participants especially appreciated seeing the immediate effects of their feedback.

At the end of each awareness workshop all participants completed an open-ended questionnaire in which they expressed their attitudes about the atmosphere of the workshop, its value to their teaching, and changes that might be made to improve future workshops. Participants in inland workshops were also asked whether they felt that Lake Erie was important to teach about in their geographic area. This overall evaluation of each workshop provided an indication of the workshops' impacts, from which it is possible to chart the continued growth and responsiveness that contributed to the Infusion Program's success. The results of these open ended evaluation forms support the conclusions above, that the workshops were very successful in accomplishing their objectives. They were received with a great deal of enthusiasm by the participants. Their success indicates in part the value of the consistent and thorough formative evaluation techniques used. The workshop organizers were able to spot any problem areas and correct them during the workshop or by the time of the subsequent workshop thus leading to a consistently high quality program.

A final form of evaluation consisted of analysis of the papers written by workshop participants. These were written after teachers returned to their homes, and they reflected how teachers used the workshop ideas and adapted them for their classes' special needs.

During the second and third years of the infusion program 12 workshops were conducted over the State of Ohio. Over 600 teachers and administrators were enrolled and some 4000 OEAGLS activities distributed through the program.

The program newsletter, <u>Middle Sea</u>, had become recognized as one of the best of its kind in marine and aquatic education. With the initiation of the infusion program, however, its focus changed from emphasis on new OEAGLS activities to one of broader service to teachers. Each issue included a feature article dealing with information on Lake Erie of use to teachers, a classroom activity, reviews of teaching materials or publications and announcements of events of interest to teachers. The variety of Middle Sea articles reemphasized the interdisciplinary nature of marine and aquatic education and highlighted the workshops, publications and plans of the Sea Grant program. This proved to be an excellent vehicle for keeping in contact with teachers who participated in the workshops. It served as a reminder of the availability of activities and materials in marine and aquatic education, and of the interest of the Sea Grant staff in the activities of the teachers it had served.

Implementation Program

The tasks of this component as specified in the proposal were to extend opportunities to Ohio teachers for obtaining in-depth background in knowledge and curricular materials related to marine and aquatic education, and to provide continuing assistance to Ohio educators.

Course structure

Two types of courses were offered, an inservice program during the regular academic year, and a summer workshop program. The inservice program was scheduled for ten three-hour evening sessions and one all day field trip. Summer workshops met for one-half day every day for two weeks and included one all-day field trip. In-depth exploration of activities was possible in implementation sessions, and as a product each teacher developed a new activity about the Great Lakes for use in their own classes. The teachers were not only participants in but contributors to the program.

The content of both types of programs was similar. Lake Erie and the Great Lakes were used as a focus for teaching content information about the world's large bodies of water. Implications of a concept for the oceans and lakes were drawn through the discussions, lectures, activities and visual aids. Content from all relevant disciplines was presented: in addition to the science related content usually associated with courses about water, significant time was devoted the visual arts, music, literature and crafts. Concepts in history, economics and transportation were presented. Each topic was developed through an activity. Most were the OEAGLS activities, but others were drawn from the Crustal Evolution Education Project, Project COAST, and Ocean Related Curriculum Activities (ORCA). Each activity used became a basis for discussing the concept in greater depth, providing teachers with the confidence necessary to adequately teach the concept in their own classes.

Field experiences were incorporated into each of the implementation workshops. These normally consisted of a one day field trip adapted to the locality. For example, in Cincinnati, along the Ohio River, the class visited a marina and docking facilities, and also a vocational program that trained workers for the river transportation industry. Since Cincinnati is a world famous collecting locality for Ordovician fossils, a lunch stop was planned so that teachers could observe and collect a variety of fossils. The Cleveland workshop included a trip along the lake shore to study erosional and depositional features, and visits to a marina, factory sites and a small maritime museum. Field experiences were designed to reflect the interdisciplinary nature of marine and aquatic education, therefore not only science localities were visited but also those of economic and historic significance.

Formative evaluation

Formative evaluation of the implementation workshops included the short three-item instrument used in the awareness workshops administered after each segment of the workshop. Daily debriefings were held by the staff members and often included program participants. A final questionnaire probing the value of various workshop components was given at the end of the course. In their course projects, the participants clearly demonstrated by their own production of activities, that they had developed plans for use of workshop information in their classrooms and were using OEAGLS as an infusion model.

SUMMATIVE EVALUATION OF THE CURRICULUM DEVELOPMENT AND TEACHER EDUCATION PROGRAM

The major thrust of the first six years of the Ohio Sea Grant Education Program was at the middle school level and consisted of the OEAGLS project and the infusion project. A unique summative evaluation was conducted for this entire program.

Questions to be Answered

A variety of data sources were used to examine questions related to the effectiveness of the overall middle school program and its two components: the OEAGLS curriculum development effort and the infusion program. The following questions have been examined:

1. Effectiveness of components:

    a. Does a four week unit comprised of OEAGLS materials improve student knowledge of Lake Erie and the world's oceans?

    b. Do extended workshops increase the probability of teachers' sustained use of OEAGLS materials preferentially as compared to the one-day workshops?

    c.   Do workshops increase the probability of teachers' sustained use of OEAGLS materials, compared to volunteer orders and to distribution of activities following a brief stage program abut Lake Erie?

2.   Overall effectiveness of the model:

    a.   Have student knowledge and attitudes regarding Lake Erie and the oceans improved over the interval in which OEAGLS materials were being actively disseminated through the infusion program?

    b.   Have student perceptions of their sources of knowledge regarding marine and aquatic education changed during this interval?

Description of Research

The evaluation program had three components, each with a different focus and methodology. The first component was designed to answer question la above. It consisted of the evaluation of a four-week earth science unit composed of OEAGLS activities using a unique time-series design for data collection. The second, designed to answer questions 1b and 1c, was a questionnaire survey of participants from different dissemination programs. The last, to answer questions 2a and 2b, was a survey of 5th and 9th graders to determine their level of knowledge of Great Lakes and ocean information and their attitudes toward Lake Erie and the oceans. The evaluation program was supported by the Sea Grant program and the Seed Grant Program of the Graduate School of Ohio State University.

1. Effectiveness of an OEAGLS unit: Intensive time-series research

In formative evaluation, the OEAGLS materials had been evaluated individually using pre-post procedures with the classes of a single teacher. Although adequate for the purposes of the formative evaluation process, this procedure did not provide the data that would permit an assessment of the effectiveness of the materials in changing student's understanding of aquatic and oceanic concepts. This type of assessment can only be made when students have had sufficient time of exposure to materials, more than the one or two days that an individual OEAGLS activity typically takes.

Method

To determine the overall effectiveness of OEAGLS activities, an earth science unit of four weeks duration designed entirely from OEAGLS activities was used in a central Ohio junior high school with all students of an earth science teacher: six eighth grade classes totalling 105 students.

These served as the pilot group. One other teacher was identified from the same school. His eighth grade earth science classes numbering 35 students served as a comparison group. The pilot and comparison groups were similar in general academic achievement.

Data were collected regarding student knowledge of the content of the unit through a unique daily testing system using six personal computers. Each student responded to a multiple choice item each day, beginning eleven days before the start of the unit and continuing for eight days beyond the end of the unit (Mayer and Raudabaugh, 1987). End of unit knowledge was assessed through the use of a multiple choice posttest. Items developed for use in the formative evaluation of the OEAGLS activities were used as the basis for both testing systems. A few additional items were developed and piloted prior to their use in the study. The same posttest was used with the pilot and comparison groups. The introduction of the OEAGLS unit was expected to positively affect the slope of the curve plotted from the data generated by the daily assessment of knowledge. A daily log of the classroom activities was also kept by the teacher to assist in the interpretation of the data.

Results and Discussion

Figure 1 displays the data accumulated concerning student knowledge of the unit objectives as reflected by performance on the multiple-choice items taken every day over the 44 days of the study. The first 11 days of the data are referred to as the baseline. They precede the introduction of the unit. The data exhibit a pattern of decreasing performance. This has been found in each of the studies using this unique data collection system. It appears that students begin to resent having to answer questions on information that they have not been taught. As a result, they tire of trying to answer the questions correctly, and thus their performance falls. The positive influence of the unit on student knowledge is apparent from the gradual rise of the curve during the next phase of the data collection, the intervention phase (when the unit was being used). It is apparent that student knowledge increased gradually as the unit progressed. The highest class average was on day 36 (73.7 percent correct), the day that the unit posttest was given following the end of the unit. The mean percent correct on the unit posttest was 68.4 percent for the pilot group and 35 percent for the comparison group. Averaging the percent correct across the 11 days prior to the beginning of the unit, the baseline phase of the data collection period, yielded 42 percent. It is therefore evident that the unit was indeed successful in raising student knowledge about Great Lakes and oceans by a significant amount. The OEAGLS activities therefore seem to be effectively designed for facilitating student learning of information about the Great Lakes and oceans.

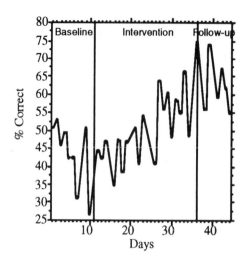

Figure 1:   Trend of student knowledge during evaluation of the OEAGLS unit

2. Evaluating modes of dissemination: Survey with canonical correlation and discriminant analysis

Four different procedures were used for disseminating OEAGLS activities. A study was conducted during the first half of 1984 to determine the relative effectiveness of the procedures in terms of the degree of usage of the materials by recipients. Research reported here has appeared in Mayer & Fortner (1987a).

The four means of dissemination were as follows:

1.   Awareness workshops. These were discussed earlier in this paper. Participants had the option of obtaining one quarter hour of graduate credit at no cost, however a small materials fee was charged. About 600 teachers enrolled in these programs.

2.   Implementation workshops. These were also discussed earlier. Participants received 3 to 4 quarter hours of graduate credit at no cost other than a small materials fee. About 180 teachers were enrolled in the 6 programs in this category.

3.   Mail orders. Over a two year period, some 200 individuals ordered OEAGLS activities as a result of their being advertised in the project newsletter or in other sources. There was a nominal charge for the activities.

4.   Museum student program. A program on Lake Erie was offered by the Center of Science and Industry (COSI) in Columbus during the 1982-83 school year. About 400 teachers who brought their students to the program were given an OEAGLS activity of their choice.

Method

A questionnaire consisting of 20 items in an objective response format was developed to determine the relative effectiveness of the different modes of dissemination, and to obtain information on teacher background characteristics. The instrument was refined through its use by science education students enrolled in a first year doctoral seminar at The Ohio State University.

A 30% random sample was drawn from the awareness workshop, implementation workshop and mail order populations and a 20% random sample from the museum student program population. The questionnaire was mailed to the individuals drawn in the samples. A combination of follow-up techniques resulted in the following response rates: awareness 78%, implementation 76%, mail orders 61%, and museum 48%. A telephone survey of a 20% random sample of the non-respondents was conducted to determine the equivalence of the respondents and non-respondents on certain variables. The actual number contacted in each group was too small to do statistical comparisons, however it appeared that there were no differences between non-respondents and respondents on use of OEAGLS activities and on other items chosen from the questionnaire. Therefore the responses obtained can be considered representative of each of the populations.

Results and Discussion

A preliminary analysis was performed through the generation and examination of two-way tables using the groups as one of the variables. An intersection between awareness and implementation workshop groups occurred with a sizeable number of teachers having participated in both activities. Their data were separated out to form a fifth group.

Three usage variables were examined. In the first, teachers were asked whether they were using the instructional materials during the current school year. Those who answered positively were then asked if they had introduced them to other teachers in their school, and to teachers in other schools. Responses are summarized in Table 1.

A one-way analysis of variance performed on the use variable between the five groups yielded between group differences were significant at the 0.001 level. Therefore the various modes of dissemination were distinctly different in their effectiveness in terms of the subsequent use of the materials by the recipients. To determine which methods were most effective additional ANOVAs were run; between the awareness group, the implementation group, and the combined awareness-implementation group, and between the awareness and implementation groups. The results of the first were significant at the 0.08 level and the second at the 0.03 level. It therefore appears that the differences between the awareness and implementation groups on use of the OEAGLS activities are significant.

TABLE 1
Use of Instructional Materials By Type of Dissemination Effort

Group	Use by Teacher		Introduced to Other Teacher		Introduced to Other School	
	N1	Percent	N	Percent	N	Percent
Awareness	102	78	82	73	74	16
Implementation	32	58	19	63	15	33
Awareness and implementation	21	81	18	72	18	17
Mail Order	26	54	22	58	14	50
Museum	25	4	1	0	0	0

1 N = Number of respondents on item

It was surprising to note that those teachers enrolled in the short awareness workshops had a significantly higher rate of usage, and also the highest rate of introduction of materials to other teachers in their schools. This is the reverse of what might be expected. In justifying the offering of the longer workshops it was believed that the longer time would permit greater depth of instruction resulting in more confidence with using the materials and thus higher usage. The relatively high usage by the mail order group was not expected since there was no direct contact nor teacher training. On the other hand it was not totally surprising, since these people had enough knowledge and interest in the activities to go to the trouble of ordering and paying for them. It is reasonable to assume that they would have the incentive to actually use them in the classroom.

Of further interest was the lack of usage among those teachers who were simply given an activity in the museum program without any formal workshop experience. The program was expected to raise interest in the subject matter to the point where teaching about it was stimulated. From these results it might be suspected that other short exposures on subject matter and materials, such as those offered at state or national conventions, may have similar low levels of impact on teachers.

Why the difference between the awareness and implementation groups? All workshops were conducted by the same people and followed similar philosophies using similar materials. Formative evaluations of the workshops indicate that the short and long ones were at least equally effective in training teachers. This leads to the conclusion that there must be differences in the teachers who elected to attend the two types of workshops.

Responses to items on the questionnaire permitted an examination of certain teacher background characteristics. A discriminant analysis program was run to determine which teacher background characteristics discriminated among the three workshop groups. Six characteristics (Table 2) were weighted on two functions with a Wilkes Lambda of 0.88 (12 df) significant at the 0.075 level for function 1 and a Wilkes Lambda of 0.094 (5 df) significant at the 0.095 level for function 2.

Background characteristics which were important in discriminating among groups were semester hours in education courses, number of years teaching, completion of Master's degree, number of education association meetings attended, and service on curriculum or textbook adoption committees.

The teachers selecting the short awareness workshops (Table 3) were less likely to have an advanced degree, more likely to attend professional meetings and more likely to participate in curriculum and textbook adoption committees. It appears therefore that they are the type who are more interested in the professional benefits derived from such participation than in the academic credit given since it is greater in the longer programs. Those teachers taking the implementation workshops may be more concerned about gaining hours toward the Masters degree or toward the next level of their districts' salary scale. This is supported by the fact that teachers taking both workshops (hence accumulating the maximum amount of credit available) had the most education courses, were most likely to have a Master's degree and had been in the teaching profession the shortest time.

The results of this study provide some intriguing insights into the relative effectiveness of common dissemination modes. Simply giving an activity to a teacher is worthless. It won't be used. Those individuals who order activities by mail will probably use them. What is surprising is that longer workshops do not lead to greater usage. This seems to be related to the type of individual attracted into each of the two types of workshops. Although similar in the usual teacher background characteristics, there seems to be a difference in several characteristics that together may imply a professional orientation that motivates the choices of workshops made by teachers.

TABLE 2
Standardized Canonical Discriminant
Function Coefficients

VARIABLE	FUNCTION 1	FUNCTION 2
Education Courses	0.893	0.264
Masters Degree	-0.036	0.471
Years Teaching	-0.620	-0.373
Education Magazines	0.369	-0.381
Education Meetings	-0.049	-0.414
Committee Memberships	-0.248	0.693

TABLE 3
Means Of Variables Used In
Discriminant Analysis

VARIABLE	AW	IM	AW-IM
Science Courses	3.79	3.69	3.76
Education Courses	4.79	4.53	5.33
Masters Degree	0.54	0.59	0.62
Years Teaching	14.99	14.50	12.67
Education Magazines	2.08	1.56	1.90
Education Meetings	1.26	0.81	0.71
Committee Memberships	1.15	1.34	1.24

For materials disseminators it is apparent that money is better spent on short workshops. They tend to attract those teachers who are more likely to use the materials presented. And obviously more workshops reaching more teachers can be offered for the money available.

3. Evaluation of Student Knowledge and Attitudes: Longitudinal Survey

Component three of the evaluation was a longitudinal study, a repeated survey of knowledge and attitudes of Ohio children regarding the Great Lakes and the oceans (Fortner & Mayer, 1983, 1988, Fortner 1989). The composite report, portions of which are reproduced here, is in press for the Journal of Environmental Education.

In 1979 the Ohio Sea Grant Education Program conducted a baseline study to determine the knowledge and attitudes of Ohio students about the oceans and Great Lakes (Fortner & Mayer, 1983). The study revealed a low level of knowledge, with fifth graders answering 37.6% and ninth graders 8.3% of questions correctly. Attitudes about the oceans and Great Lakes were related to knowledge, with high scorers having more positive attitudes. Students indicated that most of their information on the subjects was obtained through movies and television.

The Ohio Sea Grant Education Program has now been active for fourteen years. During that period many of the concerns raised by the knowledge levels revealed in the baseline test have been addressed and many of the media utilized (Mayer and Fortner 1987b). The test was repeated in 1983 and 1987, offering a longitudinal study of awareness changes among students that is currently without parallel in environmental education studies. Details on design of the study are summarized in Fortner and Mayer (1983 and 1988).

This model and the results of the individual test components have provided some valuable insights for a continuing program in environmental education, providing answers to the following questions about changes over the eight year period:

1) How have Ohio students' knowledge and attitudes about the marine and Great Lakes environments changed?

2) What trends in knowledge acquisition can be noted?

3) How are demographic characteristics of students related to their knowledge and attitudes about the oceans and Great Lakes, and have these relationships changed?

4) Has the source of student knowledge about water environments changed?

In addition, the advantages and disadvantages of this repeated measures model for assessing changes induced by environmental education programs can be evaluated.

Methods

Research design. This was a longitudinal study using a comparison group. Participating schools were selected randomly, and no school participated in any two of the three tests. Fifth graders in 1979 were therefore the cohort of ninth graders in 1983, not the same students. Likewise, fifth graders of 1983 were the cohort of ninth graders in 1987. The ninth graders of 1979 serve as the comparison group, since they had no earlier cohort in the testing and no opportunity to be exposed to the aquatic education programs being developed for middle school. Their awareness level reflects general awareness of aquatic environments among that age group. A general baseline was established in 1979 (Fortner & Mayer, 1983). With the addition of OEAGLS-specific items in 1983, a new baseline was established for the knowledge assessed by those items (Fortner & Mayer, 1988).

Survey development. The survey instrument consisted of the original 1979 instrument with some modifications. The final instrument contained the following:

(1) a test of knowledge--25 multiple choice questions on each of three test forms, used in all three test years. Within the 25, six items common to all forms served as a means of assessing equivalence of groups responding to the forms. Ten additional items per form were added to the 1983 and 1987 surveys, to test OEAGLS-specific information and important new concepts identified since 1979. All knowledge items were classified as either science, social studies or humanities, and were equally divided among the three forms.

(2)   an attitude, assessment--2 sets, of 10 semantic differential items with adjectival pairs describing the dimensions of potency evaluation and, activity of two referents, "The Ocean" and "Lake Erie." This portion was the same for all test forms in all years.

(3)   one item identifying the media source from which information was obtained relating to the content measured on the test of knowledge. The same item was used in all years.

Content validity was established through a review of all test instruments by a panel of experts in marine and Great Lakes education. The KR-20 reliability for the fifth grade test forms ranged from 0.38 to 0.51. Because of low internal consistency, no analyses were attempted for fifth grade data beyond summary statistics. For ninth graders, the KR-20 ranged from 0.56 to 0.72. Chi-square analyses of the common test items indicated no significant differences between those taking the three test forms in any of the test years. Therefore all items could be pooled for analysis.

Sample Selection. The State of Ohio was divided into Lake, Central and River regions, since results of earlier studies (Fortner & Teates, 1980) indicated that proximity to a large body of water was related to higher knowledge scores. From each of the three areas, 5% of the fifth grade schools and 10% of the ninth grade schools were randomly selected from the Ohio Educational Directory and invited to participate in the study. The principal of each school identified a cooperating teacher by a specified randomizing technique, and the teacher was asked to present the survey to the class that he or she taught during the last period of the day.

Results

In discussing the results of the testing over the three applications it must be kept in mind that the returns of the 1987 study were very low (28% of fifth grade schools contacted and 35% of ninth). It therefore cannot be assumed that they are representative of 5th and 9th graders in the state. However, the demographic measures that are available indicate that on the variables sex and race the schools providing responses were not greatly different than those in the previous two tests. Those two variables were significantly related to knowledge and attitudes in the first two administrations of the test.
Over the three test years, scores on the general items have increased slightly, from 37.6% to 39.1% correct in Grade 5 and from 48.3% to 50% in Grade 9 in 1987 (Table 4). Cohort comparison shows that over a four year period, from fifth grade to ninth grade, the students gain substantial amounts of knowledge, increasing their scores an average of over ten percentage points.

Table 4. Student Knowledge Scores by Content Area of the Statewide Survey

Content	Percent Answering Correctly in:					
	1979		1983		1987	
	5th	9th	5th	9th	5th	9th
All Baseline ------	37.6%	48.3%	38.6%	48.0%	39.1%	50.0%
Science-----------	41.0	50.6	40.5	49.9	43.0	54.3
Social Studies-----	36.8	50.0	40.5	50.6	39.5	52.1
Humanities-------	31.8	40.7	27.4	39.8	31.9	40.8
OEAGALS items ---	NA	NA	27.3	32.3	28.7	36.5

Scores on OEAGLS items also increased, especially in the ninth grade, from 32.3% in 1983 to 36.5% in 1987. Fifth graders improved from 27.3% to 28.7% over the period. A ninth grader in 1987 would therefore have gained more than nine percentage points over the fifth grade cohort.

As for the subject matter of the test, both science and social studies items have gained in the number of correct answers over the period, but humanities scores have remained constant, except for a temporary decline in 1983. For OEAGLS items, there was a greater increase in science knowledge than in social studies.

Attitudes of ninth graders were consistently more positive on the oceans and less positive on Lake Erie than fifth graders. On the whole, oceanic attitudes have been declining in both grades (Table 5). In fact, the ninth grader in 1987 was even less positive (3.64 out of 5.0) than the fifth grade cohort in 1983 (3.72). Lake Erie attitudes have declined in Grade 5, but no trend was apparent in Grade 9. Nevertheless, the ninth grade 1987 attitude mean of 2.87 must be considered negative given a range of 1 to 5.

Table 5. Student Attitudes about the Oceans and Great Lakes

Topic	Year	Attitude Mean (5 possible) 5th Grade	9th Grade
Ocean-----------------------------------	1979	3.76	3.97
	1983	3.72	3.82
	1987	3.49	3.64
Lake Erie` ------------------------------	1979	3.49	3.29
	1983	3.49	3.45
	1987	3.64	2.87

In 1979 and 1983 certain demographic variables were related to knowledge scores. Analyses of variance indicated main effects of race in Grade 5, with white students outscoring nonwhites. Main effects of region and race were noted in Grade 9, with higher scores in the coastal area and among white students. A sex-race interaction was also detected in the ninth grade, with white males scoring highest on general knowledge. In 1987 none of these variables were significantly related to either total or OEAGLS knowledge scores.

Perhaps the most important difference between responses in 1979, 1983 and 1987 was students' answers to the question, "Which of the following was the most important in teaching you about the oceans and Great Lakes?" In 1979 students in both grades selected movies and television as the greatest influence; in 1983 both groups selected classes in school as most influential, and that category of information source was still chosen most often in 1987 (Figure 2). By 1987 movies and television had fallen to fifth place for fifth graders and second place for ninth grade.

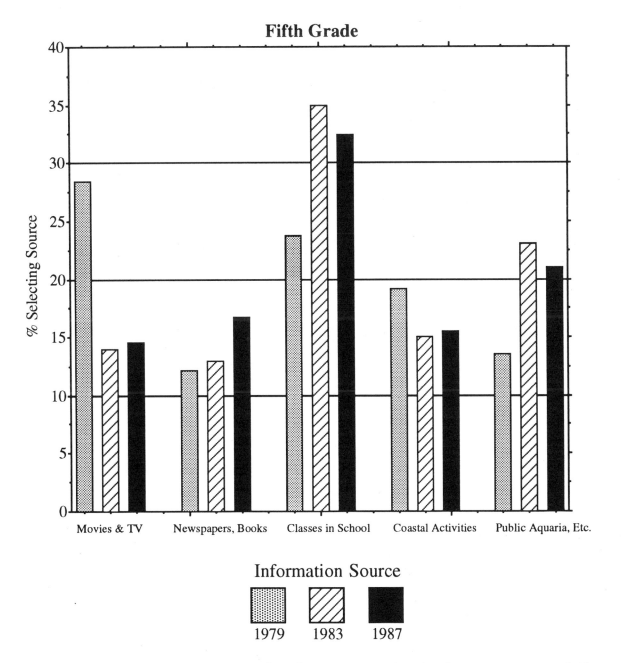

Figure 2.   Student sources of information about the oceans and Great Lakes, 1979 - 1987

Discussion

While it seems clear that Ohio students are learning a significant amount about the oceans and Great Lakes in the middle school years, the slow rise in knowledge levels among ninth graders is an indication that little progress was made in increasing general awareness of the world of water over the eight year test period. Even more discouraging is the fact that attitudes among ninth graders are slightly negative toward Lake Erie and are declining though still positive regarding the oceans.

Impact of classroom source. Perhaps both the knowledge and attitude changes are related to the shift toward greater reliance on classroom information. For example, classes that did not include environmental content in the early 1980s were beginning to include more such information by 1987, whether in the form of OEAGLS, or Science-Technology-Society (STS) lessons or as previously unemphasized text material. The content of that information was indeed somewhat negative at that point in earth's history, as once again the human race was becoming aware of the fragility of the planet. To know more about the oceans and Lake Erie, then, may be to know about their problems and to select Dirty rather than Clean, Awful rather than Nice on a semantic differential survey.

Subject matter trends. There are aspects of the knowledge portion of the survey that also deserve particular attention because of trends that have appeared. First, while almost every one of the biology items shows an improved score over the period, those items related to Earth sciences have declined or are stalled at low percentages of correct answers. This is an indication of the very low emphasis placed on Earth sciences in the curriculum (Mayer, 1991) and the need to increase basic understanding of Earth systems and how they relate to people.

More encouraging trends can be seen among the geography questions. While recent studies claim vast ignorance of geography among our population, about 60% of the ninth graders answered 80% of the map-use items correctly. Finally, it must be noted in a discussion of the content of marine and Great Lakes education that the humanities are being overlooked as a vehicle for teaching about the world of water. It is surely time to begin using our cultural heritage, especially the language arts, as a means of teaching about our planetary home (Mayer 1989; Simpson 1988).

Media impact. It is interesting to note that even though students discount the impact of television on their knowledge of the oceans and Great Lakes, those topics that have received the greatest media coverage over the recent years have all increased in percentage of correct answers. Examples include the reason for disappearance of coastal wetlands, PCBs as a cause for fish advisories, the meaning of eutrophication, and the major cause of lake level changes (Precipitation/evaporation balance).

Lessons from the model.

A major consideration in planning for environmental education is to assure that subject matter is current. In this study, however, it was important to the integrity of the test to administer it intact as a repeated measure of awareness. Of course, during the eight years many environmental characteristics have changed. Issues and answers that were appropriate in

1979 sometimes were not in 1987. Recoding and item testing should accompany future uses of the instrument.

Another lesson from repeated testing is that the classroom day is becoming too crowded to allow for research efforts, and teachers are being approached too frequently to participate in research, even if rewards are offered (a free curriculum module, in this case). The response rate for 1987 was about half that of the other years, and contact methods will be redesigned if the survey is to be offered in the future. A discussion of the implications of the low response rate is found in the complete research description in press for the <u>Journal of Environmental Education.</u>

This portion of the Sea Grant R & D program has served as a means of drawing attention to the need for aquatic environmental education in the state. The student survey mechanism has indicated a need for further curriculum development in current topics related to the Great Lakes and oceans, and it has established classrooms as a recognized source of information on these topics.

Overall, the repeated measure of marine and Great Lakes awareness has provided extremely valuable information about the patterns of change in environmental education, the importance of media, and the potential for impacting large population sectors with an educational effort. The ninth graders who took the survey in 1979 have now voted in two Presidential elections. We can only hope that the media they now encounter will exert even the small but positive effect that classrooms appear to be having on those still in school.

<u>Summary</u>

One of the strengths of Ohio Sea Grant's program for curriculum development and teacher education has been its application of research and evaluation techniques to assess needs and document results of efforts. To be familiar with numerous educational research designs is to be alert to opportunities for their use, and to know their limitations. To date the program has relied mostly on quantitative designs, but the authors acknowledge that new methods of qualitative evaluation can expand the information available and assist in identifying future program directions.

References

Fortner, R.W. (1986). A multiphased evaluation of the impact of a non-school science exhibition. Paper presented at the annual meeting of the American Educational Research Association, San Francisco (ED 272 358).

Fortner, R. W. (1989). <u>The Oceanic and Great Lakes Awareness Survey</u>. ERIC/SMEAC. Columbus, OH (ED 309 072)

Fortner, R.W. and V.J. Mayer. (1983). Ohio students' knowledge and attitudes about the oceans and Great Lakes. <u>The Ohio Journal of Science</u> 83(5): 218-224.

Fortner, R.W. and V.J. Mayer. (1988). Ocean and Great Lakes awareness among fifth and ninth grade Ohio students: A continuing study <u>The Ohio Journal of Science.</u>.

Fortner, R.W. and V. J. Mayer. Repeated measures of students' marine and Great Lakes awareness. <u>Journal of Environmental Education</u>. (in press at time of submission)

Fortner, R.W. and T.G. Teates. (1980). Baseline studies for marine education: Experiences related to marine knowledge and attitudes. <u>Journal of Environmental Education.</u> 11(4): 11-19.

Mayer, V.J. (1991 January). Earth-Systems Science. <u>The Science Teacher</u>, 34-39.

Mayer, V.J. (1990 March). Earth Appreciation. <u>The Science Teacher</u>. 60-63.

Mayer, V.J. and R.W. Fortner. (1987a). Relative effectiveness of four modes of dissemination of curriculum materials. <u>Journal of Environmental Education,</u> 19(1): 25-30.

Mayer, V.J. and R.W. Fortner. (1987b). <u>Ohio Sea Grant Education Program: Development, implementation, evaluation.</u> (Monograph) The Ohio State University Research Foundation, Columbus, OH.

Mayer, Victor J. and John S. Monk. (1983). <u>Handbook for Using the Intensive Time-Series Design.</u> College of Education, The Ohio State University, Columbus.

Mayer, V.J. and William Raudabaugh. (1987). Pilot of a system for collecting daily classroom data on learning by using microcomputers. Paper presented at the annual meeting of the American Educational Research Association, Washington, DC.

Rhodes, Gregory L. (1983). <u>The impact of formative evaluation on the development of social studies curriculum materials</u>. Unpublished doctoral dissertation, Indiana University.

Simpson, Steve. (1988). Speaking for the trees: The use of literature to convey outdoor education themes. <u>Journal of Environmental Education</u> 19(3): 25-31.

About the Authors

Victor J. Mayer is professor of Educational Studies, Geological Sciences and Natural Resources at The Ohio State University, Columbus, OH. He developed the Ohio Sea Grant Education Program in 1977 as the first Sea Grant project for the state, and served as the program coordinator until 1983. His current work in Earth Systems Education continues the interdisciplinary emphasis of this successful aquatic education model, and applies a systems approach for the complete science curriculum. His work continues to apply the results of research and evaluation reported here.

Rosanne W. Fortner is professor of Natural Resources and Educational Studies at Ohio State. She joined the Ohio Sea Grant Education Program in 1978 and has been coordinator since 1983. Her current Sea Grant project deals with global climate change in the Great Lakes and the technologies used to study the environment. The successful model of curriculum development and evaluation described here is being reconstructed with environmental change as the focus.

GETTING THE WORD OUT ABOUT RECYCLING: THE ROLE OF PUBLIC EDUCATION

Deborah Simmons
and
Ron Widmar

Abstract

Communities across the country are facing a garbage crisis, and are finding themselves searching for solutions to a growing amount of refuse with a limited amount of space for its disposal. One often mentioned solution involves reducing the amount of waste produced through recycling and reuse at the household level. Simply instituting a recycling program, however, will not insure waste reduction. Participation in recycling and reuse on a regular basis is dependent upon a variety of factors including knowing what to do and how to do it (Simmons and Widmar, 1989-90). Providing basic information on how to recycle must be a component of any solid waste reduction program.

Introduction

The task becomes one of designing education programs that can reach the public with the appropriate information. Public education campaigns traditionally have taken many different forms, utilizing the media, community organizations and even the schools to disseminate messages. Thus far, the evidence is somewhat mixed, however, as to the relative effectiveness of these various methods of providing information about recycling programs.

In designing a public education program it is tempting to rely heavily upon the influence of the mass media, assuming that because of its ability to reach large numbers of people that it will have the greatest and most efficient impact. However, it is important to consider the type of message being conveyed as well as the method being used. Several authors Cook and Berrenberg, 1981; Yates and Aronson, 1983) point out that general messages offered through the mass media have had little effect on changing environmental behaviour, while more specific information communicated through these same media may prompt participation.

At the other end of the scale, many of those who study the diffusion of information suggest that people are most receptive to new ideas that come from credible, known sources such as friends and co-workers (Darley, 1977). The personal salience and vividness of conversations with those that are known and trusted effectively gain ones attention and may then make the greatest impact on behavior (Nisbett and Ross, 1980).

The use of prompts, flyers, contests, raffles, and a host of other methods of encouraging environmental behavior have also been suggested. Various studies have examined these techniques in terms of their effectiveness at inducing short term behavior change (e.g. Witmer and Geller, 1976; McClelland and Canter, 1981). But, from a public education perspective, a long term, sustained behavior change is the ultimate goal. A technique which is designed to heighten excitement by utilizing monetary incentives, for example, may not impart the needed information that would enable a sustained change in behavior.

It seems that the degree to which people pay attention to a particular source of information may be dependent upon a variety of factors such as whether the information being communicated is general or specific, and whether the individual is already predisposed to believe the source of the ideas being presented. Consequently, those responsible for delivering a public education program, often limited by both time and funds, must make critical decisions on where to invest their resources with the hopes of effectively reaching the greatest number of people. The present study examines the perceived helpfulness of various sources of recycling information to residents participating in a country mandated recycling program.

Study Background

New Jersey instituted statewide mandatory recycling in April, 1987. Legislation required communities to create recycling programs that would reduce their waste stream by at least 25%. The first county in New Jersey to institute mandatory recycling, Somerset County, initiated a pilot program in 1985. Mandatory recycling began in the county during September, 1986 (seven months before statewide mandatory recycling became effective). The county program required each of the 21 communities within Somerset County to develop a recycling plan utilizing either curbside pickup or drop-off centers. In addition, each program provided for the recycling of at least three materials such as aluminum cans, glass bottles, newspapers and magazines.

As mandatory recycling was phased in, household participation rates increased dramatically. An estimated 47% of the households were recycling by the end of the first year of the program. But even with the power of legislative mandates, a vigorous public education program, and the impementation of support services such as curbside pick up of recyclables, full participation was not achieved. The question became what types of information are most useful in encouraging individuals to recycle?

Study Methods

To understand more about where people get their recycling information a survey was developed in cooperation with the Somerset County Offices of Recycling and Public Information. It was recognized that most people gain information from a variety of sources. Consequently, the questionnaire asked residents to indicate how helpful various methods of information dissemination had been. Residents rated 17 different methods of gaining information about recycling (newspaper stories, exhibits, newsletters, etc.) on a five point scale with 1 being not helpful and 5 being very helpful. Participants were also asked that types of information they feel they need more of. The survey of information sources was part of a larger 85 item questionnaire designed to gain data concerning why residents participate in the recycling program, how they feel about it, and the degree to which they participate in solid waste reduction behaviors (see Simmons and Widmar, 1989-90; Simmons & Widmar, 1990). Of the 1500 surveys sent to a random sample of residents in Somerset County, 567 or approximately 38% of the surveys were returned. Background data on the survey respondents is found in Table 1.

Table 1
Background Information of Respondents

Gender:

Male =	216	(43.3%)
Female =	283	(56.7%)

Age:

20	-	29	=	21	(3.8%)
30	-	39	=	122	(22%)
40	-	49	=	122	(22%)
50	-	59	=	91	(16.4%)
60	-	69	=	123	(22.1%)
70	+		=	76	(13.7%)

Households with children = 302 (35.9%)
Households without children = 362 (64.1%)

Education:

grade school	=	6	(1.1%)
some high school	=	11	(2.1%)
high school graduate	=	151	(28.2%)
some college	=	76	(14.2%)
college degree	=	177	(33.1%)
masters degree	=	87	(16.3%)
PhD, MD, law, etc.	=	27	(5%)

Income:

<15,000	=	29	(5.6%)
15-20,000	=	30	(5.8%)
21-30,000	=	41	(7.9%)
31-45,000	=	87	(16.8%)
46-60,000	=	102	(19.7%)
61-80,000	=	98	(18.8%)
81,000 +	=	132	(25.4%)

Recycled before became mandatory = 278 (50.2%)
Started recycling after became mandatory = 276 (49.8%)

Study Results

The questionnaire items reflected a broad range of potential sources of information (see Table 2). It is instructive to examine which types of information were found to be most helpful. To facilitate the discussion, the information sources have been grouped into four general categories: media as a source of information, information delivered directly to the home, community based sources of information, and informal methods of gaining information.

Media as a Source of Information

The capacity of the media (television, radio, magazine, and newspapers) to deliver messages to large audiences is reflected in the number of residents who considered various forms of media helpful in gaining information about recycling. Fifty-five percent of those responding to the survey named newspaper stories as an important source of information, 40.9% chose newspaper ads, 34.2% named TV programs, while radio programs and magazine articles were indicated by 27.5% and 26.4% respectively.

It is noteworthy that two of the most highly rated information sources were newspaper stories and newspaper ads. One would suspect that newspaper stories and ads provide specific, locally relevant information concerning recycling as compared to television, radio, and magazine coverage that may focus on the issues in general.

Table 2 -- Helpfulness of Information Sources			
Source	Mean	Percent Indicating	
		not/a little helpful	helpful	helped a lot/ very helpful
newspaper	3.63	14.3	30.7	55.0
direct-mail	3.53	20.8	26.2	53.0
news ads	3.19	28.6	30.5	40.9
TV programs	2.95	37.2	28.5	34.2
radio	2.73	43.2	29.8	27.1
magazine	2.72	42.4	31.1	26.4
ed materials*	2.69	49.0	27.4	24.6
leaflets	2.67	47.7	20.7	31.5
community	2.63	47.8	25.7	26.5
neighbors	2.57	46.0	33.9	20.1
relatives	2.37	53.5	30.2	16.4
tax inserts	2.31	59.4	21.8	18.8
exhibits	2.21	61.7	24.9	13.4
news-child*	2.19	60.5	28.5	13.7
civic groups	1.88	71.8	15.1	13.1
contests	1.72	77.8	13.9	8.2

results based only on answers given by respondents who have children living at home.

Information Delivered Directly to the Home

Information delivered directly to the home and especially information in the form of newsletters, brochures, and flyers seems to provide an effective method of reaching a large proportion of the Somerset County community. As can be seen in Table 2, materials received directly in the mail were named as important sources of information by 53% of the respondents. Similarly, leaflets or notes about recycling are left with the residents' garbage can at the curb were considered important by 31.5% of the residents. Two additional methods of reaching the public, inserts placed with the tax bill and recycling contests, were mentioned less often (18.8% and 8.2% respectively).

Interestingly, although contests may serve to raise awareness of the recycling effort when used as a promotion or incentive, they are not seen as a particularly helpful source of information. Likewise, piggy-backing information on a one-shot basis (e.g. as an insert in the tax bill) did not seem to be particularly effective compared to other direct methods of information dissemination.

Community Based Sources of Information

When people leave their homes to shop, go to work, or attend community activities, they may be exposed to both formal and informal sources of information concerning recycling. To some extent, these are chance encounters; not all residents will go by the shopping mall while a recycling exhibit is on display. Consequently, it is not too surprising that community based methods of information dissemination were not, for the most part, highly rated by a large proportion of the population.

Twenty-six percent of the residents indicated that information received through community groups (church, 4H, environmental groups, etc.) had been helpful; 13.4% named special exhibits (at shopping malls, 4H fairs, libraries, etc.) as an important source of information; and 13.1% named presentations made to local, civic or business groups (Rotary, League of Women Voters, Chamber of Commerce).

Informal Methods of Gaining Information

People talk with one another, neighbors, relatives, co-workers, all share information and, at times, misinformation. Although not considered as helpful of a source of information by 20.1% of the residents; relatives (spouse, parents, etc.) were named by 16.4%.

Similarly, although it would not be surprising to find that children learn about recycling at home from their parents, it is interesting to consider that parents learned from materials developed primarily for their sons and daughters. Twenty-four percent of the respondents who have school aged children thought that educational materials brought home by their children served as a helpful source of information; in addition, 13.7% named newspaper stories geared toward children as a helpful information source. It is significant to note that information developed and disseminated for one particular group may in actuality reach a far different audience.

What Makes the Information Helpful?

Knowing which sources of information were considered most helpful is informative, but it is equally instructive to examine what makes a source of information most useful. In an open-ended question, participants were asked to indicate which source of information was most helpful and why (Table 3). Approximately one-third of the participants responded that information sources that get their attention were most useful. Information sources in this category represent both those read on a regular basis (newspapers) and the unusual, such as flyers, brochures and leaflets.

The participants also considered information that reached them directly at their homes (25.35%) (e.g. newspapers, flyers, TV and radio) to be helpful. They appreciated information that provided them with specific details of what, when and how to recycle (18.8%), as well as sources that provided in-depth information (5.9%) and information that reinforces the need to recycle (5.6%).

Desired Information

In a second open-ended question, participants were asked what types of information they desired. Overwhelmingly, they wanted information on how, when, and what to recycle (47.2%). Even after months of public education programs, the participants still asked for prompts, leaflets, and stickers to put on their calendars as reminders to recycle.

But many of the participants (20.2%) were not content to limit their recycling effort only to those items picked up at curbside. They expressed a desire for information on how to recycle and reuse items such as plastic, clothing, household hazardous wastes, and tires. They want to be kept up-to-date (20.8%) about the county's recycling effort, requesting information on how much material is being recycled, where it goes, how much it costs, and what good it is doing. Finally, they also want to be kept informed about general environmental issues (e.g. household pollution, biodegradable products) and legislative initiatives (10.4%).

Table 3 Characteristics of Helpful Information		
Characteristic	Percent Indicating	Type of Source(s) Mentioned
gets attention/read regularly	32.4%	newspapers, flyers/brochures
delivered directly to the home/convenient	25.3%	newspaper, TV, flyers/brochures
gives specific details/clear, precise, to the point	18.8%	flyers, brochures, newspapers, newsletters
provides in-depth information	8.2%	newspapers, TV, community groups
reinforces the need to recycle	6.5%	newspapers, government officials
provides locally relevant information	5.9%	newspapers, community groups, flyers/brochures
credible source/sets positive examples	2.9%	friends/relatives, government officials

Summary and Implications

The findings of the survey confirm that people get their information from a variety of sources. And, although an effective strategy for information dissemination should most certainly include information that reaches people directly at their homes through newspaper articles, newsletters, and flyers, such diverse methods of reaching the public as the use of television, presentations to community groups, and displaying exhibits at shopping centers, etc. should also be included.

Additionally, the results suggest that in designing a public education strategy it should be recognized that messages meant for one audience may well reach another. Nearly one-fourth of those residents with school aged children felt that educational materials brought home by their children were helpful. Consequently, a robust public education program must go beyond press releases and informational brochures to include curriculum materials that tap into the educational system's ability to reach a large portion of the population.

The nature of the information itself must also be considered carefully. No matter which communication device is utilized, specific details that constantly remind people how and what to recycle should be included. Even after a program is well established, participation needs to be reinforced with notices and other prompts. Finally, environmental educators should take advantage of the interest generated in recycling and build upon the public's general level of environmental knowledge and concern. Residents requested more information on how to recycle and reuse items not currently picked up at curbside as well as general information on environmental issues. Through newsletter articles, exhibits, and other in-depth presentations of information, it is possible to widen the public's perspective and extend their involvement in environmentally responsible behaviors.

References

Cook, S. and J. Berrenberg. (1981). Approaches to encouraging conservation behavior: A review and conceptual framework, Journal of Social Issues, 37(2):73-107.

Darley, J. (1977). Energy conservation techniques as innovations and their diffusion. Energy and Buildings, 1: 339-389.

Nisbett, R. and L. Ross. (1980). Human Inference: Strategies and Shortcomings of Social Judgement. Englewood Cliffs, NJ: Prentice-Hall.

Simmons, D. and R. Widmar. (1989-90). Participation in household solid waste reduction activities: The need for public education. Journal of Environmental Systems, 19(4):323-330.

Witmer, J. and E.S. Geller. (1976). Facilitating paper recycling: Effects of prompts, raffles and contests. Journal of Applied Behavior Analysis. 9(3).

Yates, S. and E. Aronson. (1983). A social psychological perspective on energy conservation in residential buildings. American Psychologist. April.

About the Authors

Deborah Simmons is an Associate Professor of Outdoor Teacher Education at Northern Illinois University in DeKalb, Illinois and Director of Resident Programs at the Lorado Taft Field Campus. She earned a B.A. in Anthropology and a secondary teaching certificate at the University of California at Berkeley, a M.S. in Natural Resources at Humboldt State University and a Ph.D. in Natural Resources at the University of Michigan. Her research centers primarily on what motivates and facilitates environmentally responsible behaviour.

Ron Widmar is the Director of Planning for the Village of Hoffman Estates, Illinois. He earned a B.S. and M.S. in Natural Resources from Humboldt State University and a Ph.D. in Urban and Regional Planning from the University of Michigan. His research focuses on environmental planning and design.

RESPONDING TO
INFLUENCES

PHILOSOPHY OR REALITY?
DRIVING PARADIGM SHIFTS

Rick Mrazek

Abstract

It was suggested at the beginning of the monograph that the reader may be embarking upon a journey or quest for an environmental education research paradigm that could be responsive to the present and future needs of environmental education and its practitioners. Along this path one has encountered contributions which might serve as signposts addressing the nature of paradigms in environmental education research, assumptions regarding theory and practice as well as interpretations of such notions as rigor, validity, and generalizability in research. The question we now face is, does such a paradigm exist and have the signposts we have encountered directed us to it? Is this paradigm only philosophical rhetoric bantered about by a few or is it steeped in realities which have as their center the problems and issues investigated in environmental education research? Are we experiencing a paradigm shift as drastic as that which occurred when the Aristotelian view placing the earth at the centre of the universe was challenged by Copernicus' heliocentric model replacing the earth with the sun at the center of a stellar sphere? In the 20th century this has become accepted knowledge, yet we might ask what effect it had on the work of Galileo and other astronomers of the time? Is this comparable to the experiences of environmental education researchers today?

Environmental Education Researchers

In the earlier description of the evolution of this monograph, I mentioned that a survey had been distributed to individuals known to be participating in environmental education research. Many of these individuals later took part in the symposium. Symposium participants who had not been surveyed earlier were requested to provide similar information regarding types of environmental education research being engaged in, perceived problems they encountered, and supporting structures which allowed them to do their research. Including those sent to the 41 participants in the symposium, there were a total of 60 distributed with 19 surveys returned . The information obtained does not form the basis of a definitive study in this area, however, it does provide us with insights as to some of the variables that have the potential to drive a paradigm shift or necessitate change. Now that the reader has had the opportunity to reflect upon the contributions in the Monograph, it seems appropriate to share some of these additional views.

When asked to describe the research orientations they were engaged in, there was a wide variety of response ranging from grounded theory, interpretive research, critical participatory research, phenomenology, and program evaluations as well as to different combinations and permutations of these. It would seem, at least from those surveyed, that there definitely exists a number of orientations towards environmental education research operating in the field. This was further reinforced by responses describing the various perspectives toward research held by these research practitioners. Most of the responses were based on combinations of approaches to research which were dictated more by the question that was being asked than by a personal view towards research. Many indicated that it was important to keep an open mind and seek other interpretations than those to which they are most familiar. Almost half of the respondents mentioned some combination or mix of what they referred to as qualitative and quantitative research.

Not surprisingly, when asked what areas of environmental education research are required or are timely now, the two areas identified most often were aspects related to (1) educational methods and curriculum development and (2) environmental behaviour. In almost all cases there was some reference to key terms such as values, value systems and problem solving skills. This was fairly indicative of perceptions of two prominent themes which appear to be timely for the future: (1) increasing public knowledge and awareness and (2) getting a better understanding of public feelings and attitudes towards environmental behaviour.

Those surveyed were asked to identify the reasons why they had become involved in research. Almost half indicated that it was a job requirement. Others indicated that it was of personal interest because of the importance of that work, or a sense of duty. These were the top themes which were given without regard to ranking. As the reader is undoubtedly aware, it is very difficult to condense a lengthy summary of themes into one or two lines. For our purposes it does show that factors do emerge that should be considered as we explore influences on environmental education research and researchers.

In response to identification of inhibitors or reasons why these researchers had not been involved more extensively in research, the predominant responses were time restrictions and commitments to other responsibilities. While some went on to say that this was related to perceived importance of such opportunities, most stated that other areas such as teaching and community involvement were extremely time consuming by nature and, therefore, interfered with the extent to which they could engage in research. Over one-third identified lack of support in terms of staff, equipment and/or money (lack of access to funding sources) as being a major obstacle to overcome.

On the other hand when asked what supporting mechanisms were in place to assist them in accomplishing what they wished in environmental education research, it was institutional support, networks, and professional organizations such as the NAAEE which were listed most often. The central theme here seemed to be communication with and support of colleagues and other similarily interested people.

Having the advantage of reviewing all the responses, I would offer three themes which should be included in the continuation of our quest for a better understanding of environmental education research paradigms and directions they may provide: (1) perceptions of difficulty, (2) relationships of research practitioners to institutions and agencies with which they are associated, and (3) the role of collaboration between researchers and the institutions to which they belong.

One of the challenges in our quest identified in an earlier article was to not stray from the path as we focus on the different signposts we encounter. If we acknowledge that each of the contributions within this Monograph has been co-created and co-authored by each of the contributor's experiences, then we might question what influence these had on the direction of the signposts offered. It has already been indicated that at times our visions are often cramped and made remote by language, potentially distancing us through abstractions from the sensuality of the world of environmental education research with its intervening layers of social, economic and political meanings. Let us consider the three experiences identified above from the survey (and reinforced in the symposium) and see if they can't be placed in a context of influences to which our environmental education research paradigm(s) may be responding.

Influences on Environmental Education Research

First let us look at "difficulty" and its implications for environmental education research. In any research in which I engage, I encounter a number of difficulties. Some of the more superficial ones can be easily named while others are of a much more significant deeper nature. Initially there is the problem of finding a suitable, meaningful topic and deciding on my approach to it. Though I may have my particular position vis-a-vis my research orientations, this is not necessarily established or set for this particular problem. The way I perceive my research question may continually be evolving. The difficulties involved with my research question may, on the one hand, bring a sense of challenge to persevere and overcome it, yet, on the other hand, an anguish that I may not be able to accomplish or achieve what I have set about to do. Without delving indepth into the literature related to 'difficulty' we cannot make definitive statements regarding views towards it. We can, however, call on our own personal experiences in education and research. More often than not, difficulty seems to be viewed as a bad or undesirable experience which should be eliminated from our lives. It may involve removing or replacing difficult material in a curriculum or changing teaching methods. Does this desire to eliminate difficulty then reveal a longing for comfort, inertia or "the easy way." If difficulties are removed, is not the necessity to struggle with the problem or strive to move beyond also removed? In terms of our research does this then mean promotion of a more superficial way of answering potentially complex questions? What are the implications of a positive correlation between integrity and difficulty? Some maintain that life without the chance of difficulty is an impossibility so that what we are actually looking at in many cases is how we approach different levels of difficulty. The threads begin to tangle as we now are dealing with our personal philosophies of life ranging from one's personal views of environmental education research and to consideration of ourselves as human beings engaged as practitioners within that area. What happens to questions addressed in environmental education research when researchers seek a freedom from difficulty rather than ways of dealing with difficulty?

The second experience questioned here is the relationship between research practitioners and the institutions or agencies with which they may be associated. The influence of individual and institution vitality may have arisen as a dominant theme because many of those responding were faculty members associated with colleges, universities, and research institutions. Whether this is truly representative of researchers in environmental education may be debated; however, we may still be able to gain some insight from associated literature. Clark and Lewis (1985) refer to vitality as those "essential, yet intangible, positive qualities of individuals in institutions that enable purposeful production" (p. 3). How does one go about enhancing this vitality if it is indeed a dominant factor? Shuster, Wheeler and Associates (1990) suggest that the two key points to consider when thinking about strategies to enhance vitality are the interplay of faculty qualities and institutional factors; and whether faculty activities are considered productive (vital) based on the relationship both to the faculty member's personal and professional goals and to the institution's mission. If we accept their premise that the faculty comprise the heart of the academic enterprise and that the excellence of a higher education institution is inseparable from the excellence of its faculty, how does one then enhance the vigor and commitment of those engaged in environmental education research? We are all probably familiar with dozens of different approaches and suggestions that have been made. These range from environmental changes aimed at improving our welfare to personal and professional reward systems. We must ask ourselves what impact these strategies have on our quest for environmental education research? If these are driving forces in the dynamics of paradigms, does this not beg more research which focuses on the potential impact of institutional changes which tend to respond to social and economic pressures?

The last theme or experience to be addressed here arising from our preliminary survey may be viewed as an extension of the second. When asked whether there were areas of research in which the respondents would like to engage collaboratively, **all** provided a positive response. Specific areas ranged from cross-cultural comparative studies dealing with attitudes, values, ethics/morality and moral reasoning related to environmental education to specific individuals (or countries in terms of international programs) with whom they would like to work. The support and enthusiasm for this approach seems to reinforce the finding of Shuster,

Wheeler and Associates that "two of the most innovative institutional strategies found were inter-institutional consortia and institutional research centres (to guide planning and development and to contribute to the intellectual vitality on campus)" (1990:56). It is also of interest that this approach seemed to rank highly in the documented faculty renewal activities in 174 institutions (63 colleges, 79 universities, and 32 professional schools) where an additional 40 sponsors were cited in the literature representing inter-institutional consortia, professional associations and other organizations which supported collaborative efforts. We might ask what the impact would be on environmental education research if there were more opportunities for not only inter-institutional collaborative efforts but also between individuals from different institutions, including schools and non-government organizations? Also, what happens when unaffiliated individuals are involved?

How these themes influence the signposts selected in our quest needs to be explored much further. They have been offered here as contributions from researchers who may not be represented in the formal contributions contained in the Monograph.

Continuing the Quest

No matter how one attempts to answer the questions raised in this Monograph, it is the sincere hope of the contributing authors and all those associated with production of Alternative Paradigms in Environmental Education Research that the reader accepts our challenge to become an active participant (part) of our quest. Regardless of which signposts guide you or which path you take, moving along that path provides hope that we will come to a better understanding of environmental education research and maintain the vitality required to deal with the increasingly complex problems and issues that we face in our global environment. So -- where to from here? It's your choice!

Bibliography

Clark, S. M. and Lewis, D. R. (Eds.). (1985). Faculty Vitality and Institutional Productivity. New York: Teachers College Press.

Shuster, J., Wheeler, D. and Associates. (1990). Enhancing Faculty Careers: Strategies for Development and Renewal. San Francisco: Jossey-Bass Publishers.

APPENDIX I:

PRE-SYMPOSIUM

RESEARCH ARTICLES

FROM THE

<u>ENVIRONMENTAL</u>

<u>COMMUNICATOR</u>

THE EMANCIPATION OF ENVIRONMENTAL EDUCATION RESEARCH

Rick Mrazek
(Reprinted from Environmental Communicator, May/June, 1990:9)

The availability and access to accurate up-to-date information is the cornerstone to effective development of environmental education programs. There is a substantial amount of information which is not available because it has not been processed or it is in forms which cannot be readily utilized by educational organizations or the community at large. There is still other information which people do not have access to because of information policies, cost or logistical reasons.

Canadian universities and research institutions, like their American counterparts, are showing considerable progress in expanding their educational and research programs into environmental areas. Hopefully more education and science researchers will be versed on environmental topics, better equipped to apply new research techniques and problem solving strategies to the complexities of environmental problems, and more alert to the need for developing creative alternatives to the accepted ways of doing things. The contribution of post-secondary institutions and research institutes to education of the non-university public is however another matter. The distinction drawn between theory-oriented research and applied practice-oriented research and the emphasis placed upon the former by journals and granting agencies has been perceived by some to be a major obstacle to the development of environmental education as a field of study. Such a policy fails to encompass a full range of high quality research which is needed in environmental education.

Some interpret the issue of concern as one of terminology, that established research traditions use the term "theoretical" only to describe studies which are expected to produce generalizable results. If this is so, possibly the term "generalizable" may be preferred in order to avoid what may have been a major misunderstanding by both proposers and assessors of the research projects and findings.

Most often leading researchers are divided in their views as to the best strategy for acquiring generalizable knowledge in environmental education. Some advocate the traditional inductive-deductive or theory-oriented approach which requires specification of a theory followed by the deduction of hypotheses which are then tested. This dominant orientation is also referred to as 'empirical-analytic' where the primary interests lie in establishing predictive control in technical situations. Methodologies for this approach, usually highly quantitative, include the experimental, quasi-experimental, correlational and survey methods.

Other researchers advocate studies, including ethnographic and case studies, which deliberately do not begin with a specification of a theory.

Instead, these studies which are exploratory and inductive, deal with observations and seek meaning at a practical level. This second orientation is sometimes referred to as 'historical-hermeneutic' and the primary interest is associated with the understanding of meaning as attributed to situations by individuals. While the ultimate goal may be the derivation of theory, a great deal of practice oriented research must be done first.

Still other researchers take what may be called an eclectic view. These researchers prefer to employ the full range of approaches, from theory to practice, often in the same study. For some this third orientation is termed 'critical-theoretic' in which emancipation and concern for the human condition is most important. Implicit within this third orientation is the demand for action which will improve the human condition.

Whatever view is taken of the best strategy for acquisition of knowledge in environmental education, it is quite clear that the issues involved are central academic concerns which must be settled through scholarly processes rather than arbitrarily through funding and publishing criteria. All research should be planned so that results can be expected to be generalizable, however in the case of some of the newer approaches, such as case studies and ethnographic studies, the generalizability may not come from a single study but from an accumulation of such studies.

One way to overcome these potential barriers is to look at cooperative ventures which include practitioners as researchers as well. If interaction is fostered among researchers and practitioners with a common interest, the quality and comprehensiveness of a program of research would be enhanced. These research teams have a potential of combining the contributions of several researchers who differ in disciplinary perspective or methodological expertise. In addition to meeting immediate research objectives, research teams would produce secondary benefits such as providing an active and high quality educational environment. Would this work? This sounds like an excellent research question, but which approach would I use? Where would I get funding? What journal would accept my results? Where would I find the time. . .?

The Importance of Learners Doing Research

Trudi L. Volk
(Reprinted from <u>Environmental/Communicator</u>, September/October, 1990:7)

When asked if I would contribute an article on research, I quickly agreed -- and then wondered what I would write about. There are a number of important things we are learning **from** research. There are also a number of important things to be said **about** research. I'd like to talk about research as it relates to youngsters. Mind you, this is not research **about** youngsters, but rather, it is about youngsters **doing** research.

Many of us agree that a major goal of EE is to help learners become actively and responsibly involved in the remediation of environmental issues. And, as responsible educators, we do not want to indoctrinate learners; we do not want their environmental responsibility to be emotion-based. Rather we are interested in developing individuals with sound problem-solving and decision-making skills. What we must recognize is that sound decision-making and problem-solving is supported by the understanding of issues, their scientific and social consequences, and the consequences of their solutions. Simply stated, citizenship action must be preceded by gathering and evaluating information. And that is where research enters the picture.

> *After examining the benefits and costs of recycling and surveying local residents regarding their attitudes toward the recycling of aluminium beverage containers, an eighth grade student in a medium-sized town in central Illinois visited the mayor and shared the results of her issue investigation and survey. The mayor was so impressed with her findings that he invited her to address the city council. As a result of her survey and work with the city council, the town now has two recycling centers.*

It may be that few words are as misused in education -- or as misunderstood -- as is research. Elementary school students are told to *do research about* an animal, or plant, or person. In reality, they usually look up a reference from the encyclopedia in the school library. High school and college students are required to hand in *research reports*. These are often papers containing a body of information gleaned from various secondary sources. In both cases, research is regarded as a searching out and recording of facts. But research is more than that.

Research is not so much an act as an attitude. Research includes the ability to recognize a problem, to view it in light of relevant evidence, to examine what that evidence reveals about the problem, and finally, to attempt to resolve the problem as *the evidence dictates.*

Research typically requires an inquisitive mind, an awareness of problems that need resolution, and a willingness to seek purposefully the evidence that may help resolve the problems. Research also requires the ability to go straight to the evidence, to confront it squarely, and to generate only those conclusions and recommendations which can be supported by the evidence. Thus, research demands a basic honesty, uncluttered by preconceived biases.

Why aren't **we** teaching youngsters the basics of research? If we want to produce individuals who can recognize and confront problems, it would appear beneficial to teach them how to research those problems and to permit them to carry out that research. Of course, the environmental problems in which we are interested are, in reality, issues which contain differing beliefs and values. Researching those issues necessitates laying aside personal biases and emotions, and facing the cold hard facts involved in the issue.

What shape would research by a young learner take? Descriptions of student research and citizen participation are presented as boxed items throughout this page. They illustrate the link between research and action.

> *In a rural midwestern community, several junior high students became interested in a local issue which centered on the use of a section of state-owned land adjacent to a local river. After conducting a country-wide survey, these students used their findings to develop a master plan for the use and development of that public land, and submitted and defended the plan at a public hearing sponsored by the state Department of Conservation. Of those who spoke at the hearing, the students were the only participants who presented a proposal founded on databased decision-making. The master plan which was adopted was very similar to their proposal.*

We can educate youngsters about the environmental issues of today. However, we cannot educate them about the issues of tomorrow. We can best prepare learners to deal with those issues by helping them to develop the intellectual tools they will need to access information about those issues, to evaluate that information, and to use it in forming sound decisions. That being accomplished, we can have greater confidence in their production of ecologically and socially sound decisions and their participation in responsible problem-solving.

What You Can't Measure Still Exists

Arjen Wals
(Reprinted from Environmental Communicator, November/December, 1990:12)

Human ideas, experiences, and intentions are not objective things like molecules and atoms. Nevertheless, like their colleagues in the natural sciences, many educational researchers attempt to use objective methods that allow for control, predictability and the ability to generalize. The scientific method has long been claimed to be a value-free tool of inquiry, allowing many social scientists to create dichotomies between themselves, their methods and their research. This separation is a dangerous one, for it gives scientists a false authority of truth.

Knowledge and human interests are interwoven, as reflected in the choice of methods and the ends to which such methods are put. The idea that there is a world that can be totally analyzed, predicted, and controlled -- the world of positivistic science -- is frightening. Unless we reflect on the ends to be served by science, we risk that prediction and control and their associated methods might exclude other ends such as: improved understanding among people, release of human potential and formation of a sustainable relationship with our surroundings.

Many researchers have tried to structure EE content matter and the way it is presented to students using hierarchical levels of universal goals and objectives. Outside experts determine what students need in terms of knowledge, attitudes, values and skills; design a curriculum that consists of measurable/quantifiable goals and objectives; implement the program; test to what extent the goals and objectives are realized; modify the program and reinstruct the teacher. In the worst case scenario, the students become a database, the teacher an implementation instrument. Only the researcher, who gets an article published in a scientific journal, stands to benefit.

This widely used positivistic approach to education research and development often results in the ignoring of students' ideas, experiences and mini-theories, as well as the teacher's own classroom experiences and expertise. Teachers and students are not viewed as capable to determine the content of their own education, to set their own goals and objectives that are compatible with the community they live in and, finally, are not allowed to evaluate their own teaching and learning. Alienation between researchers and school community and disempowerment of teachers and students who have been denied a role in shaping and evaluating their own education, often is the result.

Is there a way of doing research that is compatible with the position taken here? One research approach that provide some answers has elements of Action Research and Phenomenology. The traditions of Action Research and

Phenomenology use -- although not exclusively -- qualitative research methods such as field research, descriptive research, and ethnography in which the researcher takes the role of observer/participant and interpreter. Research here is more than a data collecting activity in that it actively seeks to understand as well as to improve the school and its community through simultaneous action and reflection with all parties involved. (See *Journal of EE*, "Education in Action: A Community Problem Solving Program for Schools." Summer, 1990.)

The emphasis in research is no longer on finding causality, generating generalizable results and predicting the future with statistical accuracy. Instead the emphasis in on documenting and describing human experience and intentions, using diagnostic instruments, one's own observations and those of teachers and students; interpreting these with all involved participants; relating the results with the foundations, goals and objectives of EE; and discussing ways to adjust the curriculum and classroom practice as a result of newly obtained insights. The main objective is not to find out the kinds of changes that occur in the learner as a result of an EE project, but to find out whether an EE project and the structure of schooling provided for such change!

A researcher has the moral obligation to work for and with the participants in his/her study. EE research should have a pedagogical end in the sense that the participants somehow benefit from the research. Thus, research should not just be an attempt to learn about people, but to come to know with them the reality which challenges them.

I have only scratched the surface in introducing an alternative paradigm for doing EE research. Before uncritically accepting the dominant positivistic paradigm, we have to consider alternatives. It is my belief that it is the same world of positivism that allowed for environmental deterioration at its current pace and scope in the first place!

APPENDIX II:

POST-SYMPOSIUM

RESEARCH ARTICLES

FROM THE

ENVIRONMENTAL

COMMUNICATOR

Thoughts on Research Paradigms in EE

Paul Hart
(Reprinted from Environmental Communicator, January/February, 1991:5)

Research has become a hot topic within the field of environmental education, that is, if attendance at the San Antonio conference seminar on contesting paradigms in EE research is an indicator. Discussions at the symposium raised a number of key issues related to research methods, which should be set within the context of educational research. This article attempts to embed our EE research issues within what Eisner and Peshkin (1990) describe as the continuing debate concerning educational inquiry.

A tension between quantitative and qualitative research methods now characterizes the educational research literature. This tension appears to be the result of several converging influences that have arisen because the field of education has tended to rely on applied science research designs rather than develop its own unique terms of inquiry. Influences from the social sciences include an infusion of European thought containing concepts such as poststructuralism, interpretivism, and critical theory and a movement toward a postpositivistic era within the philosophy of science (see Garrison, 1986; Philips, 1987). In addition, the dominant psychometric tradition of educational research has been severely criticized for being inconclusive and inadequate to tell us anything secure and important about how teachers should proceed in the classroom (Barrow, 1984).

There is even a lack of consensus about whether the debate should focus on the particulars of various research methodologies or on the positivist and nonpositivist epistemologies that underlie alternative research paradigms (see Howe & Eisenhart, 1990). This latter aspect of the debate was manifest within the NAAEE symposium as an issue of whether the title should be described as "alternative" or "contesting". Because of these two very different ways of approaching the problem, thinkers who focus on the development and articulation of goals or standards, for example, are accused of paying little attention to the demand to frame their recommendations in terms of deeper epistemological issues, of capitulating merely to what works, and even of embracing positivism (Smith & Heshusius, 1986).

Environmental educators interested in research should understand that the debate is now deeper, more complex, and more problematic involving a reexamination of taken-for-granted assumptions and a reconsideration of how we think about *knowing*. The issues for debate not only concern subjectivity, validity, and generalizability, but also questions of intent. We tend to frame problems in relation to methods we know. These methods are powerful filters or lenses through which we have been socialized to view the world. For example, according to Eisner & Peshkin (1990), if we are predisposed toward finding measurable relationships, we see classrooms differently than if we are inclined to focus on the description of the unique features of a person or situation. Our methods influence our perceptions: our cognitive maps define different routes through the territory. Being socialized into a method means being socialized into a set of norms that define acceptable scholarship.

We in EE must recognize that there are fundamental differences underlying quantitative and qualitative methods that imply epistemological differences, that is, what it means to know and how knowledge is generated. But it is *methods* that should be debated, not personalities. Conversations about method have an important place in the field of EE. They enliven debate, raise consciousness, and, when thoughtfully advanced, are healthy (Jackson, 1990).

I would hope that the current debates about research methods will create a plurality of legitimate approaches that will shed greater light on educational matters than any single set of methods can provide.

The kind of scholarship considered acceptable for journals may need to include the fruit of such methodological debate -- a broader conception of inquiry. This does not mean that we abandon standards for educational research. We must learn to understand and appreciate perspectives not in terms of what counts as orthodox methodology. What matters most is whether warranted conclusions are obtained about important educational questions. We all want research to be done thoroughly and rigorously. However, we also need to maintain a vision, to learn how to ask questions differently, to write about matters previously unexamined and to judge quality within appropriate research frameworks. This is the essence of the new view of research within the field of education. Environmental educators, take heed!

The Scope of Research in Marine and Aquatic Education

Rosanne Fortner
(Reprinted from Environmental Communicator, July/August, 1991:5)

Marine and aquatic education (M/AE) is defined as "that part of the total educational process which enables people to develop a sensitivity to and a general understanding of the role of the seas and fresh water in human affairs and the impact of society on the marine and aquatic environments." (Goodwin & Schaadt, 1977) An an important component of EE, M/AE involves thousands of formal and nonformal educators throughout the continent.

The following is a brief review of the topics addressed in M/AE research during the last 15 years. The definition of research is the same as that used by the NACEER. We exclude program descriptions except as accompanied by needs assessment or substantive evaluation. For a list of over 60 references encompassed by this overview, send a self-addressed, stamped envelope to NAAEE headquarters and request "M/AE References."

Interest in teaching about the world of water grew to noticeable proportions in the 1970s, and with it emerged a network of leading individuals and sponsored programs. Research among this group produced an interdisciplinary conceptual framework that has been refined for use in framing objectives, structuring programs, classifying curricula, and identifying gaps in existing resources. Based on the scope of this conceptual framework, a number of researchers in the U.S. and Canada have assessed student knowledge and attitudes about the oceans and Great Lakes, finding generally that knowledge increases with grade level, with exposure to television documentaries and specialty magazines, and with proximity to the coast. Knowledge of science concepts in M/AE slightly exceeds knowledge of related social studies concepts, and both are far greater than knowledge of humanities topics in the world of water. Specific instruction in water topics has been shown to increase knowledge scores. Attitudes are directly related to knowledge levels.

Teacher awareness of marine and aquatic concepts has been assessed in relationship to what is being taught. For teachers, as well as students, more is known about marine topics than about the Great Lakes, even in the Great Lakes region. In general, teachers report spending more time teaching about those marine topics that they know best, including primarily the basic concepts of marine biology, physical oceanography, and media-interest topics related to marine mammals and ocean pollution. Conclusions from such research are frequently used as justification for new teacher education programs.

Implementation of M/AE programs has been the subject of much research. The number and nature of marine education programs have been reported for British Columbia, California, and Ohio. Program success has been examined in relation to factors such as school organizational climate, inservice teacher characteristics, content test scores of teachers, teacher willingness to innovate, students' cultural values and spiritual beliefs, and teacher experience with aquatic environments. The effectiveness of various modes of curriculum dissemination has also been evaluated, demonstrating that teacher training is a must to assure the highest level of use of curriculum materials.

Additional M/AE research deals with issues important throughout the fields of formal EE and science education: computer applications, global understanding through telecommunications, characteristics of successful student projects, and defining and responding to issues. The "pipeline" issue of educating more marine scientists to fill positions in the future may be addressed more effectively, using some 1987 research on learning styles of marine scientists.

As for nonformal M/AE, recent works include design and testing of multimedia interactive displays, evaluation of an estuarine sanctuary's outreach program for school groups, and multiphased evaluation of a museum program with an aquatic theme. Entire issues of *Current: The Journal of Marine Education* have been devoted to action research on marine debris and program developments in NOAA's National Estuarine Research Reserve Program.

Finally, M/AE research includes studies of adults' knowledge and attitudes about the oceans and Great Lakes. In most cases, adult information levels do not exceed those of high school students. Intensive studies using Piagetian development levels, concept mapping, interviews, and VEE diagrams have extended our knowledge of adults' marine learning beyond what can be assessed in standard multiple-choice tests. Experimental studies have also indicated that a single television documentary or a series of brief TV news programs can influence knowledge levels on marine and Great Lakes issues. Given the generally low level of adult knowledge of marine and Great Lake topics (frequently reported at 50-60 percent of items correct), marine and aquatic educators are cautiously rejoicing in the new higher levels of media interest in environmental topics.

Based on research in M/AE, an action agenda for increased implementation and more effective dissemination of information has been proposed in a chapter of NABT's 1990 monograph on "Oceanography for Landlocked Classrooms." The same recommendations apply to the needs of EE in general: 1) a clearinghouse for centralized information about and access to curriculum materials; 2) a speaker's bureau of subject matter experts by region; 3) an educator's network for ongoing contact; 4) coalitions of groups with similar aims; 5) creative funding arrangements; and 6) attention to publicity and promotion of marine education activities.

The National Marine Educators Association (NMEA) and others in the marine and aquatic education community are working on these ideas and others that apply the results of research in the field. Some NAAEE members are among this group, and more are encouraged to examine M/AE approaches for their applications to other EE topics. After all, good planets are hard to find, and 70 percent of this one is water!

Thinking Beyond Paradigms in EE Research

Bob Jickling
(Reprinted from Environmental Communicator, March/April, 1992:4-5)

I have noted with interest that research in environmental education has continued to be the subject of much discussion. Several articles on this topic have appeared in this publication since the symposium, "Contesting Paradigms in EE Research," was held in San Antonio a littler over a year ago. And, I for one, welcome the challenges issued by the authors of these articles; this is a healthy sign for research in environmental education. There are, however, more issues to consider and I would now like to further challenge the reader by offering yet another perspective on research in this field.

The symposium title, "Contesting Paradigms in EE Research," was in a couple of ways a good one. It was descriptively fairly accurate. There is contention within the field of environmental education about relative merits of various research traditions and the adequacy of their methodologies. The symposium also gave prominence to this contention. Discussion and debate about the nature of scholarly work is healthy in any academic setting. In other ways, however, this title could be confusing. It is not clear that use of the world "paradigm" is applicable in social sciences in general (a point raised by Kuhn himself), or in education in particular. It seems to be that education, reflects its non-paradigmatic quality, in the realization that this field of study comprises many questions of distinctly different types. It follows that an *a priori* task for any educational researcher should be to clearly identify the question to be investigated and to understand its nature. Significant discussion about such a task is conspicuously absent in the field of environmental education. In its absence we are left observing the spectacle of contestants in a paradigm tug-of-war.

Much has been made of the contest between qualitative and quantitative research methodologies. To this debate the category "action research" was added during the discussions in San Antonio. While proponents tried to create a place in the sun for each of these three methodological approaches, the need to do more than simply establish a legitimized plurality of research methodologies was overlooked; it was perhaps a moot point to argue the relative merits of "contesting" and "alternative" to describe available research methodologies. In addition to establishing the legitimacy of these approaches, we must do much more to understand the kinds of questions to which they can be usefully applied. It is possible that some of the difficulties experienced in environmental education are rooted in mis-application of technique.

Perhaps, in the current context, some such misapplication of technique is inevitable in environmental education. Such a gloomy prediction arises from two observations. First, discussion about environmental education is rarely placed within the greater debate about the nature and purpose of education.

References in the majority of papers about environmental education seldom include citations from series educational journals. Second, the breadth of legitimate research in environmental education, as represented in the structure of the San Antonio symposium, did not include the analytical work of educational philosophers. While these omissions accurately reflect the current status accorded this type of work, they do not augur well for the future of environmental education.

What we, as environmental educators, must understand is that our field is full of inherently difficult concepts. We must further understand that these concepts are not objects, but exist as abstractions in the minds of men and women. As such, they are neither static nor measurable. Many concepts such as education and environmental education are normative and thus subject to shifting values. Further, some words have never been used very precisely. What this means is that concepts central to environmental education are <u>not</u> amenable to standardization or precise definition and they <u>are</u> subject to careless application and misuse.

Fortunately researchers employing philosophical techniques such as conceptual analysis, can if given encouragement and opportunity, help in the ever-growing problem of trying to make sense of language used in environmental education. Recognizing that precise definition of completed concepts is rarely possible, philosophers seek to carefully tease out the necessary and sufficient conditions which appear to delineate a concept and give it meaning. Further, analysis of concepts is essentially a dialectical business and such analyses are in constant need of re-examination and clarification. This means, therefore, that attempts to resolve the "definitional problem" in environmental education or to define with any amount of certitude, concepts such as "environmental literacy" will amount to little more than mere chimeras, and demonstrate failure to understand the nature of the task at hand.

It has been acknowledged that environmental educators have struggled with definitional problems for some time. It has also been lamented that individuals have mis-used the term "environmental education", applying it to activities that do not reflect generally accepted principals and characteristics of the field. Worse still it is said, all this is happening at a time when "a national standard setting process coordinated by the American Society for Testing and Materials is attempting to resolve [this definitional problem]." Perhaps these problems have been mis-read. Is it not also possible: That there is not a body of generally accepted principles and characteristics of environmental education? That techniques employed to define environmental education have been inappropriate? And, that employing the American Society for Testing and Materials to assist in resolving the definitional problem will in fact exacerbate it by continued mis-application of research techniques?

Is it also possible: That environmental education could be enriched by giving greater attention to issues raised within the broader context of educational research? That philosophical techniques, particularly conceptual analysis, have been for too long overlooked in environmental education? And, that we should move beyond thinking that research in environmental education consists of a bundle of "contesting" or "alternative" paradigms?

APPENDIX III:
RESPONSES TO
SYMPOSIUM REACTORS

A Response to "Beyond Behaviorism"
Tom Marcinkowski

Preface

Having already prepared a lengthy article for presentation at the symposium on EE research paradigms, it may seem a bit unusual that I would prepare a second.   However, since I was asked to prepare remarks on the "quantitative paradigm" in educational research, my remarks have been available to any and everyone who may have sought to critique them for one reason or another.   As it turns out, one of the other reactors, Ian Robottom, has chosen to do so (1990).   In and of itself, this is not "bad", for constructive dialogue is sorely needed in this area.   However, the tone of Robottom's article is highly critical and "contestive".   In my estimation, it is unfairly so on several points.   Thus, it is incumbent upon me to address these points in this collection for several reasons.   First, I had no opportunity to review Robottom's comments in advance, such as he has had of mine.   Thus, this represents the first time I have an opportunity to respond to these comments in writing.   Second, failure to do so may leave Robottom feeling that his were fair and just comments.   Since the symposium and this monograph were intended to open up a scholarly dialogue, it is only fair that I am able to point out what I perceive to be unfair or unwarranted criticisms.   Finally, this monograph will be read by many.   In fact, one of the intended uses of it is as a reader in courses related to EE research.   I feel that it would unfair to readers to be exposed to such criticisms without having an opportunity to hear a reasoned response, and thus be granted the opportunity to think through these issues in a deeper manner.   With these in mind, I offer the following response to Robottom's article.   It is organized into three sections: points of agreement, points of disagreement, and closing comments.

Points of Agreement

On the basis of comments offered in this article, there appear to be no less then five points on which I find substantial agreement with Robottom.   First, in the face of momentous issues pertaining to educational research, there is value to be found in issue-focused dialogue.   It is important to carefully define and clarify important terms, as well as inspect their implications for educational practice, notably that in the field of EE.   Such dialogue is not easy, as Robottom himself reports (p.5).   When dialogue takes on a highly charged tone, as was true in the symposium, what may appear to a speaker to be a legitimate criticism may not be perceived as such by listeners.   In fact, it may be felt as a deep misunderstanding of their ideas and intentions, and so, may be taken quite personally.   For this reason, it is both my opinion and preference that conscious efforts be made not to escalate the tone of such dialogue.

Second, I would agree that within the realm of educational research, there are deeply divisive and problematic issues associated with the philosophical suppositions accompanying more and less traditional "kinds" of educational research. As Robottom clearly indicates, these "kinds" reflect differing "ideologies" (p.1). In my article, I supported this by clearly indicating that these philosophical issues have not been resolved, cannot easily be resolved, and in fact, may not be resolvable (see Parts II.E and IV.D). As currently described in the literature, each "kind" is based upon quite differing assumptions about what constitutes reality, truth, knowledge, and so on.

It is significant that available means for resolving such philosophical issues appear to be limited. For example, consensus building does not appear to be viable under these circumstances, since the crux of these issues involves a departure from traditional views of what constitutes legitimate educational research. Moreover, the processes to be used in discussing these issues, and the criteria for resolving them are in dispute. Given the philosophical nature of these issues, I agree with Robottom that philosophical research may well serve as a fundamental and viable option by which to address them (p.1). However, it does not appear that these issues will be resolved to anyone's satisfaction in the very near future, and so, educational research activities are not going to come to a standstill over this. Consequently, those involved in educational research in this "interim period" will continue to make choices about how they will go about their research activities, further complicating these issues.

A third point on which I find some agreement with Robottom pertains to his concern over a "behaviorist perspective" (p.2). In my extensive readings of social and educational research which pertain to "behavior", it is clear to me that differing theoretical models of environmental behavior have been put into use (e.g. , models which depict lifestyle change, social change, citizen participation, and citizen action). One common element in this body of literature is that these researchers are all interested in "human behavior towards the environment and associated problems" as a phenomenon of research interest. Literally hundreds of researchers have inquired into such behavior. However, only one of these models is a direct descendent of the "behaviorist tradition" in psychology (see Cone & Hayes, 1980; Geller, Winnett, & Everett, 1985). I have written elsewhere of various concerns I have regarding this particular model and its use in EE (Marcinkowski, 1989). Thus, while it may come as a surprise to Robottom, I largely agree with his concern over the use of "behavioral intervention strategies" and the manipulation of "situational factors in order to produce desired behavioral changes" (i.e., extrinsic motivational factors) in educational settings. Rather, I favor and even advocate those models which emphasize intrinsic motivation (see Widman, Simmons, Kaplan, & DeYoung, 1984). Thus, I do not agree with Robottom's assertion that I and my colleagues advocate the behaviorist model, and so, I will return to this point in the next section.

Closely related to this is a brief comment Robottom offers on "Responsible environmental behavior". On page 2, he points out that the defining of this construct is somewhat problematic ("as if it were unitary and consensual").

I have acknowledged in other writings that this is precisely the case (Marcinkowski, 1989, in development). People are prone to differ about what should be construed as "responsible" from ecological and/or from social perspectives. This should not be seen as "bad", for it is prone to sharpen thinking and discussion about what constitutes such behavior by interested parties in various sectors.

A fifth and final point on which I find some agreement is that educational goals in the field of environmental education should not be "reified and objectified" (p. 5), but rather should be shaped and reshaped to reflect the historical, cultural, political, social, <u>environmental</u>, and <u>educational</u> conditions which shape education and which education seeks to shape (p. 4). Beyond this, I have some rather serious disagreements with him over the one set of educational goals he criticizes (pp. 3-5); i.e., the "Goals for Curriculum Development in Environmental Education" (Hungerford, Peyton, & Wilke, 1980). I will also address these concerns in the next section of the paper.

<u>Points of Disagreement</u>

There are at least four areas in which I hold substantial disagreement with Robottom. I would prefer to address them in the order in which they appear within his article. First, he appears to suggest that I 'equate 'paradigm' with 'method' or technique'" (p. 2) in my paper. If he is not suggesting this, his writing is sufficiently ambiguous to appear as if it does. In light of the contents of my paper, that "hint" is unfair. On the other hand, if this is the case, it is a rather bold mis-statement of my views. All one has to do is to review Section I.C (Figure 2, p.) and the organization of Section II to recognize that I do not equate these. Rather, Figure 2 clearly suggests that "method" or "technique" fits somewhere between broad "paradigms" and specific "problems". I purposely included the extended quote from Bryman (1988, p. 123-125) to suggest that the <u>is</u> versus <u>ought</u> relationship amongst paradigm, method and problem is itself an epistomological issue. In other words, it is a "naturalistic fallacy" to suggest that method <u>should</u> solely reflect paradigm, or to suggest that method <u>should</u> solely reflect the problem under investigation. In the face of this unresolved issue, I attempted to present a novel view: that <u>formal designs</u> (or method) are promulgated to reflect philosophical assumptions embedded with a given paradigm, and that <u>strategic designs</u> (or methods) are reported versions of formal designs as they have been modified to meet varying conditions in the research setting. This distinction may seem subtle, though it is an important one. To suggest that these comments "deny the issue of ideology and ... make facile the treatment of differing paradigms as merely different tools in the researcher's toolbox" (p. 1) is to <u>totally</u> misinterpret and misrepresent my ideas.

A second section in which I find several of Robottom's comments unfair and misleading are those presented in "The Behaviorism of Positivistic Research" (p. 2). He begins by setting up his "straw man"; i.e., by noting the avowed purposes and apparent limitations of "positivistic" research, and by linking them to a "behaviorist" psychology. All else follows from this. For example, he asserts that NAAEE is a vocal advocate of positivistic research and of a "behaviorist" perspective (educational psychology). He fails to cite any source to support these assertions, and in fact, would find it near impossible to do so, for as a corporate body, NAAEE has never offered any formal statement related to either. Moreover, I doubt that NAAEE would ever venture to make such a statement, for the organization provides a forum for differing perspectives (e.g., this monograph), as well as for the discussion of such differences (e.g., the preceding Research Symposium).

Within this section, he offers several other bold, yet unsupported assertions. For example: "Behaviorism has become the ideology of positivist EE research" and "the task of research is seen as understanding, predicting, and modifying "responsible problem solving behavior" (emphasis added, p. 2). The former assertion is an over-generalization. Certainly there are some who use positivistic methods for behaviorist ends in environmental research circles (e.g., Cone & Hayes, 1980; Geller, Winnett, & Everett, 1985). However, this research is generally conducted in social rather than educational settings. There have been few exceptions to this (see Hines, 1985). Rather, the majority of educational studies in this area reflect "non-behaviorist" models. The latter assertion is clearly a mis-statement, albeit one which is used to advance his syllogism on positivism and behaviorism. Simply put, research does not modify behavior. Rather humans may use research to inquire into behavior or behavior change. What a researcher (or anyone else) does with observations on behavior is a quite different matter. Efforts to modify behavior is but one of a number of potential or actual uses of such data.

His 'syllogism' pertaining to positivism and behaviorism is also prone to criticism. In it, he appears to strongly infer the following: (1) that all research in the area of 'responsible environmental behavior' is positivistic in nature; and (2) that all of it is intended to support behaviorist efforts. A careful review of the research literature will clearly indicate that each of these premises is a vast over-generalization (Marcinkowski, 1989, in development). Social and educational studies of responsible environmental behavior have been reported which are "interpretivistic" in nature, in whole or in part (i.e., which are not "positivistic"). And, as noted in the previous section, only one of the many research models employed in such research is truly "behaviorist" in nature. A number of these "models" are not educational, but rather are sociological in nature (e.g., "diffusion and adoption" and "verbal commitment"). Of those that I am familiar with, I would not refer to any of the prominent educational models as "behaviorist" in orientation.

I would like to offer one final set of comments pertaining to this section on "Behaviorism". One of the educational models which focuses upon responsible environmental behavior has been developed by Hungerford, et al. In quoting only from professionals who have contributed to the evolution of this model, Robottom appears to suggest that these professionals and this model fall into the "behaviorism" camp. Nothing could be further from the truth. While they are interested in encouraging students to engage in such behavior, as called for within the Tbilisi Objectives (UNESCO, 1978), they have gone to great lengths to state in print that no student should be coerced or forced to engage in action (e.g., Hungerford, Litherland, Peyton, Ramsey, Tomera & Volk, 1985, p. VI-3; Hungerford, Volk, Dixon, Marcinkowski, & Sia, 1988, pp. 7-8; Marcinkowski, Volk & Hungerford, 1990, pp. 17-18). Instead, as Robottom advocates (p. 1), they focus upon the development of the thinking, inquiry, and data skills, as well as on an understanding of action strategies and an internal locus of control. Rather than deterministic, these are seen by teachers and students as "enabling" and "empowering" with respect to behavior (Ramsey & Hungerford, 1989; Hungerford & Volk, 1990). In light of these points, I would assert that the entire collection of ideas presented in this section is grossly misleading.

In the previous section, I also noted that I had some serious disagreement with Robottom's writings in the third section of his paper, "The Role of the Goals" (pp. 3-5) . It is appropriate to offer comments on three points. The first pertains to points raised by Disinger (1983) and others. During the 1970s, an inordinate amount of effort went into defining the field and its goals (see Harvey, 1976; Hart, 1981). In the opinions of some, this detracted from the implementation of any clear set of goals, and led to divisiveness amongst differing "schools of thought". The goals & objectives for EE adopted at the Tbilisi Conference (UNESCO, 1978) and reaffirmed ten years later (UNESCO, 1987) were intended to overcome this. However, some in North America found these goals and objectives to be vague, and called for clarification and refinement (e.g., Gustafson, 1983, p. 112). The "Goals for Curriculum Development" (GFCD) represents one of the few serious, public responses to this perceived need and recommendation.

My second set of comments pertains to Robottom's charges that the GFCD have remained static and unchallenged through the 1980's, and as a consequence have become reified. It is not true that they have gone unchallenged. The Journal of Environmental Education article containing the GFCD (1980) was fought by several editors, and as a result, barely made it into print. The call for clarifications of and refinements to the Tbilisi goals and objectives (noted above) was offered without any attention to the GFCD as one example of such an effort (Gustafson, 1983, p. 112). Further, early discussions in the ASTM-operated standard setting process involved serious challenges to the utility of the GFCD. Discussions with Hungerford would reveal that the GFCD have questioned and challenged on a consistent basis. Robottom's article is but another in a long litany.

It is also largely untrue that the GFCD are static; i.e., that they have not been revised. Revisions are reasonably apparent within the literature, though do not exist in article form in any one place. For example, there have been changes in the formulation of goal statements under existing goal levels, such as "Ecological Foundations" (Marcinkowski, Volk, & Hungerford,

1990). Broader changes have included the addition of "Environmental Sensitivity" as a pre-foundational goal level, of "Social Foundations" as a second foundational goal level, and of an "Instructional Applications" goal level for use in teacher education (Marcinkowski, Volk, & Hungerford, 1990; Held, 1991; Marcinkowski, 1991). These changes have come about as a result of perceived need, feedback, and new research findings. I expect that changes on these grounds will continue to be the made in the future.

Whether the GFCD have become reified ("cast in stone") is largely in the eyes of the beholder. It seems to me that this charge (p. 5) says more about the writer and his perceptions than about the GFCD. His views of them are very evident within this section of his article; (a) they are uniquely North American (pp. 1 & 4); (b) "they are treated as the source and embodiment of all worthwhile theory in environmental education" (p. 4); (c) the originators assume a higher intellectual and moral ground for the GFCD and themselves (p. 4), (d) the appropriateness of these may be called into question on "social, political, cultural, (and) historical" grounds (p. 4) and (e) they "impose upon the rest of us a rationalist theory of action in which definitional questions are petulantly and almost forcibly out aside" (p. 5). These comments seem to accord the GFCD powers which they simply do not claim or exhibit. That they are visible and advocated by a body of professionals does not mean that they are extensively used. To the above charges, I would offer four comments:

- No one is forcing anyone to adopt these as the goals for EE;
- If you think they need revision, take on that task yourself; and
- If others believe that they are of little or no use in another setting, such as Australia, don't use them; and
- If you are so inclined, develop whatever set of EE goals will be most useful in that setting at that time.

The basis upon which Robottom bases his own view of goals for EE is somewhat problematic. On page 1, he asserts that "the main educational aspiration of environmental education ... (is) ... the development of independent critical thinking in relation to environmental issues". This does not square with international agreements, for it reflects only one of the five objectives agreed to in Belgrade (UNESCO, 1977), in Tbilisi (UNESCO, 1978), and in Moscow (UNESCO, 1987). Whether he considers the remaining objectives to be a central and valuable part of EE is not clear. In addition, the practical dimension of this statement should be explored: "Toward what end should these skills be developed?" If a response emphasized their role in helping citizens better understand, analyze and respond to such issues, I would have to agree. However, if the response places any emphasis upon citizen response to such issues, I would ask a follow-up question: "How does one know that these skills can and do assist citizens in doing so?" It is this question that has led Hungerford, et al. to grapple seriously with this whole notion of education relative to active citizen response (i.e., behavior). While this topic area may be fraught with philosophical, ethical and practical issues, I would assert that exploration of it cannot be easily and summarily dismissed.

The fourth and final area of disagreement pertains to the use of the term "teachers". Robottom uses this term as if it were reasonable to talk about <u>all</u> teachers in all places at once. In my experience with teachers, both within and outside the field of EE, it is simply unfair to do so. Certainly, all teachers are to be treated with respect. However, teachers vary in their own levels of commitment to their education in general and their students in specific. Their knowledge of content and skills varies widely, as does their ability to apply the same. Their familiarity with teaching and assessment methods, and the accompanying skills also varies widely. This is of grave concern amongst education professionals of all kinds (including teachers) within the U.S. That these are also serious concerns within EE in the U.S. is apparent in the results of research (e.g., Peyton, 1977; Champeau, Gross, & Wilke, 1980; Volk, Hungerford, & Tomera, 1984; Wilson, 1988), and not merely a matter of "pejorative moral judgement" (p. 4). I interpret this situation to mean that pre- and in- service education should be offered in a manner which addresses such concerns (needs) in a manner which supports teachers' professional development, empowerment, and dignity. This may be, and in fact, has been, accomplished in varying ways within the field. It is certainly an important topic of discussion.

Closing Comments

In this response, I have presented some areas of agreement, as well as areas of disagreement with points offered by Robottom (1990). This response is but a small piece in the ongoing dialogue about research paradigms and methods in EE. The intent is to further careful inspection of serious issues in the field, and not to criticize an individual. In the course of detailing my disagreements with some of his points, I do criticize some of his <u>ideas</u> (e.g., perceptions, positions, reasoning, and conclusions) for I find them to be weak and/or unsupported. This is an academic prerogative no different than that which he uses in offering his own criticisms. In all fairness, "critical inspection" is a two-way street, and I have taken this prerogative to sharpen some points at issue for subsequent discussion. These issues can no more be "petulantly and almost forcibly put aside" (p. 5) than can those which Robottom raises. I hope that the comments offered herein are taken in this spirit, and do contribute positively to the discussion of these issues.

References

Bryman, A. (1988). Quantity versus quality in social research. In M. Blumer (Ed.), <u>Contemporary Social Research Series, #18</u>. London, England: Unwin Hyman.

Champeau, R., Gross, M., & Wilke, R. (1980). An assessment of teachers' understanding and use of "Goals for Curriculum Development in Environmental Education". In A. Sacks, et al. (Eds.), Current Issues VI: The Yearbook of Environmental Education and Environmental Studies (pp. 218-226). Columbus, OH: ERIC/SMEAC.

Cone, J., & Hayes, S. (1980). Environmental Problems and Behavioral Solutions. Monterrey, Cal.: Brooks/Cole Pub. Co.

Disinger, J. (1983). Environmental education's definitional problem. (Information Bulletin, No. 2). Columbus, OH: ERIC/SMEAC.

Geller, S., Winnett, R., & Everett, P. (1982). Preserving the Environment: New Strategies for Behavioral Chance. New York: Pergamon Press.

Gustafson, J. (Ed.). (1983). The First National Congress for Environmental Education Futures: Policies and Practices: Conference Proceedings - Policies. Columbus, OH: ERIC/SMEAC.

Hart, E. (1981). Identification of key characteristics of environmental education. The Journal of Environmental Education, 13(1), 12-16.

Harvey, G. (1976). Environmental education: A delineation of substantive structure. (Doctoral dissertation, Southern Illinois University at Carbondale). Dissertation Abstracts International, 38(2), 611-A.

Held, B. (Ed.). (August 6, 1991). Draft of 'Teacher Education Standards for Environmental Education'. Philadelphia, PA: Unpublished working document of the T-04 Subcommittee on Teacher Education, ASTM.

Hines, J. (1985). An analysis and synthesis of research on responsible environmental behavior. (Doctoral dissertation, Southern Illinois University at Carbondale, 1984). Dissertation Abstracts International, 46(3), 655-A.

Hungerford, H., Litherland, R., Peyton, R., Ramsey, J., Tomera, A., & Volk, T. (1985). Investigating and Evaluating Environmental Issues and Actions: Skill Development Modules. Champaign, IL: Stipes Pub. Co.

Hungerford, H., Peyton, R., & Wilke, R. (1980). Goals for curriculum development in environmental education. The Journal of Environmental Education, 11(3), 42-47.

Hungerford, H., & Volk, T. (1990). Changing learner behavior through environmental education. The Journal of Environmental Education, 12(3), 8-21.

Hungerford, H., Volk, T., Dixon, B., Marcinkowski, T., & Sia, A. (1988). An Environmental Approach to the Training of Elementary Teachers: A Teacher Education Programme. (Environmental Education Series #27). Paris, France: UNESCO.

Marcinkowski, T. (1989). An analysis of correlates and predictors of responsible environmental behavior. (Doctoral dissertation, Southern Illinois University at Carbondale, 1988). Dissertation Abstracts International, 49 (12), 3677-A.

Marcinkowski, T. (1991). Suggested additions: Teacher Education Standards for Environmental Education. St. Louis, MO: Unpublished proposal to the T-04 Subcommittee on Teacher Education, ASTM. Presented at the Annual Conference of the North American Association for Environmental Education, Minneapolis, MN, Sept. 27-28, 1991.

Marcinkowski, T. (in development). The modeling, measurement, and prediction of responsible environmental behavior: A review of the research literature, with recommendations. Monographs in Environmental Education and Environmental Studies, Volume. Troy, OH: NAAEE.

Marcinkowski, T., Volk, T., & Hungerford, H. (1990). An Environmental Education Approach to the Training of Middle Level Teachers: A Prototype Programme. (Environmental Education Series #30). Paris, France: UNESCO.

Peyton, R. (1977). An assessment of teachers' abilities to identify, teach, and implement environmental action skills. (Doctoral dissertation, So. Illinois University at Carbondale). Dissertation Abstracts International, 38 (10), 6071-A.

Ramsey, J., & Hungerford, H. (1989). So. . . You want to teach issues? Contemporary Education, 60(3), 137-142.

Robottom, I, (1990). Beyond behaviorism: Making EE research educational. Paper submitted for publication in R. Mrazek and P. Hart (Eds.), Paradigms in Environmental Education Research. Troy, OH: NAAEE.

UNESCO. (1977). Trends in Environmental Education. Paris, France: UNESCO.

UNESCO. (1978). Final Report: Intergovernmental Conference on Environmental Education. Paris, France: Author.

UNESCO. (1987). Moscow '87: UNESCO-UNEP International Congress on Environmental Education and Training (USSR, 17-21 August 1987). Connect, 12(3), 1-2.

Volk, T., Hungerford, H., & Tomera, A. (1984). A national survey of curriculum needs as perceived by professional environmental educators. The Journal of Environmental Education, 16(1), 10-19.

Widman, R., Simmons, B., Kaplan, R., & DeYoung, R. (1984). Behavioral Approaches to Energy Conservation in Organizations: A Selected Review of the Literature. (CPL Bibliography No. 143). Chicago, IL: Council of Planning Librarians.

Wilson, T. (1988). A study into the attainment of goals for environmental education through the inservice teacher education efforts of a university-based network of centers for environmental education. Paper presented at the Seventeenth Annual Meeting of the North American Association for Environmental Education, Orlando, Florida, 1988.

APPENDIX IV:

RESEARCH

PUBLICATION

GUIDELINES

TYPES OF MANUSCRIPTS SOLICITED FOR AND PUBLISHED IN JOURNAL OF ENVIRONMENTAL EDUCATION BY HELDREF PUBLICATIONS

Over the past year and a half, Heldref has begun soliciting a wider variety of manuscripts for The Journal of Environmental Education (JEE) than it has in the recent past. This sheet contains a brief description of each type of manuscript Heldref currently solicits for JEE. Unless noted otherwise, manuscripts may range up to 3,500 words in length. All manuscripts should follow The Chicago Manual of Style and should be submitted in triplicate.

1. **Editorials:** Editorial pieces are written by the JEE's Executive and Consulting Editors. These articles focus upon timely and critical insights into activities or events in the field of environmental education, as well as into those that may affect it. These articles should not exceed 2,500 words.

2. **Forefront:** These articles focus upon recent developments in the field of environmental education. They should be descriptive in nature, and may include tables and figures, and should not exceed 2,500 words.

3. **Viewpoint:** Viewpoint articles are opinion pieces written by environmental educators. Like "Editorials," these articles focus upon timely and critical insights into activities or events within the field of environmental education, as well as those that may affect it. These articles should not exceed 2,500 words.

4. **Research Reports:** Research reports can be based on qualitative and/or quantitative methods, and must include the following components: (a) an abstract of 100 words; (b) a problem statement; (c) a review of relevant literature; (d) a description of the research methodology; (e) a report of results; (f) a discussion and summary; and (g) a list of references. Where conclusions are made, they must be supported by appropriate research methodology and documentation. Recommendations and/or conjecture are encouraged, as long as they are identified as such. The manner in which qualitative and quantitative reports address these components may vary.

5. **Research Reviews and Critiques:** Research manuscripts of these kinds can take a variety of forms. They may be: (a) a critical review of one study, or of a collection of studies; (b) an interpretive analysis and/or synthesis of research results from a collection of studies; (c) a review of developments in research methodology; (d) an interpretive and/or critical analysis of research methods used in a collection of studies; or (e) an interpretive and/or critical analysis of substantive frameworks employed in a collection of studies. When appropriate, these

325

manuscripts should address the various components and concerns associated with research reports.

6. **<u>Program and Project Reports</u>**: Reports are sought for programs, projects and initiatives that have led or will lead to innovative advances in the field. Articles should: (a) state goals and objectives; (b) document what was done and the results; (c) evaluate effectiveness where possible; and (d) describe the relevance and implications for other practitioners. Anecdotal information that illustrates specific points is encouraged. These reports should describe what was done without making unsubstantiated claims.

7. **<u>Essays and Analyses</u>**: Critical essays and analyses are sought which are related to policy issues, philosophies or historical perspectives on environmental education. These articles should be based upon literature, events, and the like, and not on research data.

8. **<u>Reviews of Educational Materials</u>**: Review articles are sought for the variety of educational materials and resources in use in the field. Thus, reviews may focus upon books, films, videos, software, course designs, curricula, and the like. These reviews should be descriptive of the material and informative to the readership, and they should not exceed 750 words.

APPENDIX V: CONTACT INFORMATION FOR CONTRIBUTING AUTHORS

BREITING, Søren Emdrupvej 101 DENMARK	CANTRELL, Dianne Assistant Chief of Public Information and Education Ohio Department of Natural Resources 1930 Belcher Drive D-3 Columbus, Ohio U.S.A. 43224-1387
DEL PILAR JIMENEZ SILVA, Maria Miguel Angel Del Quevedo 33-3 Depto. 3 Col. Ermita San Angel Mexico DF. MEXICO CP 01070	DI CHIRO, Giovanna 202 Berkshire Avenue, Santa Cruz, California U.S.A.
DISINGER, John The Ohio State University School of Natural Resources 2021 Coffey Road Columbus, Ohio U. S. A.43210-1085	FORTNER, Rosanne W. The Ohio State University School of Natural Resources 2021 Coffey Road Columbus, Ohio U. S. A.43210-1085
GOUGH, Noel Victoria College 662 Blackburn Road Clayton, Victoria 3168 AUSTRALIA	HART, Paul, SIDRU Faculty of Education University of Regina Regina, Saskatchewan S4S 0A2
JICKLING, Bob Yukon College Box 2799 Whitehorse, Yukon, CANADA Y1A 5K4	KAPLAN, Stephen University of Michigan Ann Arbor, Michigan U.S.A.
MARCINKOWSKI, Tom Florida Institute of Technology Science Education Department 150 West University Boulevard Melbourne, Florida, U.S.A. 32901-6988	MAYER, Victor J. College of Education The Ohio State University 1945 N. Hugh Street Columbus, Ohio 43210 U.S.A.
MONROE, Martha C. 1255 - 33rd Street N.W./Suite 400 Washington, D.C., U.S.A. 20037	MRAZEK, Rick Faculty of Education The University of Lethbridge 4401 University Drive Lethbridge, Alberta, CANADA T1K 3M4
PALMER, Jackie Southwest Educational Development Laboratory 211 East Seventh Street Austin, Texas 78701-3281 U.S.A.	ROBOTTOM, Ian Deakin University Victoria 3217 AUSTRALIA

SIMMONS, Deborah 864 N 11th DeKalb, Illinois, U.S.A. 60115	VOLK, Trudi L. Department of Curriculum & Instruction Southern Illinois University Carbondale. Illinois, U.S.A.
WALS, Arjen E. J. Agricultural University Department of Agricultural Education Box 8130 6700 EW Wageningen THE NETHERLANDS	WIDMAR, Ron

APPENDIX VI:
MONOGRAPHS AND
PUBLICATIONS OF
THE NORTH
AMERICAN
ASSOCIATION FOR
ENVIRONMENTAL
EDUCATION

Publications available through NAAEE

NAAEE publishes conference proceedings, monographs and other documents as a service to its members and the EE community. In addition, we make available certain items from outside publishers that we feel will be of interest and use to our members. Most publications are offered at or near cost. The following publications are available as of May, 1991. Some are in limited supply or are one-time offers made possible by special arrangements with authors or publishers. All prices include postage and handling.

Title	Price Per Copy (member/non-member)	
Essential Learnings in Environmental Education	$12.00/$16.00	
Computer-Aided EE	$12.00/$16.00	
Monograph Volume V	$6.00/$10.00	
Monograph Volume IV	$8.00/$12.00	
Monograph Volume III	$8.00/$12.00	
Conference Proceedings 1990; 1989; 1988; 1987; 1986 1985, 1984	$8.00/$12.00 (Any 3) $16.00/$24.00 (Set of 7) $29.00/$41.00	
Recent Graduate Works 1989; 1983; 1979; 1987; 1982; 1986; 1981; 1985; 1980	$5.00/$8.00 (Any 3) $10.00/$15.00 (Set of 9) $25.00/$35.00	
Resource Fair Catalogs 1988; 1985; 1987;	$3.00/$5.00 (Set of 3) $5.00/$8.00	
Film and Video Festival List 1988; 1987; 1986; 1983	$2.00/$3.00	
You Are an Environment	$5.00/$8.00	
Environmental Protection in the United States	$5.00/$8.00	